W9-AFC-653

CHEMICAL EQUILIBRIUM

ROBERT B. FISCHER

California State College, Dominguez Hills

DENNIS G. PETERS

Indiana University

BRIAR CLIFF COLLEGE
LIBRARY
SIOUX CITY, IOWA

W. B. SAUNDERS COMPANY

PHILADELPHIA · LONDON · TORONTO · 1970

SAUNDERS GOLDEN SERIES

W. B. Saunders Company: West Washington Square
Philadelphia, Pa. 19105

12 Dyott Street
London W.C.1

1835 Yonge Street
Toronto 7, Ontario

QD
501
.F632

Chemical Equilibrium

© 1970 by W. B. Saunders Company. Copyright under the International Copyright
Union. All rights reserved. This book is protected by copyright. No part of it may be
reproduced, stored in a retrieval system, or transmitted in any form or by any means,
electronic, mechanical, photocopying, recording, or otherwise, without written permission
from the publisher. Made in the United States of America. Press of W. B. Saunders
Company. Library of Congress catalog card number 70-113025.

Print Number: 1   2   3   4   5   6   7   8   9

Preface

Chemical equilibrium is a frequently encountered topic in virtually every course in the undergraduate curriculum. Numerous subjects require consideration of the equilibrium properties of a system: in analytical chemistry, the preparation of a certain buffer solution; in biochemistry, the extent of ionization of an amino acid in an aqueous environment; in inorganic chemistry, the evaluation of the concentrations of the various metal ion complexes in a solution containing palladium(II) and chloride; in organic chemistry, the amounts of the chair and boat conformers of cyclohexane; and, in physical chemistry, the measurement of electromotive force in order to determine an equilibrium constant.

In these days of large undergraduate enrollments, and when students have such diverse backgrounds and goals, one of the effective methods for emphasizing specific subjects such as chemical equilibrium is by means of short, single-topic books which can be used to supplement the more broadly based, regular texts. Single-topic, supplementary texts are especially valuable when a student desires more intensive study of a particular subject than is ordinarily provided by standard textbooks.

Accordingly, one of the purposes of the present book is to provide students in courses of general chemistry with reasonably detailed discussions of the principles underlying chemical equilibrium as applied to dissolution and precipitation phenomena, to acid-base reactions, to the formation of metal ion complexes, and to oxidation-reduction processes. We have sought to give students a sound basis for using equilibrium principles in quantitative calculations, as well as to offer considerable guidance and practice in the application of these principles and calculations. An effort has been made to treat the subject matter in depth and breadth so

59152

as to supplement the study of chemical equilibrium in general college chemistry courses, both for students having difficulty in this area and for students and classes desiring to expand their study of equilibrium. In addition, this book is intended to serve as the primary text in a separate course in chemical equilibrium in those curricula which include such a course.

Much of the material in this book is similar to relevant portions of our texts, "Quantitative Chemical Analysis" and "A Brief Introduction to Quantitative Chemical Analysis," published in 1968 and 1969, respectively. However, many of the discussions have been revised and rearranged in accordance with present purposes. Numerous examples of fully solved problems have been inserted throughout each of the five chapters, in order to illustrate many of the points raised in the text and to show the student in detail how various types of problems can be set up and solved in a complete and logical fashion. Wherever they appear, these sample problems are indicated by a shaded vertical bar along the left-hand edge of a page. At the end of each chapter is provided an ample selection of questions and problems, many of them new, designed both to give practice in the common computations of chemical equilibrium and to offer a challenge to the advanced or especially well-prepared student. Answers to all of the numerical problems are listed in Appendix 5.

It is a pleasure to acknowledge the assistance and advice of a number of friends and associates in the preparation of this book. In particular, Professor William L. Masterton of the University of Connecticut and Professor Harry L. Pardue of Purdue University have been very helpful.

We invite comments and suggestions from students and from professors.

ROBERT B. FISCHER

Dominguez Hills, California

DENNIS G. PETERS

Bloomington, Indiana

Contents

v

Chapter 3

EQUILIBRIA IN ACID-BASE REACTIONS

Chapter 1

PRINCIPLES OF CHEMICAL EQUILIBRIUM

A chemical reaction is any process in which a bond between atoms is broken or formed, or both. Chemistry is, in essence, that branch of science which deals with chemical reactions, including such broad and interrelated factors as the structural properties of all species involved in chemical reactions, the rates and mechanisms of reactions, and the equilibrium conditions for reactions. A thorough knowledge of the principles underlying equilibrium is essential to the understanding of chemistry, and the ability to apply these principles is a prerequisite both to the ongoing refinement and expansion of the science of chemistry and to the reasoned application of chemistry in other fields of science, in many areas of technology, and in life itself.

SOME QUALITATIVE CONSIDERATIONS

Before we attempt to place chemical equilibrium on a firm mathematical foundation, it is worthwhile to examine qualitatively some of the characteristics of chemical systems in order to see what an equilibrium state is and how to recognize that a system has reached such a state of equilibrium.

Let us consider the reaction in aqueous solution between iron(III) and iodide ion to form iron(II) and triiodide ion,

$$2 \, Fe^{+++} + 3 \, I^- \rightleftharpoons 2 \, Fe^{++} + I_3^-$$

This equation is written with a double arrow to indicate that the reverse reaction, the combination of iron(II) and triiodide ion to form iron(III) and iodide ion, can also occur. In fact, the state of equilibrium may be

1

defined as the condition which prevails when both the forward and the reverse reactions are occurring at the same rate.

Suppose that a reaction mixture containing 0.200 M iron(III) and 0.300 M iodide ion is prepared and that we wish to determine *when* and *if* chemical equilibrium is established. As the reaction proceeds in the forward direction, the concentrations of iron(III) and iodide ion will diminish and, simultaneously, the concentrations of iron(II) and triiodide will build up. We can follow this process experimentally by measuring the concentration of any of the four substances as a function of time. For example, we can determine the concentration of triiodide by measuring the intensity of the yellow-orange color which is characteristic of this species. Color-intensity measurements can be made quite readily in the laboratory and, within limits which can be readily established and experimentally verified, the intensity of color is directly proportional to the concentration of triiodide ion. If this is done in the present example, we find that the concentration of triiodide reaches a maximum value of 0.0866 M and that any further net formation of triiodide ceases within a fraction of a second; these observations are represented by curve A of Figure 1-1. Therefore, since no detectable change in the triiodide concentration occurs after this time, one is tempted to conclude that chemical equilibrium has been reached.

However, such a conclusion is invalid unless the same final concentration of triiodide ion is approached when reaction occurs in the reverse direction, that is, when only iron(II) and triiodide are initially present. Accordingly, we could prepare another solution, this one 0.200 M in iron(II) and 0.100 M in triiodide, being certain that the *total* amounts of iron and iodine are identical to those in the preceding experiment. We could then study the changes with time in the concentrations of the four species. If, as before, the intensity of the yellow-orange color of triiodide were measured to indicate the progress of the reaction, the triiodide concentration would be found to decrease rapidly, although exponentially, to a value of 0.0866 M, as shown by curve B of Figure 1-1. Because there is no decrease in the triiodide concentration below this value, and because the final state of the system appears to be independent of the direction of the reaction, we can now assert that chemical equilibrium has definitely been attained. To point out the fact that the rate of approach to equilibrium from two opposite directions is usually different, curves A and B in Figure 1-1 have purposely been drawn so that equilibrium is reached somewhat more rapidly from the forward direction than from the backward direction. However, depending upon the initial concentrations of the various species, equilibrium can be attained more quickly from either direction.

It is important to stress that the absence of a detectable change in the concentrations of reactants and products does not by itself constitute a criterion for the state of chemical equilibrium. Some familiar reactions proceed toward equilibrium at such an infinitesimally slow rate that no

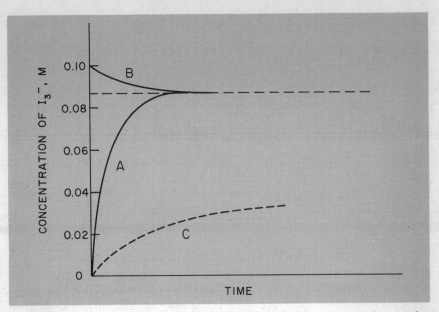

FIGURE 1-1 Hypothetical rate of change of triiodide concentration as the reaction

$$2\ Fe^{+++} + 3\ I^- \rightleftharpoons 2\ Fe^{++} + I_3^-$$

approaches a state of equilibrium. *Curve A:* approach to equilibrium in the *forward* direction. *Curve B:* approach to equilibrium in the *backward* direction. The horizontal, dashed line indicates the equilibrium triiodide concentration. *Curve C:* approach to equilibrium in the *forward* direction at a much slower reaction rate than Curve A. (See text for data on concentrations of starting solutions and for discussion.)

variations in the concentrations occur even after long periods of time. For example, a two-to-one mixture of hydrogen and oxygen gases should combine to form water,

$$2\ H_2 + O_2 \rightleftharpoons 2\ H_2O$$

the position of equilibrium for this reaction lying so far to the right that virtually no unreacted hydrogen or oxygen should remain. Nevertheless, in the absence of a suitable catalyst, such as spongy platinum, the reaction does not proceed at any measurable rate. Yet the mixture of hydrogen and oxygen must not be regarded as the true equilibrium state of the system. One should always verify the existence of true chemical equilibrium by showing that the same equilibrium state is reached from two directions. Such a procedure is mandatory whenever a chemical system is being investigated for the first time, but evidence that this procedure is valid for the iron(III)-iodide reaction can be seen from the following consideration. If the rate of the forward reaction had been relatively slow, the triiodide concentration might have increased only gradually, as shown by curve C of Figure 1-1. Furthermore, if the rate of the forward reaction was sufficiently slow, and if the technique employed to observe changes in the triiodide concentration was not too sensitive, one might decide that the triiodide concentration was not changing after a certain length of time. Thus, one could conclude erroneously that equilibrium had been attained at some point along curve C long before the triiodide concentration ever reached 0.0866 M. Fortunately, this error need not arise when equilibrium is approached from opposite directions, because any difference in the apparent equilibrium states attained from the forward and backward directions would be recognized immediately.

Sometimes, when the forward and backward reactions are so slow that it is inconvenient to wait for true equilibrium to be established, one may attempt to extrapolate a set of experimental results to obtain information about the equilibrium state. Notice that curves A and B in Figure 1-1 both approach asymptotically a triiodide concentration of 0.0866 M. If one makes measurements of the triiodide concentration as a function of time for the forward and backward reactions and then plots the experimental data as in Figure 1-1, it may be feasible to extrapolate each curve to the equilibrium triiodide concentration, even though true equilibrium has not yet been reached. In order for the extrapolation procedure to be meaningful, however, data reasonably close to the equilibrium state must be obtained, so that the limiting slopes of the experimental curves can be accurately identified. For example, it would be useless to extrapolate two curves such as B and C in an effort to find the equilibrium triiodide concentration.

Experimental techniques employed to follow the progress of a chemical reaction toward equilibrium are extremely varied, but they rely on the specific nature of the reactants and products as well as on the environment in which the reaction occurs. Above all, it is essential to select for observation or measurement a property of the chemical system which has a value at equilibrium distinctly different from that for any other state of the system. For the iron(III)-iodide equilibrium just discussed, the color intensity measurement of the concentration of yellow-orange triiodide ion is especially suitable. This measurement can be made readily with a colorimeter or a spectrophotometer, an instrument which permits a beam of light of the desired color or wavelength to impinge upon the system, and which measures the fraction of the light energy of this beam absorbed by the system.

Alternatively, similar spectrophotometric measurement involving other predetermined and preselected colors or wavelengths of light in the visible and ultraviolet regions of the electromagnetic spectrum could be used to measure the concentration of either iron(III) or iron(II). Other methods of chemical analysis could be used, the one requirement being that the method provide distinctive measurement of a component which is either consumed or produced in the forward reaction and, conversely, which is either produced or consumed in the backward reaction.

We shall now turn our attention from an essentially qualitative picture to a more formal mathematical representation of chemical equilibrium. Two theoretical approaches may be employed to derive a fundamental relation pertaining to the state of equilibrium. The first of these methods, involving a consideration of reaction kinetics, relates closely to the descriptive concepts or models which we use to visualize what actually happens as a chemical system attains a state of equilibrium. The second method is based upon the concepts of thermodynamics, which deal in turn with the energies possessed by the chemical substances involved in the system and with the changes in energy which accompany the forward and backward reactions.

KINETIC APPROACH TO EQUILIBRIUM

Fundamentally, the rate of a chemical reaction depends upon only two factors—the total number of collisions per unit of time between the reacting species and the fraction of these collisions which is fruitful in accomplishing reaction. The fraction of collisions which is successful in promoting any specific reaction is, in turn, dependent upon the temperature of the system as well as the presence of catalysts. When such conditions are held constant, a reaction rate is simply a function of the total number of collisions per unit of time between the reactants. If the number of these collisions doubles, the rate of the reaction likewise doubles. Similarly, if the number of these collisions is decreased by a factor of ten, the rate of the reaction is decreased ten-fold.

Consider the simple bimolecular reaction

$$A + B \rightarrow C + D$$

whose mechanism, we shall assume, involves the collision of a single particle of species A with a single particle of B to form one particle each of substances C and D. If the concentration of A is suddenly doubled, that is, if the number of A particles in a fixed volume is doubled, it is reasonable to expect that the number of collisions per unit time between A and B will momentarily double and that the rate of reaction will be doubled accordingly. Similarly, if the concentration of A is maintained constant and the concentration of B is doubled, the reaction rate will be doubled. Now, if the concentrations of both A and B are doubled, the number of collisions per unit time between A and B particles is quadrupled, so that the rate of reaction is quadrupled. These considerations suggest that the rate or the velocity of the forward reaction, v_f, may be expressed by the equation

$$v_f = k_f \, [A] \, [B]$$

where k_f is the rate constant and [A] and [B] are the concentrations of A and B, respectively.

All chemical reactions are reversible, at least to a slight extent. In fact, some degree of reversibility is necessary in order for a state of equilibrium to be established since, as we have already noted, a state of equilibrium exists in a chemical system when a forward reaction and a reverse reaction are occurring at the same rate. Consequently, it is more correct to formulate the previous reaction as

$$A + B \rightleftharpoons C + D$$

to indicate that the backward reaction between one particle of C and one particle of D has definite significance. If the assumption is made that the mechanism of this process entails collision of one particle of C with one particle of D, the rate of the backward reaction, v_b, can be expressed by the equation

$$v_b = k_b \, [C] \, [D]$$

When A and B are first mixed, with no C or D present, the reaction will proceed toward the right at a finite rate. As this forward reaction continues, the concentrations of A and B diminish, and the rate of the forward reaction, v_f, decreases. Initially, the rate of the backward reaction, v_b, is zero since neither C nor D is present. However, as the forward reaction proceeds, the concentrations of C and D build up, so that the rate of the backward reaction begins to increase. Thus, v_f starts at its maximum value and then diminishes, whereas, during the same time, v_b starts at zero and increases. Sooner or later, as these trends continue, the two rates inevitably become equal to each other, and the system is then said to be in a state of equilibrium. Thereafter, the individual concentrations of A, B, C, and D remain constant. Substances A and B are, from that time on, being used up at the same rate at which they are being produced, while C and D are likewise being used up at the same rate at which they are being formed.

It must be emphasized that the forward and backward reactions do not stop when the equilibrium condition is achieved. Rather, they both continue, but at equal rates. This means that the system is in a dynamic state of equilibrium, not a static one. The dynamic nature of equilibrium can be demonstrated, in principle, for any chemical system. To illustrate one way in which this may be verified experimentally, let us recall the iron(III)-iodide reaction. Suppose that we know, in advance, just one of the infinite number of sets of iron(III), iodide, iron(II) and triiodide concentrations corresponding to the state of chemical equilibrium, and suppose that we mix solutions of the four species together in such a way that equilibrium prevails immediately at the start of the experiment. If we used a solution of radioactive iodide ion and non-radioactive triiodide ion for the preparation of this equilibrium mixture, we would eventually find experimentally that the radioiodine was distributed randomly between triiodide and iodide ions, thus indicating that the forward and backward reactions

$$2\,Fe^{+++} + 3\,I^- \rightleftharpoons 2\,Fe^{++} + I_3^-$$

occur at equal rates, even though a state of chemical equilibrium was preserved throughout the experiment. On the other hand, if chemical equilibrium were a stationary state, all the radioiodine would remain as iodide ion, the form in which it was introduced.

Returning now to the reaction of one particle each of substances A and B to form one particle each of substances C and D, we may represent the equilibrium state mathematically by equating the rates of the forward and backward reactions as follows:

$$v_f = v_b$$

$$k_f\,[A]\,[B] = k_b\,[C]\,[D]$$

It is difficult to evaluate the individual rate constants k_f and k_b. Nevertheless, they may be combined into a single constant by rearrangement of the preceding equation,

$$\frac{k_f}{k_b} = \frac{[C]\,[D]}{[A]\,[B]}$$

$$K = \frac{[C]\,[D]}{[A]\,[B]}$$

where K is called the equilibrium constant for this reaction.

We have assumed that in this process only one particle of each reactant combines in the forward reaction, and one particle of each in the backward reaction. Let us now extend this treatment to the process

$$2\,A + B \rightleftharpoons C + 2\,D$$

which could conceivably occur according to the following two mechanistic steps:

$$A + B \rightleftharpoons Z + D$$

$$A + Z \rightleftharpoons C + D$$

For the first step,

$$v_f = k_f[A]\,[B] \quad \text{and} \quad v_b = k_b[Z]\,[D] \quad \text{and} \quad K_1 = \frac{[Z]\,[D]}{[A]\,[B]}$$

where K_1 is the equilibrium constant for this first step. For the second step,

$$v_f = k_f[A][Z] \quad \text{and} \quad v_b = k_b[C][D] \quad \text{and} \quad K_2 = \frac{[C][D]}{[A][Z]}$$

where K_2 is the equilibrium constant for the second step. Now, let us multiply K_1 by K_2:

$$K_1 \times K_2 = \frac{[Z][D]}{[A][B]} \times \frac{[C][D]}{[A][Z]}$$

$$K = \frac{[C][D]^2}{[A]^2[B]}$$

Note that the latter relation is exactly the same as what we would have derived for the overall process if we had assumed that the mechanism of the forward reaction consisted of simultaneous collision of two particles of A with one particle of B and that the backward reaction involved simultaneous collision of two particles of D with one particle of C. Thus, we are led to the **Law of Chemical Equilibrium:** For the generalized reaction

$$a A + b B \rightleftharpoons c C + d D$$

in which a, b, c, and d signify the stoichiometric numbers of particles of A, B, C, and D, respectively, involved in the completely balanced reaction, the equilibrium constant may be expressed by the relation

$$K = \frac{[C]^c[D]^d}{[A]^a[B]^b}$$

regardless of the detailed mechanism of the reaction. Even though the true reaction mechanism may differ markedly from the stoichiometry of the overall process, the equilibrium properties of a system do not depend upon the pathway by which equilibrium is reached.

In this discussion we have used the concentrations of the various species both in rate equations and in equilibrium-constant equations. For any given chemical system, the several concentrations in a rate expression are essentially independent of each other, and each one may assume any value. However, the concentrations of A, B, C, and D in the equilibrium-constant expression are the values which exist only at equilibrium. There is an infinite number of sets of concentrations which correspond to the equilibrium state, but no one concentration can vary independently of the concentrations of the other substances without destroying the equilibrium condition. To illustrate this point, let us examine a specific chemical system.

EXAMPLE 1

In a study of the gas-phase dimerization of nitrogen dioxide at 25°C according to the reaction

$$2\,NO_2(g) \rightleftharpoons N_2O_4(g)$$

the following equilibrium molar concentrations of the two gaseous species were observed in four different experiments:

Experiment	$[NO_2(g)]$	$[N_2O_4(g)]$
I	0.052	0.595
II	0.024	0.127
III	0.068	1.02
IV	0.101	2.24

Verify that the experimental data conform to the equilibrium expression for the overall process, and determine the equilibrium constant for the dimerization reaction.

When the ratio of the concentration of N_2O_4 to the square of the NO_2 concentration is computed for each of the experiments, we obtain:

For Experiment I:

$$\frac{[N_2O_4(g)]}{[NO_2(g)]^2} = \frac{(0.595)}{(0.052)^2} = 220$$

For Experiment II:

$$\frac{[N_2O_4(g)]}{[NO_2(g)]^2} = \frac{(0.127)}{(0.024)^2} = 220$$

For Experiment III:

$$\frac{[N_2O_4(g)]}{[NO_2(g)]^2} = \frac{(1.02)}{(0.068)^2} = 221$$

For Experiment IV:

$$\frac{[N_2O_4(g)]}{[NO_2(g)]^2} = \frac{(2.24)}{(0.101)^2} = 220$$

Regardless of the fact that the equilibrium concentrations of NO_2 and N_2O_4 are different in each experiment, the concentration of N_2O_4 divided by the square of the NO_2 concentration is always constant within the limits of accuracy of the data. This agreement among all four experiments, as well as any additional studies we might perform, demonstrates the correctness and significance of the equilibrium expression and allows us to conclude that the equilibrium constant for the reaction is very close to 220 at a temperature of 25°C. Whenever NO_2 and N_2O_4 are present together in a system at equilibrium, the individual concentrations must satisfy the equilibrium expression. If, for any reason, the concentration of NO_2 is increased, the N_2O_4 concentration must likewise increase to some new value such that

$$\frac{[N_2O_4(g)]}{[NO_2(g)]^2} = 220$$

at equilibrium. Similarly, if the NO_2 concentration falls, the concentration of N_2O_4 must undergo a decrease so that the equilibrium expression is satisfied. These concepts will be encountered again in the following paragraphs.

Attention should be directed to the convention — originally chosen quite arbitrarily, but now a matter of international agreement — that the numerical value of an equilibrium constant refers to the ratio in which the concentrations of the *products* of a reaction appear in the *numerator* and the concentrations of the *reactants* in the *denominator*. With this convention in mind, one can frequently tell by glancing at the numerical magnitude of the equilibrium constant whether a reaction has a tendency to proceed far toward the right, or only slightly so, before reaching equilibrium.

For a reaction having a large K, equilibrium is attained only after the reaction has proceeded far to the right. A two-to-one mixture of hydrogen and oxygen gases, as we have previously mentioned, has a strong tendency to form water vapor

$$2\,H_2 + O_2 \rightleftharpoons 2\,H_2O$$

although the reaction does not occur readily without a catalyst. At 25°C the equilibrium expression for the process is

$$\frac{[H_2O(g)]^2}{[H_2(g)]^2\,[O_2(g)]} = 1.7 \times 10^{80}$$

so that the numerator of the relation is exceedingly large compared to the denominator, indicating that very little hydrogen and oxygen remain unreacted at equilibrium. Another system, involving the reaction of iron(II) with cerium(IV) in a sulfuric acid solution,

$$Fe^{++} + Ce^{++++} \rightleftharpoons Fe^{+++} + Ce^{+++}$$

has an equilibrium-constant expression given by

$$\frac{[Fe^{+++}][Ce^{+++}]}{[Fe^{++}][Ce^{++++}]} = 7.9 \times 10^{12}$$

which reveals that the numerator of the equation is considerably greater than the denominator and implies that the concentration of at least one, and possibly both, of the reactants is small when equilibrium is attained. In other words, if one mixes equal amounts of iron(II) and cerium(IV), practically all of these species will be converted to iron(III) and cerium(III).

EXAMPLE 2

If a sulfuric acid solution initially containing 0.10 M concentrations of iron(II) and cerium(IV) is prepared, show that the reaction between these two species is virtually complete, by calculating the equilibrium concentrations of all the reactants and products.

On the basis of the preceding discussion, we can write the pertinent chemical reaction

$$Fe^{++} + Ce^{++++} \rightleftharpoons Fe^{+++} + Ce^{+++}$$

and the equilibrium expression

$$\frac{[Fe^{+++}][Ce^{+++}]}{[Fe^{++}][Ce^{++++}]} = 7.9 \times 10^{12}$$

From the stoichiometry of the overall process, it should be evident that identical concentrations of Fe^{+++} and Ce^{+++} will be formed and that the residual Fe^{++} and Ce^{++++} concentrations will be equal:

$$[Fe^{+++}] = [Ce^{+++}] \quad \text{and} \quad [Fe^{++}] = [Ce^{++++}]$$

In addition, we can state that the final equilibrium concentration of Fe^{++} is given by the original Fe^{++} concentration (0.10 M) minus the concentration of Fe^{++} which reacts (the latter being simply the concentration of Fe^{+++} formed):

$$[Fe^{++}] = 0.10 - [Fe^{+++}]$$

A similar relation can be written for the equilibrium concentration of Ce^{++++}:

$$[Ce^{++++}] = 0.10 - [Ce^{+++}] = 0.10 - [Fe^{+++}]$$

If this information is substituted into the equilibrium expression, we obtain

$$\frac{[Fe^{+++}][Ce^{+++}]}{[Fe^{++}][Ce^{++++}]} = \frac{[Fe^{+++}][Fe^{+++}]}{(0.10 - [Fe^{+++}])(0.10 - [Fe^{+++}])}$$

$$= 7.9 \times 10^{12}$$

which, when solved for the concentration of iron(III), yields

$$[Fe^{+++}] = 0.10\,M$$

Since the concentration of the other product, cerium(III), has the same value, we may immediately write

$$[Ce^{+++}] = 0.10\,M$$

Although our calculations show that essentially all the iron(II) and cerium(IV) react to form iron(III) and cerium(III), respectively—as earlier qualitative predictions suggested—small concentrations of both reactants do remain. To find these values, we can take note of the facts that

$$[Fe^{+++}] = [Ce^{+++}] = 0.10\,M$$

and that

$$[Fe^{++}] = [Ce^{++++}]$$

When these two relations are inserted into the original equilibrium expression, one obtains

$$\frac{[Fe^{+++}][Ce^{+++}]}{[Fe^{++}][Ce^{++++}]} = \frac{(0.10)(0.10)}{[Fe^{++}]^2} = 7.9 \times 10^{12}$$

from which it follows that

$$[Fe^{++}] = 3.6 \times 10^{-8}\,M$$

and

$$[Ce^{++++}] = 3.6 \times 10^{-8}\,M$$

Some familiar chemical processes have K values much smaller than unity, so that equilibrium is reached before the reactions have gone very far toward the right. For example, the dissolution of silver chloride in water may be represented by the reaction

$$AgCl(s) \rightleftharpoons Ag^+ + Cl^-$$

for which the equilibrium expression* at 25°C is

$$[Ag^+][Cl^-] = 1.78 \times 10^{-10}$$

Such an equilibrium constant indicates that the concentrations of silver ion and chloride ion (equal to each other in a saturated aqueous solution of silver chloride) are quite small, which simply confirms our knowledge of the low solubility of silver chloride. Acetic acid is well known as a weak electrolyte in aqueous solution because the extent of its ionization (dissociation) into hydrogen ion and acetate ion

$$CH_3COOH \rightleftharpoons H^+ + CH_3COO^-$$

does not usually occur to an appreciable extent. Such a conclusion can be drawn, at least in part, from an inspection of the appropriate equilibrium expression:

$$\frac{[H^+][CH_3COO^-]}{[CH_3COOH]} = 1.75 \times 10^{-5}$$

Here we see that the equilibrium constant is much less than unity and that the numerator is very small in comparison to the denominator of the equation. From this information alone, we expect that at equilibrium the concentration of either H^+ or CH_3COO^-, or perhaps the concentration of each ion, will be small relative to the acetic acid concentration.

Some words of caution should be interjected at this point. Although it is true that the magnitude of an equilibrium constant is a criterion by which to judge whether a chemical reaction has a pronounced or only a slight tendency to proceed from left to right as written, the initial concentrations of the reactants and products provide a second and equally important criterion for deciding the direction in which a reaction will actually go in order to attain a state of equilibrium. For example, a chemical reaction may have a *large* equilibrium constant, yet it may proceed from *right to left* if the initial concentrations of species on the right-hand side of the balanced chemical equation happen to be much greater than the concentrations of substances on the left-hand side of the chemical

---

*The concentration (activity) of solid silver chloride does not appear in this equilibrium expression because, as described in detail in Chapter 2, the concentration of a pure solid phase is unity.

equation. A system we have already discussed, namely the iron(III)-iodide reaction,

$$2\ Fe^{+++} + 3\ I^- \rightleftharpoons 2\ Fe^{++} + I_3^-$$

illustrates these considerations. The position of equilibrium for the reaction lies toward the right because the equilibrium constant is moderately large ($K = 5.55 \times 10^4$), so the formation of iron(II) and triiodide ion is favored. Nevertheless, curve B of Figure 1-1 clearly confirms that, if the original concentrations of iron(II) and triiodide are very large compared to the initial concentrations of iron(III) and iodide, the reaction actually proceeds from *right to left*.

Effects of the relative initial concentrations of reactants and products are sufficiently important that we should examine a specific system in a quantitative way.

EXAMPLE 3

At 600°C one form of the equilibrium expression for the gas-phase reaction

$$2\ SO_2(g) + O_2(g) \rightleftharpoons 2\ SO_3(g)$$

is

$$\frac{[SO_3(g)]^2}{[SO_2(g)]^2 [O_2(g)]} = 5.8 \times 10^3$$

Suppose that three different gas mixtures are prepared in which the following initial molar concentrations of each species are taken:

Mixture	Initial Concentration, moles/liter		
	$SO_2(g)$	$O_2(g)$	$SO_3(g)$
I	0.150	0.100	0.200
II	0.010	0.050	0.500
III	0.035	0.070	0.705

Predict the direction in which reaction will actually proceed as a state of chemical equilibrium is approached in each gas mixture.

Observing the equilibrium constant to be significantly greater than unity, one might be tempted immediately to conclude that the reaction should proceed from left to right. However, to determine the true behavior of each gas mixture, we must compare the *initial* value of the concentration quotient

$$\frac{[SO_3(g)]^2}{[SO_2(g)]^2[O_2(g)]}$$

to the concentration quotient *at equilibrium,* the latter quantity being simply the equilibrium constant itself (5.8×10^3).

For mixture I, the initial value of the concentration quotient is

$$\left(\frac{[SO_3(g)]^2}{[SO_2(g)]^2[O_2(g)]}\right)_{initial} = \frac{(0.200)^2}{(0.150)^2(0.100)} = 17.8$$

which is considerably smaller than 5.8×10^3.

$$\left(\frac{[SO_3(g)]^2}{[SO_2(g)]^2[O_2(g)]}\right)_{initial} < \left(\frac{[SO_3(g)]^2}{[SO_2(g)]^2[O_2(g)]}\right)_{equilibrium}$$

In order for equilibrium to be attained, the concentration of SO_3 must increase, while the SO_2 and O_2 concentrations must correspondingly decrease. This means that SO_2 and O_2 will react to form more SO_3 and that *reaction will proceed spontaneously from left to right.* Once chemical equilibrium is reached, no further net reaction will occur.

For mixture II, the initial value of the concentration quotient is

$$\left(\frac{[SO_3(g)]^2}{[SO_2(g)]^2[O_2(g)]}\right)_{initial} = \frac{(0.500)^2}{(0.010)^2(0.050)} = 5.0 \times 10^4$$

which is seen to be substantially larger than 5.8×10^3.

$$\left(\frac{[SO_3(g)]^2}{[SO_2(g)]^2[O_2(g)]}\right)_{initial} > \left(\frac{[SO_3(g)]^2}{[SO_2(g)]^2[O_2(g)]}\right)_{equilibrium}$$

Accordingly, in order for a state of equilibrium to be reached, the SO_3 concentration must decrease, while the concentrations of SO_2 and O_2 must increase. Therefore, SO_3 will decompose to give more SO_2 and O_2—and *reaction will occur spontaneously from right to left*—until equilibrium is established, after which time there will be no additional net reaction.

For mixture III, the initial value of the concentration quotient is

$$\left(\frac{[SO_3(g)]^2}{[SO_2(g)]^2[O_2(g)]}\right)_{initial} = \frac{(0.705)^2}{(0.035)^2(0.070)} = 5.8 \times 10^3$$

which happens to be identical to the equilibrium constant.

$$\left(\frac{[SO_3(g)]^2}{[SO_2(g)]^2[O_2(g)]}\right)_{initial} = \left(\frac{[SO_3(g)]^2}{[SO_2(g)]^2[O_2(g)]}\right)_{equilibrium}$$

Thus, we can conclude that the system is already at equilibrium and that *no net reaction will occur.*

In conclusion of this section, it should be reëmphasized that the concept of chemical equilibrium tells us absolutely nothing about either the rate at which the equilibrium state has been reached or, once that state is reached, the direction from which it was approached. Furthermore, it is highly significant that the characteristics of the state of equilibrium do not depend in any way on the detailed mechanism of the process whereby equilibrium is attained. No matter how complicated the mechanisms of the reactions leading to equilibrium are, however, the equilibrium-constant expression can always be written after an inspection of the balanced chemical equation.

THERMODYNAMIC CONCEPT OF EQUILIBRIUM

The second of our two methods of deriving a fundamental relation pertaining to the state of equilibrium is based upon energy considerations and utilizes some of the basic concepts of thermodynamics. The word thermodynamics is formed from two terms, one signifying heat, which is a form of energy, and the other meaning power or work. Thus **chemical thermodynamics** is that branch of chemistry which deals with the energies of chemical systems and, of particular significance here, the energy transformations and work done during chemical reactions.

Our purposes now are to use thermodynamic considerations to obtain verification of the Law of Chemical Equilibrium, which we have already established from the kinetic approach, and also to obtain equations relating the equilibrium constant to thermodynamic data. These equations are especially important because they make possible the calculation of numerical values of many equilibrium constants from the large quantities of thermodynamic data which have been obtained and tabulated, and also because they permit us to assess the effects of changes in experimental conditions upon chemical systems.

One of the fundamental laws of nature is that a chemical system always tends to undergo a spontaneous and irreversible change from some initial, nonequilibrium state to a final, equilibrium state. Once the system reaches a state of equilibrium, no additional change will occur unless some new stress is placed upon the system. Although the preceding two sentences apply to physical processes as well as chemical ones, we are concerned here primarily with chemical reactions and chemical equilibria.

In describing equilibrium in thermodynamic terms, one must define a property of a chemical system which can be related to the concentrations of the various species involved in an equilibrium state. The thermodynamic parameter which is most useful in this respect is G, the **Gibbs free energy.** A chemical system which is initially in some nonequilibrium state has a tendency to change spontaneously until the free energy for the system becomes minimal and the system itself reaches equilibrium. It is strictly correct to speak only of a *tendency* for change to occur, since thermodynamics offers no information at all about the rate of a particular process. The driving force which causes a system to pass from an initial state to a certain final state is measured by the free-energy change for that process. In turn, the free-energy change is defined as the difference between the free energies of the final and initial states, and is symbolized by ΔG when the system undergoes a finite change of state:

$$\Delta G = G_{final} - G_{initial}$$

Sometimes the free-energy change is referred to as the *maximum amount of useful work or energy other than pressure-volume work* which can be obtained from a physical or chemical process at constant temperature and pressure. This definition is especially appropriate for the discussion in Chapter 5 concerning oxidation-reduction phenomena. However, our immediate objectives are to evaluate the free-energy change for a particular chemical reaction and to relate the free-energy change to the state of equilibrium for that reaction.

STANDARD STATES AND FREE ENERGIES OF FORMATION

In general, the free energy of a chemical species is dependent upon temperature and pressure, as well as upon the nature and quantity of the substance itself. Therefore, standard-state conditions have been established for the various kinds of chemical species, so that values for the absolute free energy of an element or the free energy of formation of a compound can be precisely specified and tabulated.

Our choice of **standard state** for a substance depends on whether it is a gaseous, liquid, solid, or solute species; however, all standard states pertain to a temperature of 298°K or 25°C. A gaseous substance, if ideal, exists in its standard state when present at a pressure of exactly one atmosphere. For a liquid or solid, the standard state is taken to be the *pure* liquid or *pure* solid, respectively, at a pressure of one atmosphere. Dissolved or solute species, including electrolytes, nonelectrolytes, and individual ions, are in their standard states if their activities or "effective" concentrations are unity in molar quantities, again at a pressure of one atmosphere. Activity or effective concentration is not necessarily the same as the actual concentration which can be obtained, for example, by titrimetric or gravimetric methods of chemical analysis. Symbols used to distinguish between the two should be mentioned: the actual concentration in molar units is designated with square brackets, such as $[Na^+]$ and $[Cl^-]$, whereas the activity may be written with parentheses, (Na^+) and (Cl^-), or may be expressed as a_{Na^+} and a_{Cl^-}. We will consider reasons for the differences between activities and analytical concentrations later in this chapter. It suffices to state here that the activity of an ionic solute is affected by the presence of other ions in solution as well as by molecules of the solvent, whereas actual concentrations are independent of such factors. Similar considerations are involved with gaseous substances as well.

By convention, the most stable form of any pure element in its standard state is assigned a free energy of zero. For a chemical compound, one must measure or determine the free-energy *change* for the reaction by which that compound is formed from its elements, when all reactants and products are in their standard states. This free-energy change is termed the **standard free energy of formation, ΔG_f°,** for the substance of interest. In Table 1-1 are listed standard free energies of formation for some representative compounds. Standard free energies of formation may be determined experimentally from the direct measurement of either equilibrium constants or the electromotive force of galvanic cells. It is common to express the free energy of formation in heat units, and for each value to pertain to one mole of the substance; thus, the standard free energies of formation in Table 1-1 are expressed in kilocalories per mole of the substance formed. It should be recognized that the free-energy change attending the formation of two moles of a substance under standard-state conditions will be twice the value of ΔG_f° shown in the table. Similarly, the formation of n moles of a compound corresponds to a free-energy change of $n(\Delta G_f^\circ)$.

We should examine briefly the significance of one or two entries in Table 1-1. For example, the standard free energy of formation of one mole of water vapor at 298°K from hydrogen and oxygen gases is listed as −54.64 kilocalories.

$$H_2(g) + \tfrac{1}{2} O_2(g) \rightleftharpoons H_2O(g); \quad \Delta G_f^\circ = -54.64 \text{ kcal}$$

Since we learned earlier that this process is spontaneous—although kinetically slow—it can be stated here that *if ΔG_f° is negative the reactants will be spontaneously converted into products,* all species being in their standard states. Further inspection of Table 1-1 shows that the standard free energy of formation of nitric oxide from nitrogen and oxygen has a value of +20.72 kilocalories per mole:

$$\tfrac{1}{2} N_2(g) + \tfrac{1}{2} O_2(g) \rightleftharpoons NO(g); \quad \Delta G_f^\circ = +20.72 \text{ kcal}$$

If one wishes to consider the formation of two moles of nitric oxide, the appropriate reaction and free-energy change are

TABLE 1-1 STANDARD FREE ENERGIES OF FORMATION (ΔG_f°) FOR VARIOUS SUBSTANCES AT 298°K (kilocalories/mole)*

Gases		Solids	
H_2O	−54.64	AgCl	−26.22
H_2O_2	−24.7	AgBr	−22.39
O_3	39.06	AgI	−15.81
HCl	−22.77	BaO	−126.3
HBr	−12.72	$BaSO_4$	−350.2
HI	0.31	$BaCO_3$	−272.2
SO_2	−71.79	CaO	−144.4
SO_3	−88.52	$CaCO_3$	−269.8
H_2S	−7.89	$Ca(OH)_2$	−214.3
N_2O	24.9	SiO_2	−192.4
NO	20.72	Fe_2O_3	−177.1
NO_2	12.39	Al_2O_3	−376.8
NH_3	−3.97	CuO	−30.4
CO	−32.81	Cu_2O	−34.98
CO_2	−94.26	ZnO	−76.05

Organic compounds
Gases

Methane, CH_4	−12.14	Ethylene, C_2H_4	16.28
Ethane, C_2H_6	−7.86	Acetylene, C_2H_2	50.00
Propane, C_3H_8	−5.61	1-Butene, C_4H_8	17.09
n-Butane, C_4H_{10}	−3.75	cis-2-Butene, C_4H_8	15.74
Isobutane, C_4H_{10}	−4.3	trans-2-Butene, C_4H_8	15.05
n-Pentane, C_5H_{12}	−2.0	Isobutene, C_4H_8	13.88
Isopentane, C_5H_{12}	−3.5	1,3-Butadiene, C_4H_6	36.01
Neopentane, C_5H_{12}	−3.6	Methyl chloride, CH_3Cl	−14.0

Liquids

Methanol, CH_3OH	−39.73	Benzene, C_6H_6	29.76
Ethanol, C_2H_5OH	−41.77	Chloroform, $CHCl_3$	−17.1
Acetic acid, CH_3COOH	−93.8	Carbon tetrachloride, CCl_4	−16.4

Aqueous ions

H^+	0.0	OH^-	−37.59
Na^+	−62.59	Cl^-	−31.35
K^+	−67.47	Br^-	−24.57
Ag^+	18.43	I^-	−12.35
Ba^{2+}	−134.0	HS^-	3.01
Ca^{2+}	−132.18	S^{2-}	20.0
Cu^{2+}	15.53	SO_4^{2-}	−177.34
Zn^{2+}	−35.18	SO_3^{2-}	−126.2

Gaseous atoms

H	48.57	I	16.77
F	14.2	C	160.84
Cl	25.19	N	81.47
Br	19.69	O	54.99

*Reproduced with permission from B. H. Mahan: *Elementary Chemical Thermodynamics*, W. A. Benjamin, Inc., New York, 1963, pp. 90-91.

$$N_2(g) + O_2(g) \rightleftharpoons 2\ NO(g); \Delta G_f^\circ = +41.44 \text{ kcal}$$

In any event, *the positive sign of ΔG_f° reveals that the conversion of nitrogen and oxygen in their standard states to nitric oxide in its standard state is nonspontaneous.* Some nitric oxide will be formed, however, but the reaction between nitrogen and oxygen, each at one atmosphere pressure, will not proceed far enough to yield this substance in its standard state at one atmosphere pressure.

FREE-ENERGY CHANGE FOR A REACTION

From information such as that compiled in Table 1-1, it is possible to compute the **standard free-energy change**, ΔG°, for each of a large number of chemical reactions. First, we should recall the simple equation presented in the introduction of this section, namely,

$$\Delta G = G_{\text{final}} - G_{\text{initial}}$$

which states mathematically that the free-energy change for any process is the difference between the free energies of the final and initial states. Now, if we choose to allow reactants in their standard states (the initial state of the system) to go to products in their standard states (the final state of the system), the preceding general expression can be rewritten as

$$\Delta G^\circ = \sum \Delta G_f^\circ \text{ (products)} - \sum \Delta G_f^\circ \text{ (reactants)}$$

where the summation signs permit us to consider as many reactants and products as necessary. According to this defining equation, the standard free-energy change for a reaction is the sum of the standard free energies of formation of the products minus the sum of the standard free energies of formation of the reactants. Let us apply this relationship to several specific cases.

EXAMPLE 4

From data listed in Table 1-1, compute the standard free-energy change, ΔG°, for the following reaction:

$$H_2O(g) + CO(g) \rightleftharpoons H_2(g) + CO_2(g)$$

On the basis of the previous equation, we can write

$$\Delta G^\circ = \Delta G_f^\circ(H_2(g)) + \Delta G_f^\circ(CO_2(g))$$
$$- \Delta G_f^\circ(H_2O(g)) - \Delta G_f^\circ(CO(g))$$

Since the standard free energy of formation for an elemental substance, such as hydrogen, is zero by definition, we obtain

$$\Delta G° = \Delta G_f°(CO_2(g)) - \Delta G_f°(H_2O(g)) - \Delta G_f°(CO(g))$$

Substitution of appropriate values from Table 1-1 gives

$$\Delta G° = -94.26 - (-54.64) - (-32.81)$$
$$\Delta G° = -6.81 \text{ kilocalories}$$

which indicates that the formation of products in their standard states from reactants in their standard states is a spontaneous process.

EXAMPLE 5

Calculate the standard free-energy change for the reaction

$$BaCO_3(s) \rightleftharpoons BaO(s) + CO_2(g)$$

from information given in Table 1-1.

As a first step in obtaining the desired result, one may write

$$\Delta G° = \Delta G_f°(BaO(s)) + \Delta G_f°(CO_2(g)) - \Delta G_f°(BaCO_3(s))$$

Next, one can insert $\Delta G_f°$ values found in the table:

$$\Delta G° = -126.3 - 94.26 - (-272.2)$$
$$\Delta G° = +51.6 \text{ kilocalories}$$

Such a positive free-energy change reveals that barium carbonate has very little tendency to decompose thermally into barium oxide and carbon dioxide at 25°C.

EXAMPLE 6

Determine the standard free-energy change for the reaction

$$6\ NO_2(g) + 4\ H_2S(g) \rightleftharpoons 3\ N_2(g) + 4\ SO_2(g) + 4\ H_2O(g)$$

from data presented in Table 1-1.

This problem differs from the two preceding ones in that the stoichiometric coefficients of the balanced chemical reaction are not unity. Therefore, our relation for $\Delta G°$ must take account of this fact as follows:

$$\Delta G° = 3 \ \Delta G_f°(N_2(g)) + 4 \ \Delta G_f°(SO_2(g)) + 4 \ \Delta G_f°(H_2O(g)) \\ - 6 \ \Delta G_f°(NO_2(g)) - 4 \ \Delta G_f°(H_2S(g))$$

Inasmuch as the standard free energy of formation of nitrogen is zero, we need only obtain $\Delta G_f°$ values from Table 1-1 for the four remaining species. Thus,

$$\Delta G° = 4(-71.79) + 4(-54.64) - 6(+12.39) - 4(-7.89) \\ \Delta G° = -548.5 \text{ kilocalories}$$

We are now ready to extend the results of the preceding discussion to a consideration of the general process

$$a\text{A} + b\text{B} \rightleftharpoons c\text{C} + d\text{D}$$

If it is assumed that all reactants and products exist in their standard-state conditions, the standard free-energy change for the reaction is

$$\Delta G° = c[\Delta G_f°(C)] + d[\Delta G_f°(D)] - a[\Delta G_f°(A)] - b[\Delta G_f°(B)] \qquad (1.1)$$

In most chemical systems, we encounter reactant and product species under conditions of concentration different from those specified for their standard states. For example, gaseous compounds may be present at pressures other than one atmosphere, whereas the activities or effective concentrations of dissolved substances are very likely not equal to unity. Fortunately, from the second law of thermodynamics, we can derive an expression to relate ΔG_f, the free energy of formation of a dissolved substance at *any* activity, to the standard free energy of formation, $\Delta G_f°$, which is

$$\Delta G_f = \Delta G_f° + RT \ln a$$

where R, the universal gas constant, is 0.001987 kilocalorie per mole-degree, T is the absolute temperature ($298°K$), and $\ln a$ is the natural logarithm of the activity or effective concentration of the species of interest in moles per liter. For gaseous substances the preceding equation is usually written in the slightly modified form

$$\Delta G_f = \Delta G_f° + RT \ln P$$

in which $\ln P$ represents the natural logarithm of the pressure in atmospheres.

Let us now formulate an expression for the free-energy change for the general process

$$aA + bB \rightleftharpoons cC + dD \tag{1.2}$$

under *non-standard-state* conditions with respect to the activities or effective concentrations of the reactants and products. Here again, the free-energy change for the reaction is defined as the sum of the free energies of formation of the products minus the sum of the free energies of formation of the reactants. However, in order to indicate the generality of the experimental conditions, we must employ ΔG and ΔG_f rather than $\Delta G°$ and $\Delta G_f°$, since the latter terms pertain only to reactions occurring under standard-state conditions. Since the quantities of A and B which do react, and the amounts of C and D which are formed, must still be stoichiometrically related to each other, it follows that

$$\Delta G = c[\Delta G_f(C)] + d[\Delta G_f(D)] - a[\Delta G_f(A)] - b[\Delta G_f(B)] \tag{1.3}$$

Subtraction of equation 1.1 from equation 1.3 and rearrangement of terms yield

$$\Delta G - \Delta G° = c[\Delta G_f(C) - \Delta G_f°(C)] + d[\Delta G_f(D) - \Delta G_f°(D)]$$

$$- a[\Delta G_f(A) - \Delta G_f°(A)] - b[\Delta G_f(B) - \Delta G_f°(B)] \tag{1.4}$$

Recalling the relationship for the free energy of formation of any substance,

$$\Delta G_f = \Delta G_f° + RT \ln a$$

or

$$\Delta G_f - \Delta G_f° = RT \ln a$$

applying it to each of the four substances A, B, C, and D, and substituting the resulting expressions into equation 1.4, one obtains

$$\Delta G - \Delta G° = cRT \ln a_C + dRT \ln a_D - aRT \ln a_A - bRT \ln a_B$$

Further rearrangement and combination of logarithmic terms may be performed as follows:

$$\Delta G - \Delta G° = RT \ln (a_C)^c + RT \ln (a_D)^d - RT \ln (a_A)^a - RT \ln (a_B)^b$$

$$\Delta G - \Delta G° = RT \ln \frac{(a_C)^c (a_D)^d}{(a_A)^a (a_B)^b}$$

or

$$\Delta G = \Delta G^\circ + RT \ln \frac{(a_C)^c (a_D)^d}{(a_A)^a (a_B)^b} \tag{1.5}$$

Equation 1.5 reveals that the free-energy change for a chemical reaction is dependent upon two factors: the standard free-energy change for the reaction which, according to equation 1.1, is related to the standard free energies of formation of the substances involved in the reaction; and the activities or effective concentrations of the reactants and products.

FREE ENERGY AND THE EQUILIBRIUM STATE

We have already noted that free-energy change is a measure of the driving force which causes a chemical reaction to tend to proceed spontaneously from a nonequilibrium state to an equilibrium state. When the system is at equilibrium, the driving force is zero; thus the free-energy change, ΔG, is zero. Therefore, for the system of equation 1.2 under equilibrium conditions, equation 1.5 becomes

$$0 = \Delta G^\circ + RT \ln \frac{(a_C)^c (a_D)^d}{(a_A)^a (a_B)^b}$$

or

$$\Delta G^\circ = -RT \ln \frac{(a_C)^c (a_D)^d}{(a_A)^a (a_B)^b} \tag{1.6}$$

Recognizing that the ratio of factors in the logarithmic term of equation 1.6 contains the *equilibrium* activities of all reactants and products involved in the general chemical reaction of equation 1.2, we may identify this ratio as a **thermodynamic equilibrium constant, K**. Thus,

$$K = \frac{(a_C)^c (a_D)^d}{(a_A)^a (a_B)^b} \tag{1.7}$$

and

$$\Delta G^\circ = -RT \ln K \tag{1.8}$$

or, if base-ten or decimal logarithms are employed,

$$\Delta G^\circ = -2.303 RT \log K \tag{1.9}$$

This equilibrium constant is the same as that derived from a consideration of kinetics, except that one is written in terms of actual or analytical concentrations, and the other in terms of activities or effective concentrations. However, it should be pointed out that even in the kinetic approach the use of activities would have been more rigorously correct than the use of actual analytical concentrations. Therefore, the two approaches to the derivation of the equilibrium-constant expression do, in fact, lead to exactly the same result, and this result may be taken as a mathematical statement of the Law of Chemical Equilibrium. Thus, from both kinetic and thermodynamic considerations, we have derived the fundamental equation which governs a chemical system in a state of equilibrium. In addition, we have obtained mathematical relationships between thermodynamic quantities and the equilibrium state.

Before leaving this discussion, it is worthwhile to see, by means of some specific examples, how to evaluate the equilibrium constant from thermodynamic data.

EXAMPLE 7

Calculate the equilibrium constant at 25°C for the reaction

$$H_2(g) + I_2(s) \rightleftharpoons 2\ HI(g)$$

from information given in Table 1-1.

It should be evident from earlier work in this chapter that we can obtain the standard free-energy change for the production of two moles of hydrogen iodide gas from the relationship

$$\Delta G° = 2\ \Delta G_f°(HI(g)) - \Delta G_f°(H_2(g)) - \Delta G_f°(I_2(s))$$

and that the equilibrium constant can, in turn, be determined with the aid of the equation

$$\Delta G° = -RT \ln K$$

Since the standard free energies of formation of hydrogen gas and solid iodine are defined to be zero, we have

$$\Delta G° = 2\ \Delta G_f°(HI(g))$$
$$\Delta G° = 2\,(0.31) = +0.62 \text{ kilocalorie}$$

When this latter result is substituted into the expression

$$\Delta G° = -RT \ln K$$

along with the values for R and T of 0.001987 kilocalorie per mole-degree and 298°K, respectively, one obtains

$$0.62 = -(0.001987)\,(298) \ln K$$

$$\ln K = -\frac{0.62}{(0.001987)\,(298)} = -1.05$$

If we convert natural logarithms to base-ten logarithms, taking note of the fact that $\ln K = 2.303 \log K$, the preceding relation becomes

$$\log K = -\frac{1.05}{2.303} = -0.46 = 0.54 - 1.00$$

and

$$K = 3.5 \times 10^{-1} = 0.35$$

EXAMPLE 8

Determine the equilibrium constant for the formation of carbon tetrachloride and hydrogen chloride from methane and chlorine at 25°C:

$$CH_4(g) + 4\ Cl_2(g) \rightleftharpoons CCl_4(l) + 4\ HCl(g)$$

As in the previous examples, we can evaluate the standard free-energy change for this reaction by means of the relation

$$\Delta G° = \Delta G_f°(CCl_4(l)) + 4\ \Delta G_f°(HCl(g))$$
$$- \Delta G_f°(CH_4(g)) - 4\ \Delta G_f°(Cl_2(g))$$

However, since the standard free energy of formation for chlorine is zero, it is only necessary to be concerned about the $\Delta G_f°$ values for carbon tetrachloride, hydrogen chloride, and methane. Accordingly, from data listed in Table 1-1, we find that

$$\Delta G° = -16.4 + 4(-22.77) - (-12.14)$$
$$\Delta G° = -95.4 \text{ kilocalories}$$

To obtain the equilibrium constant from the standard free-energy change, one can utilize the equation

$$\Delta G° = -RT \ln K$$

or, since base-ten logarithms are preferable, the expression

$$\Delta G° = -2.303\ RT \log K$$

If the second of these two relationships is used, we have

$$\log K = -\frac{\Delta G°}{2.303\ RT}$$

$$\log K = -\frac{(-95.4)}{(2.303)(0.001987)(298)} = 70.0$$

$$K = 1.0 \times 10^{70}$$

As the last sample calculation of this section, let us consider a reaction involving ionic species.

EXAMPLE 9

Calculate the equilibrium constant at 25°C for the following reaction, which shows the dissolution of silver chloride in water:

$$AgCl(s) \rightleftharpoons Ag^+ + Cl^-$$

First, let us formulate the expression for the standard free-energy change of this process:

$$\Delta G° = \Delta G_f°(Ag^+) + \Delta G_f°(Cl^-) - \Delta G_f°(AgCl(s))$$

Each of the three required standard free energies of formation is available in Table 1-1, so that we can write

$$\Delta G° = 18.43 + (-31.35) - (-26.22)$$
$$\Delta G° = +13.30 \text{ kilocalories}$$

This value substantiates our knowledge that silver chloride is relatively insoluble in pure water. Clearly, the formation of silver ion and chloride ion in their standard states at an activity or effective concentration of one mole per liter does not occur.

Next, we can substitute the appropriate known quantities into the relation

$$\log K = -\frac{\Delta G°}{2.303\, RT}$$

which, when solved, gives

$$\log K = -\frac{13.30}{(2.303)(0.001987)(298)} = -9.76$$

$$K = 1.74 \times 10^{-10}$$

Further consideration of this result — particularly in light of subsequent discussion in Chapter 2 — reveals that we have just calculated the solubility product for silver chloride from free-energy data.

THERMODYNAMIC CRITERION FOR A CHEMICAL REACTION

In the preceding section we were concerned with the driving force of a chemical reaction, primarily because it enabled us to derive certain information about the eventual equilibrium state of the system. However, this driving force is of considerable importance in its own right. Many chemical operations involve bringing reagents together in such a way that the system is not initially at equilibrium, regardless of whether or not we desire or expect the system sooner or later to attain its equilibrium state. We shall now consider the following fundamental question: If arbitrary quantities of substances A, B, C, and D are mixed, and if these species can interact according to the reversible reaction

$$a\mathrm{A} + b\mathrm{B} \rightleftharpoons c\mathrm{C} + d\mathrm{D}$$

how may we predict the direction, forward or backward, in which the reaction will proceed? The answer to this question can be obtained in several different ways, one of which was described in connection with Example 3, but for our present discussion we will base our answers on relations for the free-energy change of a reaction and for the ratios of activities of the substances involved.

Equation 1.6 deals with the activities of reactants and products at equilibrium with one another,

$$\Delta G^\circ = -RT \ln \frac{(a_\mathrm{C})^c (a_\mathrm{D})^d}{(a_\mathrm{A})^a (a_\mathrm{B})^b}$$

whereas equation 1.5, which contains activities of species not necessarily at equilibrium, may be written in the form

$$\Delta G = \Delta G^\circ + RT \ln \frac{(a'_\mathrm{C})^c (a'_\mathrm{D})^d}{(a'_\mathrm{A})^a (a'_\mathrm{B})^b} \tag{1.10}$$

We have used prime marks in equation 1.10 to distinguish these activities from those in equation 1.6, because the latter are valid only at equilibrium. In other words, a'_C is, for example, any actual activity of substance C, and a_C is its equilibrium activity. Substitution of equation 1.6 into equation 1.10 yields

$$\Delta G = -RT \ln \frac{(a_\mathrm{C})^c (a_\mathrm{D})^d}{(a_\mathrm{A})^a (a_\mathrm{B})^b} + RT \ln \frac{(a'_\mathrm{C})^c (a'_\mathrm{D})^d}{(a'_\mathrm{A})^a (a'_\mathrm{B})^b}$$

When we examine the significance of this relation with respect to the chemical reaction of equation 1.2, three important conclusions can be drawn.

First, if

$$\frac{(a'_C)^c (a'_D)^d}{(a'_A)^a (a'_B)^b} < \frac{(a_C)^c (a_D)^d}{(a_A)^a (a_B)^b}$$

the reaction will proceed in the forward direction, A and B combining to form C and D until equilibrium is established. In terms of the free-energy change, the process will tend to go in the forward direction if ΔG for the reaction is less than zero, that is, if ΔG is negative.

Second, if

$$\frac{(a'_C)^c (a'_D)^d}{(a'_A)^a (a'_B)^b} = \frac{(a_C)^c (a_D)^d}{(a_A)^a (a_B)^b}$$

then the system is already at equilibrium, and no net reaction will occur. In terms of the free-energy change, the system is at equilibrium if ΔG for the process is zero.

Third, if

$$\frac{(a'_C)^c (a'_D)^d}{(a'_A)^a (a'_B)^b} > \frac{(a_C)^c (a_D)^d}{(a_A)^a (a_B)^b}$$

the reaction will proceed in the backward direction, C and D combining to form A and B until equilibrium is established. In terms of the free-energy change, the reaction will tend to go in the backward direction if ΔG for the process is greater than zero, that is, if ΔG is positive.

FACTORS WHICH INFLUENCE CHEMICAL EQUILIBRIUM

In this section, the effects of several factors, which may be experimentally adjusted and controlled, upon systems which are in a state of chemical equilibrium will be described. Qualitative predictions of the influence of specific variables can be based on the principle of Le Châtelier, whereas the equilibrium constant itself provides a basis for quantitative considerations. Specific examples and numerical calculations pertaining to the points raised in this section will be found throughout this book, in conjunction with the discussion of the applications of equilibrium concepts to various types of chemical reactions.

The **principle of Le Châtelier**, which enables the chemist to make qualitative predictions of the effects of specific variations, may be stated in the general form: when a stress is applied to a system at equilibrium, the position of equilibrium tends to shift in such a direction as to diminish or relieve that stress. This principle is entirely consistent with relationships we have already developed to describe the equilibrium state, as will be seen in some of the examples to be discussed subsequently.

EFFECT OF CONCENTRATION

We noted in our description of the kinetic approach to equilibrium that the rate of any reaction is some function of the concentrations of the reacting species and that, when the system is in a state of equilibrium, the rates of the forward and backward reactions are equal. It is evident, therefore, that an increase or decrease in the concentration of a reactant or product in a system which is initially in an equilibrium state will cause an imbalance in the rates of the forward and backward reactions and that the system must shift in one direction or the other to establish a new position of equilibrium. A change in concentration of any component of the system does not alter the numerical value of the equilibrium constant. However, such a change does result in different concentrations of all species when equilibrium is restored, as well as corresponding variations in the actual rates of both the forward and the backward reactions at the new equilibrium state.

Le Châtelier's principle provides a qualitative guide to the direction in which an equilibrium is shifted by a change in the concentration of one of the chemical species. Since the stress in this case is a change in concentration, it may be predicted that the position of equilibrium will shift in such a way as to minimize this change. Thus, if the concentration of one of the components of the equilibrium mixture is diminished, the system will reach a new position of equilibrium by reacting in such a direction as to restore in part the concentration of the component which was withdrawn. Consider, for example, the system involving the dissociation of the silver-ammine complex in an aqueous medium,

$$Ag(NH_3)_2^+ \rightleftharpoons Ag^+ + 2\,NH_3$$

Removal from the solution of some of the silver ion by addition of chloride ion,

$$Ag^+ + Cl^- \rightleftharpoons AgCl(s)$$

will cause further dissociation of the $Ag(NH_3)_2^+$ complex in order to restore a condition of equilibrium. Similarly, when an additional amount of one of the components is introduced to a system at equilibrium, the system shifts toward a new position of equilibrium in such a direction as to consume part of the added material. Thus, introduction of some silver ion in the form of silver nitrate, for example, would promote the formation of more of the silver-ammine complex, the reaction proceeding from right to left as written.

EFFECT OF CATALYSTS

By influencing or altering the rate of a reaction, a catalyst hastens the approach of a chemical system to a state of equilibrium. However, and this is very important, catalysis always affects the rates of both forward and backward reactions to the same extent. When a system is at equilibrium, the forward and backward reaction rates may be greater in the presence of a catalyst than in its absence, but in each situation the forward and backward rates equal each other. In general, the catalyst enters into a chemical or physical process at some step in the overall reaction mechanism and is regenerated in a subsequent step. Although the physical properties of a catalyst may be altered, it does not undergo permanent chemical change. Thus, the catalyst does not appear as a reactant or product in the chemical equation representing the overall reaction, and catalysis never under any circumstance alters the numerical value of the equilibrium constant for a specific reaction.

We noted on page 3 that the rate of the reaction between hydrogen and oxygen gases to form water molecules, as well as the time required for equilibrium to be established in this system, is very markedly influenced by the presence of a catalyst. As another example of catalysis, consider the isotope exchange reaction occurring in the vapor phase between water and deuterium molecules,

$$H_2O + D_2 \rightleftharpoons HD + HDO$$

A mixture of H_2O and D_2 gases in a clean vessel reacts only slowly, typically requiring hours for the system to attain a state of equilibrium. In the presence of finely divided platinum oxide, however, the same initial mixture reaches its state of equilibrium in a few minutes. Nevertheless, both equilibrium mixtures contain exactly the same concentrations of each of the four species, whether the catalyst is present or not.

EFFECT OF TEMPERATURE

Unlike a change in concentration or the presence of a catalyst, neither of which alters the value of an equilibrium constant, variations in temperature may produce substantial changes in the numerical values of such constants. Increasing the temperature of a system at equilibrium, in effect, supplies heat or thermal energy. Many chemical reactions absorb heat as they proceed in one direction and are called **endothermic** processes, whereas those reactions which liberate thermal energy are designated as **exothermic** processes.

Usually, the quantity of heat liberated or absorbed during the occurrence of a chemical reaction is referred to as the **enthalpy change** and is given the symbol ΔH. In a manner similar to our earlier presentation of the concepts of free energy, each element in its standard state is assigned an enthalpy of zero, and a **standard enthalpy of formation,** ΔH_f°, is associated with the production of one mole of a compound in its standard state from the appropriate elements in their standard states. Furthermore, the **standard enthalpy change**, ΔH°, for any process is the sum of the standard enthalpies of formation for the products minus the sum of the standard enthalpies of formation for the reactants; that is

$$\Delta H^\circ = \sum \Delta H_f^\circ \text{ (products)} - \sum \Delta H_f^\circ \text{ (reactants)}$$

Like the standard free-energy change mentioned earlier in this chapter, the value of ΔH° is typically expressed in kilocalories. In addition, like the standard free energies of formation, the standard enthalpies of formation (ΔH_f°) are tabulated in units of kilocalories per mole of the substance of interest. Processes for which ΔH° is negative are exothermic, and the products of such reactions tend to be stable relative to the reactants. Conversely, endothermic reactions, for which the products are apt to be less stable than the reactants, have ΔH° values which are positive.

Now let us consider again a chemical system in a state of equilibrium. If the forward reaction is endothermic, the backward reaction is exothermic. However, the backward reaction will be endothermic if the forward reaction is exothermic. If the temperature of the system is increased, that is, if heat is supplied to the system, the position of equilibrium will shift in such a direction as to consume at least part of this extra thermal energy. Le Châtelier's principle enables us to predict that an increase in temperature will favor an endothermic reaction over an exothermic process. Therefore, if the forward reaction is exothermic, a rise in temperature will favor the backward reaction and thus make the numerical value of the equilibrium constant smaller; conversely, a drop in temperature favors the forward reaction and increases the value of the equilibrium constant. However, if the forward reaction is an endothermic process, the numerical value of the equilibrium constant increases with a rise of temperature and decreases if the temperature drops.

Thermodynamics allows us to derive an explicit equation to describe quantitatively how variations in temperature affect the magnitude of the equilibrium constant for a reaction. Although the desired relationship is reasonably easy to obtain from the second law of thermodynamics, it is sufficient here just to state the final expression. Thus, if K_1 and K_2 are equilibrium constants at absolute temperatures T_1 and T_2, respectively, we discover that

$$\ln \frac{K_2}{K_1} = -\frac{\Delta H^\circ}{R}\left(\frac{1}{T_2} - \frac{1}{T_1}\right)$$

where ΔH° is the standard enthalpy change for the process of interest and R is the universal gas constant. When base-ten logarithms are employed, the preceding equation takes the form

$$\log \frac{K_2}{K_1} = -\frac{\Delta H^\circ}{2.303\, R}\left(\frac{1}{T_2} - \frac{1}{T_1}\right)$$

These relationships may be utilized in either of two ways. First, if the equilibrium constant for a reaction at one temperature is known, along with the value of $\Delta H°$, one can determine the equilibrium constant at another temperature. One possible source of difficulty in this procedure is the need to assume that $\Delta H°$ remains constant within the temperature range of concern; however, for most purposes no serious error is incurred, because $\Delta H°$ changes only slightly with temperature. A second application of these expressions is in the calculation of the standard enthalpy change from knowledge of the equilibrium constant for a reaction at two different temperatures.

EXAMPLE 10

Given that the standard enthalpy change ($\Delta H°$) for the reaction

$$2 \text{ HI(g)} \rightleftharpoons \text{H}_2\text{(g)} + \text{I}_2\text{(g)}$$

is +3.03 kilocalories and that the equilibrium constant is 0.0162 at 667°K, what is the value of the equilibrium constant at 760°K?

If $T_1 = 667°\text{K}$, $T_2 = 760°\text{K}$, and $K_1 = 0.0162$, and if these values are substituted into the equation

$$\log \frac{K_2}{K_1} = -\frac{\Delta H°}{2.303 \, R} \left(\frac{1}{T_2} - \frac{1}{T_1} \right)$$

we have

$$\log \frac{K_2}{(0.0162)} = -\frac{(3.03)}{(2.303)(0.001987)} \left(\frac{1}{760} - \frac{1}{667} \right)$$

which can be solved for K_2, the equilibrium constant at 760°K, as follows:

$$\log \frac{K_2}{(0.0162)} = -\frac{(3.03)(-0.00018)}{(2.303)(0.001987)} = 0.120$$

$$\frac{K_2}{(0.0162)} = 1.32$$

$$K_2 = (0.0162)(1.32) = 0.0214$$

EXAMPLE 11

If the equilibrium constant for the reaction

$$\text{PCl}_5\text{(g)} \rightleftharpoons \text{PCl}_3\text{(g)} + \text{Cl}_2\text{(g)}$$

is 1.8×10^{-7} at 25°C and 1.8 at 250°C, determine the enthalpy change for the process.

Before performing the necessary calculations, we should note that only an average enthalpy change for the temperature interval between 25 and 250°C can be obtained, even though ΔH does not vary more than one per cent between the two extremes of temperature. Therefore, in the computations which follow, it is preferable to use ΔH instead of $\Delta H°$ in the equation

$$\log \frac{K_2}{K_1} = -\frac{\Delta H}{2.303\,R}\left(\frac{1}{T_2} - \frac{1}{T_1}\right)$$

From the statement of the problem, we have $K_1 = 1.8 \times 10^{-7}$, $K_2 = 1.8$, $T_1 = 298°K$, and $T_2 = 523°K$. Substitution of these quantities, along with the value of R, into the previous relationship yields

$$\log \frac{(1.8)}{(1.8 \times 10^{-7})} = -\frac{\Delta H}{(2.303)(0.001987)}\left(\frac{1}{523} - \frac{1}{298}\right)$$

$$\log (1.0 \times 10^7) = -\frac{(\Delta H)(-0.00145)}{(2.303)(0.001987)} = (0.317)(\Delta H)$$

$$7.00 = (0.317)(\Delta H)$$

$$\Delta H = \frac{7.00}{0.317} = 22.1 \text{ kilocalories}$$

It is of interest to note that, along with its influence upon the position of a chemical equilibrium, temperature has a pronounced effect on the rates of both the forward and backward reactions involved in the equilibrium. Many reactions increase in rate by a factor of approximately two or three for every 10 degree rise in temperature. This increase in the rate of a chemical process arises because the number, and particularly the average energy, of collisions between reacting species is enhanced at elevated temperatures. However, inasmuch as the equilibrium constant is altered by a change in temperature, it follows that an increase in temperature does not increase the rates of the forward and backward reactions to the same extent. For example, we have noted that an increase in temperature causes an increase in the equilibrium constant for the endothermic dissociation of hydrogen iodide into hydrogen and iodine gases. This means that the temperature rise causes the rate constant k_f for the forward reaction to increase to a greater extent than the rate constant k_b of the backward reaction, even though both rate constants become larger.

Let us now consider further the effect of temperature upon the free-energy change for a chemical process. An equation relating the free-energy change, ΔG, for a reaction to the enthalpy change, ΔH, may be derived from the second law of thermodynamics. Suffice it to state here that the result of that derivation is the Gibbs-Helmholtz equation,

$$\Delta G = \Delta H - T\Delta S \tag{1.11}$$

where T is the absolute temperature and ΔS is the change in a quantity called the **entropy** of the system. A definite amount of entropy, like free-energy and enthalpy, is associated with each chemical substance. More specifically, entropy is a measure of the *degree of disorder* in a substance. Consequently, the entropy is greater for a given species in the gaseous state, where the particles are highly disordered with respect to each other, than for the same substance in the form of a crystalline solid, which consists of a well-organized geometric structure. For example, the absolute entropies of helium, nitrogen, and n-pentane (C_5H_{12}) at 25°C are 30.1, 45.7, and 83.4 calories per mole-degree (entropy units), respectively. Helium, which has the lowest entropy of the three gases, is monatomic and is capable only of translational motion. However, as a diatomic molecule, nitrogen has a larger entropy because both translational and rotational movement can contribute to its degree of disorder. Finally, n-pentane, which consists of a chain of five carbon atoms, may exhibit large vibrational and rotational as well as translational disorder. It is interesting to compare two familiar solids, diamond which is very hard and silver which is a relatively soft metal; the absolute entropy of diamond is extremely low, 0.6 calorie per mole-degree, and that of silver is 10.2 calories per mole-degree. Such factors as the weakness of the attractive forces between individual atoms or molecules and the high mobility of the molecules or atoms tend to increase the disorder of a substance, and hence its entropy.

According to equation 1.11, the entropy change is a factor which contributes to the driving force of a chemical reaction. This fact may be interpreted as signifying that there is a natural tendency for all substances to become disorganized. Such a tendency for a system to attain maximal entropy is actually the major driving force for some chemical processes.

As we have mentioned earlier, numerical values of ΔH for various reactions are essentially independent of temperature. For the reaction in which carbon dioxide is formed from carbon monoxide and oxygen,

$$CO(g) + \tfrac{1}{2}\, O_2(g) \rightleftharpoons CO_2(g)$$

the standard enthalpy change ($\Delta H°$) is -67.64 kilocalories at 298°K and -67.79 kilocalories at 398°K. Likewise, values of ΔS for numerous processes are largely invariant with changes in temperature. Therefore, the $T\Delta S$ term is directly proportional to temperature, and ΔG is very strongly temperature-dependent. At ordinary room temperatures, on the order of 25°C, numerical values of $T\Delta S$ for most chemical reactions are much smaller than the magnitudes of ΔH. This means that the major component of ΔG is the ΔH term, which in turn agrees with the fact that most exothermic reactions (ΔH negative) are spontaneous (ΔG negative). However, at room temperatures for a few reactions, and at higher temperatures for many reactions, the $T\Delta S$ term is sufficiently large compared to ΔH, and is of the appropriate sign, so that an exothermic process may be nonspontaneous and an endothermic process may be spontaneous. At a pressure of one atmosphere and a temperature of 298°K, the reaction

$$4\ Ag(s) + O_2(g) \rightleftharpoons 2\ Ag_2O(s)$$

is exothermic, having a $\Delta H°$ value of -14.62 kilocalories. In addition, the standard entropy change ($\Delta S°$) for this process is -0.0316 kilocalorie per degree. It is of considerable interest to determine the influence of temperature on the direction of this reaction, which we can accomplish by evaluating the free-energy change at different temperatures with the aid of the Gibbs-Helmholtz equation:

$$\Delta G = \Delta H - T\Delta S$$

In performing these calculations, we must assume that the values of $\Delta H°$ and $\Delta S°$ are applicable throughout a wide range of temperature, a point which has been discussed previously. Accordingly, let us employ the relation

$$\Delta G = \Delta H° - T\Delta S°$$

for the calculation of the free-energy change at five selected temperatures.

At 298°K: $\Delta G = \Delta H° - T\Delta S°$
$\Delta G = -14.62 - (298)(-0.0316)$
$\Delta G = -14.62 + 9.42 = -5.20$ kilocalories

At 375°K: $\Delta G = \Delta H° - T\Delta S°$
$\Delta G = -14.62 - (375)(-0.0316)$
$\Delta G = -14.62 + 11.86 = -2.76$ kilocalories

At 463°K: $\Delta G = \Delta H° - T\Delta S°$
$\Delta G = -14.62 - (463)(-0.0316)$
$\Delta G = -14.62 + 14.62 = 0$

At 550°K: $\Delta G = \Delta H° - T\Delta S°$
$\Delta G = -14.62 - (550)(-0.0316)$
$\Delta G = -14.62 + 17.38 = +2.76$ kilocalories

At 700°K: $\Delta G = \Delta H° - T\Delta S°$
$\Delta G = -14.62 - (700)(-0.0316)$
$\Delta G = -14.62 + 22.13 = +7.51$ kilocalories

At temperatures below 463°K, the reaction is spontaneous as written, because the free-energy change is negative. However, for temperatures above 463°K, the value of $T\Delta S$ actually exceeds the magnitude of ΔH, so that ΔG becomes positive and the *reverse* process occurs spontaneously at one atmosphere pressure.

EFFECT OF PRESSURE

Changes in pressure may exert either a considerable influence upon the position of a chemical equilibrium, or almost none at all. As should be expected, the effects are most pronounced for gas-phase systems, which will be considered in detail in a later section of this chapter. Therefore, only a qualitative discussion will be included at this point.

Consider, for example, a system in which the gas-phase equilibrium

$$2\ SO_2(g) + O_2(g) \rightleftharpoons 2\ SO_3(g)$$

prevails. A rise in the overall pressure of the system would be expected to cause a marked change in the position of equilibrium. Such a result is explicable on the basis of Le Châtelier's principle, interpreted for the present situation to state that any increase in pressure favors a shift in the equilibrium position in whichever direction tends to reduce the number of molecules present. Notice that three molecules of reactants — two molecules of sulfur dioxide and one molecule of oxygen — combine to form two molecules of sulfur trioxide. Consequently, any rise in pressure will favor the formation of a higher percentage of sulfur trioxide, because the system can most readily relieve this stress through a decrease in the total number of molecules.

For a gas-phase equilibrium such as

$$2\ HI(g) \rightleftharpoons H_2(g) + I_2(g)$$

in which the *same* total number of molecules appears on both the reactant and product side of the chemical process, no change in the number of molecules accompanies the decomposition of hydrogen iodide at a specified temperature and pressure. Therefore, the position of equilibrium is not influenced by variations in the total pressure of the system.

Equilibria occurring in condensed phases, such as aqueous solutions, are usually not greatly altered by variations in pressure because liquids are so much less compressible than gaseous systems. However, slight changes in the position of an equilibrium which do occur follow the principle of Le Châtelier; that is, a system always responds to an increase in pressure by undergoing a decrease in volume. The autoprotolysis or self-ionization of water, for example,

$$H_2O + H_2O \rightleftharpoons H_3O^+ + OH^-$$

takes place with a very small decrease in volume because the orientation of other water molecules around the ionic species, H_3O^+ and OH^-, leads to a more compact structure than exists hypothetically before any ionization occurs. Consequently, if the pressure upon a sample of water is raised from one atmosphere to several thousand atmospheres, the extent of ionization of water increases by a factor of two or three.

COMPLETENESS OF REACTION

It is frequently important that reactions used in laboratory work and in industrial chemistry go substantially to completion. For example, when chloride is to be determined in an analytical chemistry laboratory by the precipitation and weighing of silver chloride, essentially all of the chloride present in the unknown sample must be converted to silver chloride:

$$Cl^- + Ag^+ \rightleftharpoons AgCl(s)$$

The precipitation of an indeterminate fraction of the chloride as silver chloride would clearly be worthless. In this example, the precipitation reaction may be considered as quantitatively complete when the amount of material remaining unprecipitated is a negligible fraction of the total weight of silver chloride. Thus, if the precipitate is to be weighed on an analytical balance with a sensitivity limit of 0.0001 gram, any amount of material left in solution which weighs less than this is of no consequence. Similarly, when a substance is manufactured industrially by means of a chemical process, it is important that the reaction go as far toward completion as is economically feasible.

It is worthwhile to consider under what conditions reversible reactions will go to practical completion. It should be noted first that any process for which the numerical value of the equilibrium constant is large — that is, for which the standard free-energy change is negative and of large magnitude — is a reaction for which the position of equilibrium inherently lies far to the right. Second, for any reaction, free-energy considerations and Le Châtelier's principle both suggest that the position of a chemical equilibrium can be shifted toward the right if one or more reaction products are removed from the system. Under such conditions, the desired reaction may proceed far to the right in an effort to re-form and to replace the component as fast as it is withdrawn. Even a reaction with a relatively small equilibrium constant goes to practical completion if the removal of one or more reaction products is continuous and extensive. Four important ways in which a reaction product may be effectively removed from a system are (1) by allowing a gaseous product to escape, (2) by precipitating a product in a relatively insoluble form, (3) by complexing one of the products as a stable ion in solution, and (4) by forming a stable molecule, such as when water is produced in an acid-base reaction. If one or more of these mechanisms is operative, the reaction should proceed to completion—the degree of completeness depending on the effectiveness with which the reaction product is removed.

We will now consider two additional sample problems which illustrate the principles discussed throughout this section.

EXAMPLE 12

At 1000°K the standard enthalpy changes for two different reactions are as follows:

$$H_2(g) + CO_2(g) \rightleftharpoons H_2O(g) + CO(g) \; ; \; \Delta H° = +8.3 \text{ kcal}$$
$$2 \, H_2S(g) \rightleftharpoons 2 \, H_2(g) + S_2(g) \; ; \; \Delta H° = -43.1 \text{ kcal}$$

Suppose that each of these processes is at equilibrium at a temperature of 1000°K and a total pressure of 0.500 atmosphere. For each of the following experimental changes, state (i) whether no net reaction occurs, (ii) whether net reaction occurs to the right, or (iii) whether net reaction occurs to the left:

(a) If additional hydrogen gas is introduced into the system at 1000°K, and if the total pressure is maintained constant by appropriate increase in the volume:

Since hydrogen gas is a *reactant* for the process

$$H_2(g) + CO_2(g) \rightleftharpoons H_2O(g) + CO(g)$$

any addition of this substance to an equilibrium mixture will cause reaction to occur toward the *right* until a new position of equilibrium is attained. On the other hand, hydrogen gas is a *product* for the reaction

$$2 \, H_2S(g) \rightleftharpoons 2 \, H_2(g) + S_2(g)$$

so, if more of it is added to a system initially at equilibrium, there will be some net reaction occurring to the *left*.

(b) If the temperature of the equilibrium mixture is decreased to 500°K, while the total pressure is kept at 0.500 atmosphere:

With a $\Delta H°$ of +8.3 kilocalories, the first reaction

$$H_2(g) + CO_2(g) \rightleftharpoons H_2O(g) + CO(g)$$

is *endothermic;* thus a *drop* in temperature from 1000 to 500°K will cause the numerical value of the equilibrium constant

$$K = \frac{[H_2O(g)][CO(g)]}{[H_2(g)][CO_2(g)]}$$

to *decrease,* which means that the concentrations of hydrogen and carbon dioxide will increase and net reaction occurs to the *left.* For the second reaction

$$2 H_2S(g) \rightleftharpoons 2 H_2(g) + S_2(g)$$

the standard enthalpy change ($\Delta H°$) is -43.1 kilocalories, which indicates that the process is *exothermic* and that the equilibrium constant

$$K = \frac{[H_2(g)]^2[S_2(g)]}{[H_2S(g)]^2}$$

will *increase* with decreasing temperature. Thus, there will be some net reaction to the *right* and more hydrogen and gaseous sulfur will be formed.

(c) If the total pressure is increased to 5 atmospheres without a change in the temperature:

We have seen earlier that an increase in pressure for a gas-phase equilibrium will favor a shift in the position of equilibrium in whichever direction tends to reduce the total number of gas molecules present. Since the *same* total number of particles appears on each side of the reaction

$$H_2(g) + CO_2(g) \rightleftharpoons H_2O(g) + CO(g)$$

there will be *no net reaction* when the pressure is increased. However, the other process

$$2 H_2S(g) \rightleftharpoons 2 H_2(g) + S_2(g)$$

does show three molecules of products and two molecules of reactants, so that an increase in pressure will cause some net reaction toward the *left.*

EXAMPLE 13

At a temperature of 1000°K, the gas-phase reactions listed below have standard enthalpy changes and equilibrium constants as indicated.

Reaction	$\Delta H°$, kcal	K
(i) $CO_2(g) + C(s) \rightleftharpoons 2\ CO(g)$	+40.8	1.7
(ii) $H_2(g) + I_2(g) \rightleftharpoons 2\ HI(g)$	−3.2	29.1
(iii) $2\ SO_3(g) \rightleftharpoons 2\ SO_2(g) + O_2(g)$	+46.4	0.30

(a) Which of these reactions is exothermic?

Since an exothermic process is one which has a negative standard enthalpy change ($\Delta H°$), only reaction (ii) falls into this category.

(b) Which of these reactions has a negative $\Delta G°$ value?

We must recall that the relationship between the standard free-energy change and the equilibrium constant for a reaction is

$$\Delta G° = -2.303\ RT \log K$$

In order for $\Delta G°$ to be negative, the value of $\log K$ must be a positive number and K itself must be greater than unity. Consequently, both reactions (i) and (ii) have negative standard free-energy changes.

(c) For which of the preceding reactions will the equilibrium constant increase with increasing temperature?

According to our earlier discussion, a reaction which has a positive standard enthalpy change ($\Delta H°$), and which is endothermic, will have its equilibrium constant increase with increasing temperature. Conversely, a process which is exothermic has a negative standard enthalpy change and its equilibrium constant decreases as the temperature increases. Therefore, reactions (i) and (iii) with positive $\Delta H°$ values have equilibrium constants which increase when the temperature is raised.

(d) For which of the preceding reactions will the equilibrium constant increase with increasing pressure?

Except for one form of the equilibrium constant involving mole fractions (page 60), which is rarely employed for gaseous equilibria, changes in pressure do not influence the magnitude of an equilibrium constant, if ideal gas behavior is assumed.

(e) For which of the preceding reactions will the position of equilibrium shift toward the right if the volume of the system is increased at constant temperature?

Since an *increase* in volume at constant temperature corresponds to a *decrease* in total pressure, there should be a shift in the equilibrium position which favors the formation of a greater total number of molecules. Reaction (i)

$$CO_2(g) + C(s) \rightleftharpoons 2\ CO(g)$$

involves conversion of one molecule of carbon dioxide to two molecules of carbon monoxide, and reaction (iii)

$$2 \, SO_3(g) \rightleftharpoons 2 \, SO_2(g) + O_2(g)$$

shows decomposition of two molecules of sulfur trioxide into two sulfur dioxide molecules and one oxygen molecule. Both of these reactions will shift toward the right when the volume of the system is increased; however, there will be no net change in the position of equilibrium for reaction (ii), since it involves an identical number of molecules on both the reactant and product sides.

ACTIVITIES AND ACTIVITY COEFFICIENTS IN SOLUTION

DISTINCTION BETWEEN ACTIVITY AND ANALYTICAL CONCENTRATION

In this section the distinctions between activity, or effective concentration, and actual concentration in chemical reactions and in chemical equilibrium will be considered. Our primary concern will be with ionic species in aqueous solution. Similar considerations involving gas-phase substances will be described subsequently.

It is well known that certain properties of solutions – called **colligative properties** – such as vapor pressure, boiling point, and freezing point, are dependent upon the number, and not the kind, of dissolved solute particles. For example, one mole (6.023×10^{23} particles) of any nonelectrolyte dissolved in 1000 grams of water (that is, a one molal solution) produces the same freezing-point lowering of water, $-1.86°C$, as one mole of any other nonelectrolyte, because one mole of any such substance contains the same number of particles. If a strong electrolyte, such as sodium chloride, is completely dissociated in aqueous solution into sodium and chloride ions, it could be expected to lower the freezing point of water twice as much as an equal molal concentration of a nonelectrolyte. Actually, for a one molal solution of sodium chloride, the freezing point of water is lowered 1.81 times – but not twice – as much as for a nonelectrolyte solution of identical concentration. A similar discrepancy occurs in boiling-point elevation. These deviations from ideality can be accounted for on the basis of the effect of the solution environment on the behavior of the solute ions. For the sodium chloride solution, one must recognize that a sodium ion and a chloride ion have mutual attraction for each other, that two chloride ions, or two sodium ions, repel one another, and that sodium ion and chloride ion both undergo ion-solvent interactions with the water in which they are dissolved. In addition, if other cations and anions are present, these species will interact with the sodium ions and chloride ions. If a solution containing 0.1 M sodium ion and 0.1 M chloride ion, and possibly other species, behaved in a perfectly ideal manner, we would expect each of these ions to act as if its concentration were 0.1 M. On the other hand, if a certain fraction of the sodium ions is attracted to anionic species, including chloride, the ions do not behave as independent particles, and the solution will exhibit the properties of one in which the concentration of sodium ion is less than 0.1 M. Depending on the relative importance of factors such as ion-dipole attractions and ion-ion repulsions, sodium ion or chloride ion in a solution containing 0.1 M sodium chloride may behave in chemical reactions and in chemical equilibria as if its concentration were less than, equal to, or greater than 0.1 M.

To distinguish the effective concentration of a solute, which accounts for its non-ideal behavior, from the molar concentration, which is actually present and which can be determined as already stated by a titrimetric or gravimetric method of chemical analysis, the term **activity** has been defined to be the effective concentration. It is customary to relate the activity of an individual species to its analytical concentration through the simple expression

$$a_i = f_i C_i \tag{1.12}$$

in which a_i is the activity of substance i, f_i is the **activity coefficient** of substance i, and C_i is its analytical concentration. Using the symbols introduced on page 18 to represent activity and analytical molar concentration, we may write the activity of sodium ion as

$$a_{Na^+} = f_{Na^+} [Na^+] \quad \text{or} \quad (Na^+) = f_{Na^+} [Na^+]$$

and that of chloride ion as

$$a_{Cl^-} = f_{Cl^-} [Cl^-] \quad \text{or} \quad (Cl^-) = f_{Cl^-} [Cl^-]$$

Activity and concentration are always expressed in such a way that both terms have identical units, usually moles per liter for solute species, so the activity coefficient is a dimensionless parameter.

Data presented in Table 1-2 are especially impressive in emphasizing the fact that there really are marked differences between activity and actual concentration, and, therefore, that interionic attractions and repulsions or ion-dipole interactions do exist. This table lists the activity, or effective concentration, which exists for each of several different molar concentrations of hydrochloric acid. It is clear that the activity of this solute does differ from the analytical concentration, especially in the more highly concentrated solutions.

Important features of the data in Table 1-2 can be described most readily if the behavior of hydrochloric acid solutions is depicted in graphical form. When we rearrange equation 1.12 to the relation

$$f_i = \frac{a_i}{C_i}$$

we can see that three situations prevail:

(1) If the activity a_i of a substance is exactly equal to its concentration C_i, the activity coefficient f_i is unity and the substance is said to behave in an *ideal* manner. Since the activity of a species reflects all possible physical and chemical interactions which can occur in a solution, and since these interactions become vanishingly small when the concentrations of ionic species approach zero, we can rightly expect that f_i should be unity in infinitely dilute solutions of electrolytes.

(2) If the activity a_i of a substance is smaller than its concentration C_i, the activity coefficient f_i is less than unity and the substance is said to exhibit *negative* deviations from ideal behavior.

(3) If the activity a_i of a substance is larger than its concentration C_i, the activity coefficient f_i is greater than unity and the substance is said to display *positive* deviations from ideal behavior.

From a plot of the activity coefficient f_i of a species as a function of its analytical concentration, we should be able to tell at a glance for a given concentration whether the substance exhibits nearly ideal behavior, negative deviations from ideality, or positive deviations from ideality. Figure 1-2 shows a plot of the quantity $f_{\pm}$, which is called the **mean activity coefficient,** versus the molar concentration of hydrochloric

TABLE 1-2 ANALYTICAL CONCENTRATION
AND ACTIVITY OF HYDROCHLORIC
ACID SOLUTIONS

Concentration, M	Activity, M
0.00500	0.00464
0.0100	0.00907
0.0500	0.0416
0.100	0.0796
1.00	0.809
2.00	2.02
3.00	3.95
5.00	11.9
6.00	19.3
7.00	30.6
8.00	47.2
9.00	71.5
12.0	207.

acid solutions. Although the significance of the mean activity coefficient will become evident later, it suffices to mention here that $f_\pm$ is employed because the individual behavior of hydrogen ion and of chloride ion in a hydrochloric acid medium cannot be sorted out; each ion influences the activity of the other species. However, the use of $f_\pm$ does not alter our interpretation of the behavior of hydrochloric acid solutions.

Figure 1-2 confirms that the mean activity coefficient $f_\pm$ for hydrochloric acid is unity at infinite dilution, that is, at a hydrochloric acid concentration of virtually zero. As the hydrochloric acid concentration is increased, the activity coefficient decreases, reaching a minimum value of approximately 0.76 at a hydrochloric acid concentration near 0.500 M. If one continues to increase the concentration of hydrochloric acid above 0.500 M, the mean activity coefficient climbs steadily until it attains a value of unity at a concentration slightly less than 2.00 M. For concen-

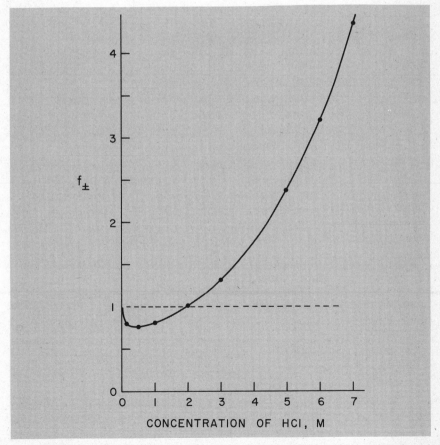

FIGURE 1-2 Mean activity coefficient $f_\pm$ for hydrochloric acid as a function of the analytical concentration of the acid. (See text for discussion.)

trations greater than $2.00\ M$, the activity coefficient rises very abruptly, indicating that such solutions exhibit large positive deviations from ideality.

One especially interesting feature of the behavior of hydrochloric acid is that the mean activity coefficient is unity for an approximately $2\ M$ solution. This observation could be interpreted to mean that the solution behaves ideally. Actually, the activity coefficient is unity only because two opposing phenomena offset each other perfectly. The first factor is that the ion-ion attractions between hydrogen ion and chloride ion cause the activity to be *less* than the concentration of hydrochloric acid and the activity coefficient to be *less* than unity. The second factor is that the solvation of hydrogen ions and chloride ions by water molecules decreases the available quantity of free or unbound solvent, thereby tending to make the activity *greater* than the concentration and the activity coefficient *greater* than unity. These two effects just happen to counteract each other in $2\ M$ hydrochloric acid. For solutions less concentrated than $2\ M$, the first factor is of greater importance, whereas the second factor predominates in hydrochloric acid media more concentrated than $2\ M$. We shall consider these effects in more detail subsequently.

Another interesting observation is that $12\ M$ hydrochloric acid, which is the commercially available concentrated reagent, behaves as if the hydrochloric acid concentration is really $207\ M$ (see Table 1-2). Actually, this is by no means extreme behavior. For example, a $20\ M$ solution of lithium bromide in water acts as if the lithium ion and bromide ion concentrations were each approximately $10{,}000\ M$, and the hydrogen ion activity in a $12\ M$ perchloric acid solution is $6000\ M$!

It should be emphasized that the behavior shown in Figure 1-2 for hydrochloric acid is quite typical of ionic solutes. A plot of activity coefficient versus the concentration of an electrolyte usually exhibits a curve which is qualitatively similar to that for hydrochloric acid. Naturally, the absolute values of the activity coefficients, as well as the solute concentration at which the activity·coefficient is minimal and at which the activity coefficient rises to unity again, depend on the nature of the solute.

In view of the important difference between activity and analytical concentration for an ionic solute such as hydrochloric acid, it is essential that activities or activity coefficients be used when rigorously correct equilibrium calculations are to be performed. For many rough calculations, however, including those made for predictive purposes in much of chemistry, it suffices to use equilibrium-constant expressions involving concentrations rather than activities.

Information about the activity of an ionic solute may be obtained in either of two general ways—direct experimental measurement or theoretical calculation. First, the activity of a species can be determined experimentally, for example, by measurement of the electromotive force of a galvanic cell, as will be described in Chapter 5. Alternatively, the mean activity coefficient of a solution of a single electrolyte can be experimentally measured through a determination of the freezing-point depression or from some other colligative property of the solution. Second, the activity of an ionic solute can be calculated from the simple equation

$$a_i = f_i C_i$$

provided that both the activity coefficient and the analytical concentration of the desired substance are known. Unfortunately, as we shall discover in the next several paragraphs, activity coefficients themselves can be calculated reliably only for electrolyte solutions up to a concentration level of perhaps $0.1\ M$. For the more concentrated solutions of single electrolytes normally encountered in much chemical work, the theoretical relations from which one can predict activity coefficients are invalid, and one must resort to one of the experimental methods of evaluating activities; however, for solutions containing mixtures of electrolytes, even the latter approach is unsuccessful. Nevertheless, by examining some of the theoretical equations which have been derived for the calculation of activity coefficients, and by comparing calculated results with those measured experimentally, we can gain considerable insight into the nature of electrolyte solutions.

DEBYE-HÜCKEL LIMITING LAW

One of the most significant contributions to our understanding of the nature of electrolyte solutions is the **Debye-Hückel limiting law,** the derivation of which was published in 1923. We shall begin this discussion with a description of some fundamental assumptions underlying the development of the limiting law. Then, by considering how well the predictions of this law agree with experimental observations, we may verify or revise our concepts of how ionic solutes behave.

One key assumption in the derivation of the Debye-Hückel limiting law is that interactions between charged solutes are purely electrostatic in character. Electrostatic forces are strictly long-range interactions. All short-range forces, including those due to van der Waals attractions, ion-pair formation, and ion-dipole interactions, are ignored.

Second among the assumptions underlying the Debye-Hückel limiting law is that, although the long-range electrostatic forces are operative, ions in solution are subject to random, thermal motion which serves to disrupt the orientation of oppositely charged species caused by specific interionic attractions. A third simplifying assumption in the derivation of the limiting law is that ionic species have spherical charge distribution, they cannot be polarized or distorted, and in fact they can be regarded as point charges. Furthermore, it is assumed that the dielectric constant and viscosity of pure water are applicable for all solutions, that is, that these parameters are uniform and independent of the concentration of the solute. Finally, it must be added that the theoretical model assumes complete dissociation of all electrolytes in the solution or at least dissociation of known fractions of these electrolytes.

No attempt will be made in this text to present a derivation of the Debye-Hückel limiting law because, in spite of the simplifying assumptions, the final equation is obtained only after considerable effort.

For a single ionic species such as sodium ion or chloride ion, the Debye-Hückel limiting law is usually written in the form

$$-\log f_i = 0.512\ z_i^2 \sqrt{\mu} \qquad (1.13)$$

where f_i is the activity coefficient, z_i is the charge of the ion of interest, μ is the ionic strength of the solution, and the constant, 0.512, is valid for water at 25°C. Ionic strength, μ, is defined as one-half the sum of the analytical concentration C_i multiplied by the square of the charge z_i for each ionic species in the solution, i.e.,

$$\mu = \tfrac{1}{2} \sum C_i z_i^2$$

For a solution containing K^+, Ca^{++}, Cl^-, and $SO_4^=$ ions, for example, the ionic strength is

$$\mu = \tfrac{1}{2}\ (C_{K^+} z_{K^+}{}^2 + C_{Ca^{++}} z_{Ca^{++}}{}^2 + C_{H^+} z_{H^+}{}^2 + C_{Cl^-} z_{Cl^-}{}^2 + C_{SO_4^=} z_{SO_4^=}{}^2)$$

$$\mu = \tfrac{1}{2}\{[K^+](1)^2 + [Ca^{++}](2)^2 + [Cl^-](-1)^2 + [SO_4^=](-2)^2\}$$

Although equation 1.13 can be employed to evaluate the activity coefficient for any single ionic species such as K^+ or Cl^-, this expression cannot be tested experimentally because it is impossible to prepare a solution containing just one kind of ion. For example, to obtain a solution of K^+, one might dissolve potassium chloride crystals in water. However, the interaction of potassium ion with chloride will influence the behavior of K^+. Thus, any technique which one utilizes to measure activity coefficients for this particular system will yield, in reality, the activity coefficient of K^+ in the presence of an equal concentration of Cl^-. Fortunately, by defining a new term, called the **mean activity coefficient** ($f_\pm$), we obtain a parameter which can be evaluated both experimentally and theoretically. The mean activity coefficient for a binary salt, $M_m N_n$, whose cation M has a charge z_M and whose anion N has a charge z_N, is related to the single-ion activity coefficients f_M and f_N by the equation

$$(f_\pm)^{m+n} = (f_M)^m (f_N)^n$$

Combining this relationship with equation 1.13 yields the result

$$-\log f_\pm = 0.512 \ z_M z_N \sqrt{\mu}$$

It is important to note here that only the *absolute* magnitudes of z_M and z_N are used in this equation.

Let us now consider some actual calculations involving the use of the Debye-Hückel limiting law. For example, let us determine the mean activity coefficient for $0.10 \ M$ hydrochloric acid. First, we must evaluate the ionic strength of the solution. Hydrogen ion and chloride ion are the only species present, so it follows that

$$\mu = \tfrac{1}{2} \ (C_{H^+} z_{H^+}^2 + C_{Cl^-} z_{Cl^-}^2)$$
$$\mu = \tfrac{1}{2} \ [(0.10)(1)^2 + (0.10)(-1)^2]$$
$$\mu = 0.10$$

Strictly speaking, ionic strength should be expressed in concentration units, such as moles per liter, but in most, if not all, reference books and research publications, ionic strength is reported as a dimensionless number. Next, since the absolute values of the charges on hydrogen ion and chloride ion are unity, the mean activity coefficient may be obtained from the expression

$$-\log f_\pm = 0.512 \ z_{H^+} z_{Cl^-} \sqrt{\mu}$$
$$-\log f_\pm = 0.512(1)(1) \ \sqrt{0.10}$$
$$-\log f_\pm = 0.162$$
$$f_\pm = 0.689$$

For purposes of comparison, the mean activity coefficient for $0.10 \ M$ hydrochloric acid has been experimentally measured and found to be 0.796.

As a second example, we shall calculate the mean activity coefficient for $0.10 \ M$ aluminum chloride solution. The ionic strength is

$$\mu = \tfrac{1}{2} \ (C_{Al^{+++}} z_{Al^{+++}}^2 + C_{Cl^-} z_{Cl^-}^2)$$
$$\mu = \tfrac{1}{2} \ [(0.10)(3)^2 + (0.30)(-1)^2]$$
$$\mu = 0.60$$

Notice that the ionic strength is six times greater than the concentration of the aluminum chloride solution. Substitution of the values for ionic strength and for the charges of the ions into the Debye-Hückel limiting law yields

$$-\log f_{\pm} = 0.512 \; z_{Al^{+++}} z_{Cl^-} \sqrt{\mu}$$
$$-\log f_{\pm} = 0.512(3)(1)\sqrt{0.60}$$
$$-\log f_{\pm} = 1.189$$
$$f_{\pm} = 0.0647$$

This calculated mean activity coefficient is less than one-fifth of the experimentally measured value, which is 0.337.

Numerous similar calculations were performed for other concentrations of hydrochloric acid and aluminum chloride, and the results are shown diagrammatically in Figure 1-3. Actual experimental values of the mean activity coefficients are included in this plot. One, and perhaps the most important, conclusion to be drawn from Figure 1-3 is that the Debye-Hückel limiting law is quantitatively useful only in very dilute solutions. A second distinctive feature of the plot is that the mean activity coefficients calculated from the limiting law (dashed lines) become significantly smaller than the true or observed values as ionic strength increases. Third, the Debye-Hückel limiting law does not account at all for the upward trend in activity coefficients at relatively high ionic strengths. In summary, the theoretical and experimental curves do converge at low ionic strengths and extrapolate to a mean activity coefficient of unity at zero ionic strength, so the concepts and assumptions implicit in the Debye-Hückel limiting law are valid, particularly for small electrolyte concentrations. In general, activity coefficients can be evaluated by means of the limiting law with an uncertainty not exceeding approximately five per cent for salts consisting of singly charged species up to $\mu = 0.05$, for salts consisting of doubly charged species up to ionic strengths of about 0.01, and for salts consisting of triply charged species, such as Al^{+++}, up to an ionic strength of about 0.005. These limits concerning the applicability of the Debye-Hückel limiting law must be regarded as rough guidelines only, because the specific nature of the ions in question has a great influence on the behavior of an electrolyte. Thus, for a given electrolyte concentration the mean activity coefficient varies with the nature of the substance. For example, the student may wish to verify from the Debye-Hückel limiting law that the mean activity coefficient of $0.005 \, M$ $MgCl_2$ is predicted to be 0.75, whereas that of $0.005 \, M$ $MgSO_4$ is expected to have a value of 0.51.

Let us now attempt to understand why the limiting law is inadequate and how the theoretical model can be modified so that a more accurate equation can be formulated. Two of the basic assumptions listed previously were that the ionic species are affected only by long-range forces and that thermal motion causes the particles to behave essentially in-

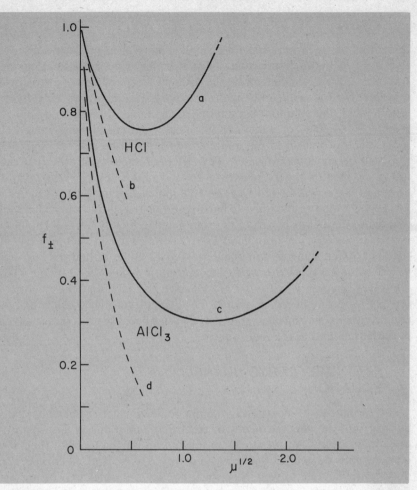

FIGURE 1-3 Comparison of the observed mean activity coefficients for hydrochloric acid and aluminum chloride with the theoretical mean activity coefficents calculated from the Debye-Hückel limiting law. *Curve a:* observed mean activity coefficients for HCl. *Curve b:* calculated mean activity coefficients for HCl. *Curve c:* observed mean activity coefficients for $AlCl_3$. *Curve d:* calculated mean activity coefficients for $AlCl_3$.

dependently of each other. In a dilute solution, where one may envisage a given ion to be insulated from other ions by a sheath of water molecules, these assumptions appear to be valid. In more concentrated solutions, ions are close to each other, and thus a number of highly specific interactions, such as ion-pair formation, may occur. Ion triplets and larger ion aggregates can conceivably form as well, particularly in the case of multiply charged species. These phenomena can do much to account for the increasing discrepancies between calculated and experimental values of the mean activity coefficients as the concentration increases beyond the limits listed in the preceding paragraph.

In addition, one can explain why activity coefficients become larger than unity in concentrated electrolyte solutions by considering the interactions between ions and water molecules. For example, we discover that a 12 M hydrochloric acid solution behaves as if the acid concentration is 207 M, indicating that the mean activity coefficient exceeds 17. Consider the following crude picture. If we have one liter of 12 M hydrochloric acid, the solution will contain 12 moles of the acid and approximately 55.6 moles of water. If the acid is completely dissociated, 12 moles each of hydrogen ion and chloride ion will be present, and these ions will be solvated by water. Then, if we assume arbitrarily that each ion is solvated on the average by 2.2 water molecules, the total quantity of bound water will be (24)(2.2) or 52.8 moles, leaving only 2.8 moles of water not bound to the ions. It must be emphasized that the water coordinated to these ions is part of the solute and definitely not solvent. Now, if 55.6 moles of water occupies 1 liter, 2.8 moles would occupy a volume of about 50 ml. Imagine that one dissolved 12 moles of hydrochloric acid in 50 ml of water — the acid concentration would be 240 M, which compares favorably with 207 M. Despite the fact that this picture is terribly oversimplified, it should be evident that very high activity coefficients in concentrated solutions do arise because most of the solvent is actually bound to the ionic species.

EXTENDED DEBYE-HÜCKEL EQUATION

It is difficult to incorporate the phenomena which we have been discussing into the general theory of electrolyte solutions in any rigorous, quantitative way. All these effects tend to be highly specific; they vary considerably depending on the geometry, charge, and electronic configuration of an ion, as well as on the other species which may be present. Several proposals have been made to modify the mathematical statement of the Debye-Hückel limiting law in order to include one or more of these refinements into the equation for an activity coefficient. One of these, which is intended primarily to provide recognition of the single fact that ions are of finite size rather than being point charges, as assumed in the derivation of the limiting law, is called the **extended Debye-Hückel equation**,

$$-\log f_{\pm} = 0.512 \; z_M z_N \left(\frac{\sqrt{\mu}}{1 + 0.328 \, a\sqrt{\mu}} \right)$$

in which a, expressed in angstrom units, is said to correspond to the average effective size (diameter) of the hydrated ions. Let us calculate the mean activity coefficient of 0.10 M hydrochloric acid by means of this relation. As found earlier, the ionic strength for this solution is 0.10,

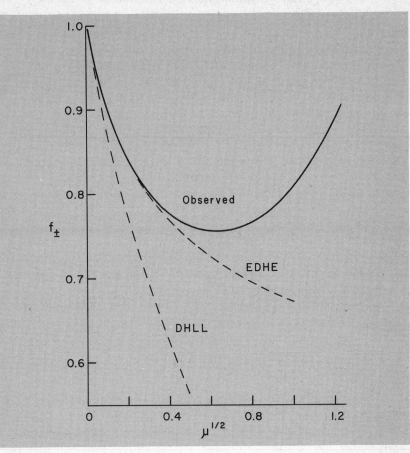

FIGURE 1-4 Comparison of mean activity coefficients for hydrochloric acid computed from Debye-Hückel limiting law (DHLL) and the extended Debye-Hückel equation (EDHE) with observed mean activity coefficients. The results based on the extended Debye-Hückel equation correspond to $a = 6$ angstroms.

and the average size of hydrogen ion and chloride ion is probably about 6 Å, a value which we will use here even though it is surely a rough estimate. Thus, the mean activity coefficient is given by

$$-\log f_{\pm} = 0.512\,(1)\,(1)\left[\frac{\sqrt{0.10}}{1+(0.328)(6)\,\sqrt{0.10}}\right]$$

$$-\log f_{\pm} = 0.0998$$

$$f_{\pm} = 0.794$$

This result, which agrees very well with the experimentally observed value of 0.796, lends strong support to the conclusion that the ionic size factor, incorporated into the derivation of the extended Debye-Hückel equation but omitted from the Debye-Hückel limiting law, is of significance. Nevertheless, some chemists contend that the parameter a should not be viewed as an ion diameter but as an empirical term which merely improves the agreement between experiment and theory.

In order to see how well the predictions of the extended Debye-Hückel equation follow the true behavior of hydrochloric acid, note the graph shown in Figure 1-4, which repeats some of the information given in Figure 1-3. It is evident that the extended Debye-Hückel equation provides much better agreement between theory and experiment than does the limiting law. However, neither relation predicts an increase in the mean activity coefficient at high ionic strengths, because the theoretical model does not include the solvation of ions by water molecules.

Several additional modifications of the basic Debye-Hückel equations have been developed. In every instance, however, these modifications take the form of empirical correction terms which are added to or subtracted from the extended Debye-Hückel equation in order to improve the agreement between observed and calculated activity coefficients. Because it is difficult, if not impossible, to assign any physical significance to these correction terms, we shall not discuss these relationships further in this text.

ACTIVITY COEFFICIENTS OF NEUTRAL MOLECULES

If one considers the behavior of neutral molecules or nonelectrolytes in the light of the Debye-Hückel theory, the conclusion is reached that such substances, being uncharged, should have activity coefficients of unity. Generally, in pure water the activity of a neutral solute is within one per cent of its analytical concentration. Therefore, the activity coefficients of such species will be taken as unity in all calculations throughout this text. However, let us briefly consider the factors which do account for the slight deviations observed.

In the presence of electrolytes the activity coefficient of an uncharged solute varies in accordance with the equation

$$\log f = k\mu$$

where f is the activity coefficient, μ is the ionic strength, and k, the "salting coefficient," may be either positive or negative. For small molecules, such as nitrogen, oxygen, and carbon dioxide, k is usually positive, with a value near 0.1, but for sugars and proteins k may be larger. If k is positive, $\log f$ is always greater than zero, provided that some electrolyte is present, so the activity coefficient f will be greater than unity and the activity will exceed the analytical concentration of the neutral solute. It is useful to remember that most solutes which have dielectric constants less than water generally behave in this manner.

Hydrogen cyanide is an example of a solute which exhibits the reverse behavior. Its dielectric constant (111 at 25°C) is much greater than that of water (78.5). Thus, the value of k is negative for this solute, and its activity is always less than its analytical concentration.

In addition, it may be noted that if k is positive the solubility of a neutral solute in an aqueous medium decreases with an increase in the ionic strength. Conversely, solutes having negative k values become more soluble at higher ionic strengths.

CONCENTRATION FACTORS IN GAS-PHASE EQUILIBRIA

We will now consider two important aspects of gas-phase equilibria: the distinction between pressure and fugacity of a gaseous substance, and the practical use of units other than atmospheres of pressure to express the quantity of each gaseous substance involved in a gas-phase equilibrium.

PRESSURE AND FUGACITY OF A GASEOUS SUBSTANCE

It will be recalled, from our discussion of electrolyte solutions in the preceding section of this chapter, that deviations from ideal behavior are reflected by the activity coefficient, which is the ratio of the activity or effective concentration of a substance to the actual or analytical concentration of that species. When the activity is greater than the analytical concentration, the activity coefficient exceeds unity and the particular substance shows positive deviations from ideality. On the other hand, if the analytical concentration is larger than the activity, the species of interest exhibits negative deviations from ideality and the activity coefficient is smaller than unity. Finally, if the activity coefficient of a solute is exactly unity, indicating that the activity and analytical concentration are identical, the substance is said to behave ideally.

A similar, but not identical, situation prevails for chemical systems containing gas-phase components. For an ideal gas, the **equation of state** is

$$PV = nRT \qquad (1.14)$$

where P, V, and T are, respectively, the pressure in atmospheres, the volume in liters, and the absolute temperature of n moles of the gas, and where R, known as the universal gas constant, is the same parameter encountered elsewhere in this chapter, although its value in the present relationship is 0.0821 liter-atmosphere per mole-degree. In general, the validity of equation 1.14 as being representative of the behavior of gases is well established in theory and in experiment. In fact, this expression correctly predicts the behavior (with an uncertainty no greater than a few per cent) of all real gases at or near room temperature and at pressures up to approximately one atmosphere. Nevertheless, significant deviations are found in the application of this relation to real gases under more extreme conditions of pressure and temperature.

Deviations of a real gas from ideal behavior can be described in terms of the ratio of the effective pressure, exhibited by a gas as it does behave, to the idealized pressure calculated from equation 1.14 for appropriate values of n, V, and T. Usually, the term **fugacity** is used to designate the effective pressure of a gaseous substance in units of atmospheres. Like the activity of a dissolved solute, the fugacity of a gaseous substance is equal to an activity coefficient multiplied by the idealized pressure. As we shall see, activity coefficients for gases, like those for solutes, may be numerically equal to unity, less than unity, or greater than unity.

Three factors influence the magnitude of the deviation of a real gas from ideal behavior—the identity of the gas, its temperature, and its pressure. A comparison of data for chlorine and oxygen, both at 25°C and at one atmosphere pressure, serves to illustrate the effect of the identity of the gas. The deviation of fugacity from idealized pressure is about 0.1 per cent for oxygen and about 1.6 per cent for chlorine. Both deviations are negative, which means that the activity coefficients are slightly less than unity.

As a general rule, the behavior of a real gas is essentially ideal at very low pressures. However, as the pressure is increased, at a fixed temperature, the fugacity becomes less than the idealized pressure. This is interpreted on the basis of intermolecular attractions. At the higher pressures, the gas molecules are closer together and are thus more susceptible to the attractive forces of one molecule for another. Even though these forces may not be very strong, as compared, for example, to the forces of mutual attraction of oppositely charged ions in an aqueous solution, intermolecular attractions in gases do exist. As a result of these intermolecular attractions, there is a tendency for the molecules to be drawn toward each other and for the effective pressure exerted by the gas to decrease.

With reference again to the comparison of chlorine and oxygen gases, it is interesting to note that at room temperature chlorine is much closer to its boiling point, −34.6°C, than is oxygen, which boils at −183.0°C. Thus, the intermolecular forces of attraction should be stronger in chlorine; and, as stated previously, the deviation from ideality is greater for chlorine than for oxygen.

As pressure is increased still more, the effective pressure approaches the idealized pressure. In fact, the effective pressure can actually exceed what it would be if the gas behaved ideally. Such behavior may be explained as resulting from an additional factor — at a very high pressure, the volume of the molecules themselves becomes a significant fraction of the total volume of the gas, and the molecules themselves are considerably less compressible than is the rest of the space occupied by the gas. Consequently, the gas tends to resist further compression, which means that for a fixed volume there is a tendency for the effective pressure to increase substantially.

Thus, there is one factor — intermolecular attractions — which tends to make the effective pressure less than the idealized pressure, and there is a second factor — the volume of the gas molecules themselves relative to the total volume occupied by the gas — which tends to make the effective pressure greater than the idealized pressure. Obviously, the direction and magnitude of the discrepancy between actual and ideal behavior is dependent upon the relative magnitudes of these two effects. Figure 1-5 presents a plot of the activity coefficient (or the ratio of the effective pressure to the idealized pressure) for five different gases as a function of total pressure. For carbon dioxide, methane, and nitrogen, the initial decrease in the activity coefficients at moderate pressure is attributable to the dominance of intermolecular attractions. At high pressure, however, the activity coefficients exceed unity because the incompressibility of the gas molecules becomes the more important

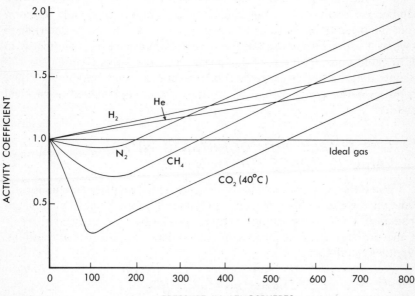

FIGURE 1-5 Plot of activity coefficient (or ratio of the effective pressure to the idealized pressure) versus pressure for carbon dioxide at 40°C and for methane, nitrogen, helium, and hydrogen at 0°C. (See text for discussion.) (Modified from Masterton, W. L., and Slowinski, E. J.: Chemical Principles. Phila., W. B. Saunders Co., 1969, 2nd edition.)

factor. With helium and hydrogen, which do not exhibit appreciable intermolecular attraction, the activity coefficient is observed to rise steadily above unity as the pressure is increased. It is interesting to compare the general trends depicted in Figure 1-5 with the behavior of the activity coefficients for ionic solutes shown in Figures 1-2 and 1-3.

Several attempts have been made to incorporate the two effects mentioned in the preceding paragraph into the equation of state for an ideal gas. One of these has yielded, as an equation of state for a real gas, the **van der Waals equation**

$$\left(P + \frac{a}{V^2}\right)(V - b) = nRT$$

in which a is a term relating to the intermolecular attractions and b is a parameter pertaining to the molecular volume. In the light of the preceding discussion, the student should verify the reasonableness of these two empirical correction factors (taking both a and b as positive numbers).

When one wishes to perform *rigorous* calculations concerning gas-phase equilibria, it is necessary to employ fugacities rather than pressures. This is because a value of K based on fugacities is a true thermodynamic constant, whereas an equilibrium expression consisting of pressure terms will vary as the total pressure of the system changes. Unfortunately, a serious difficulty in the use of fugacities for gas-phase equilibrium calculations is that the fugacity of a gaseous species in a mixture of gases — the number we really desire, but cannot easily obtain — is usually *different* from the fugacity of the same gaseous species — which can be determined — when it is present by itself at the same total pressure. Consequently, in subsequent considerations of gas-phase systems in this chapter, we will assume that the fugacity or effective pressure of each compound is equal to the pressure which would be exerted if the gas behaved in an ideal manner.

GAS EQUILIBRIUM CONSTANTS WITH VARIOUS CONCENTRATION UNITS

When thermodynamic data are employed to calculate an equilibrium constant for a gas-phase reaction, the amount of each substance, which appears in the corresponding equilibrium relation, is expressed in terms of the pressure in atmospheres of that substance. Accordingly, for the hypothetical all-gas reaction

$$a\text{A} + b\text{B} \rightleftharpoons c\text{C} + d\text{D}$$

one designates the equilibrium constant as K_p and uses the symbols

p_A, p_B, p_C, and p_D to represent the pressure in atmospheres of each reactant and product involved in the process. Therefore,

$$K_p = \frac{p_C^c \, p_D^d}{p_A^a \, p_B^b} \tag{1.15}$$

However, in practical calculations of equilibria involving gas-phase systems, it is often convenient to express quantities of gases in units other than atmospheres of pressure.

Another common concentration unit, even for gas-phase systems, is moles per liter. Using the symbol K_c along with square brackets to represent molar concentrations of the various substances (remember that we are assuming no distinction between activity and analytical concentration), we may write

$$K_c = \frac{[C]^c \, [D]^d}{[A]^a \, [B]^b}$$

A simple relationship between the two constants, K_p and K_c, may be determined by substitution of the equation of state for an ideal gas, equation 1.14, into the definition of K_p, equation 1.15. Applying equation 1.14 to each of the four gaseous species, we obtain

$$p_A = \frac{n_A RT}{V}, \quad p_B = \frac{n_B RT}{V}, \quad p_C = \frac{n_C RT}{V}, \quad p_D = \frac{n_D RT}{V}$$

However, each n/V factor in the preceding expressions is a molar concentration, so

$$p_A = [A]RT, \quad p_B = [B]RT, \quad p_C = [C]RT, \quad p_D = [D]RT$$

Substituting each of these relations into equation 1.15, we have

$$K_p = \frac{([C]RT)^c \, ([D]RT)^d}{([A]RT)^a \, ([B]RT)^b} = \frac{[C]^c [D]^d}{[A]^a [B]^b} \times (RT)^{c+d-a-b}$$

$$K_p = K_c (RT)^{c+d-a-b}$$

Thus, the value of K_p is equal to K_c multiplied by the quantity RT raised to a power equal to the difference between the total number of moles of products and the total number of moles of reactants appearing in the balanced reaction. In illustration of this generalized formulation, consider the following examples of all-gas reactions:

$$2\,HI \rightleftharpoons H_2 + I_2 \qquad c+d-a-b=0 \qquad so, K_p = K_c$$

$$PCl_5 \rightleftharpoons PCl_3 + Cl_2 \qquad c+d-a-b=1 \qquad so, K_p = K_c(RT)$$

$$2\,NH_3 \rightleftharpoons N_2 + 3\,H_2 \qquad c+d-a-b=2 \qquad so, K_p = K_c(RT)^2$$

$$4\,NO_2 + 6\,H_2O \rightleftharpoons 4\,NH_3 + 5\,O_2 \quad c+d-a-b=-1 \quad so, K_p = K_c(RT)^{-1}$$

A third form of the equilibrium constant for a gas-phase reaction is that in which the quantities of the different substances are expressed as mole fractions, the mole fraction X_A of a species A being given by the relation

$$X_A = \frac{p_A}{p}$$

where p_A is the pressure exerted by substance A, and p is the total pressure of all components in the system. Using the symbol K_X for the equilibrium constant and representing the mole fractions of the other three gases in the system by X_B, X_C, and X_D, we may write

$$K_X = \frac{X_C^c X_D^d}{X_A^a X_B^b}$$

For a given chemical system, K_X may be related to K_p as follows:

$$K_X = \frac{X_C^c X_D^d}{X_A^a X_B^b} = \frac{\left(\dfrac{p_C}{p}\right)^c \left(\dfrac{p_D}{p}\right)^d}{\left(\dfrac{p_A}{p}\right)^a \left(\dfrac{p_B}{p}\right)^b}$$

$$K_X = \frac{p_C^c p_D^d}{p_A^a p_B^b} \times \frac{\left(\dfrac{1}{p}\right)^c \left(\dfrac{1}{p}\right)^d}{\left(\dfrac{1}{p}\right)^a \left(\dfrac{1}{p}\right)^b}$$

$$K_X = K_p(p)^{a+b-c-d}$$

Thus, the numerical value of K_X is equal to K_p multiplied by the total pressure, p, raised to a power equal to the difference in the numbers of moles of reactants and products in the reaction as written.

To illustrate the interrelationships between K_p, K_c, and K_X, let us consider the gas-phase reaction

$$N_2O_4 \rightleftharpoons 2\,NO_2$$

for which the K_X value is 0.67 at 320°K and a total pressure of two atmospheres. Let us calculate K_c and K_p for this system, recognizing that the equation as written shows one mole of reactant and two moles of product. To obtain K_p we write

$$K_X = K_p(p)^{-1} \quad \text{or} \quad K_p = K_X(p)$$
$$K_p = (0.67)(2) = 1.34 \text{ atm}$$

and K_c can be readily calculated as follows:

$$K_p = K_c(RT) \quad \text{or} \quad K_c = \frac{K_p}{RT}$$

where R is 0.0821 liter-atmosphere/mole-degree

$$K_c = \frac{1.34}{(0.0821)(320)}$$

$$K_c = 0.0510 \text{ mole/liter}$$

It is significant to note that K_X is a function of the total pressure of the system, unless the number of moles of products equals the number of moles of reactants, whereas both K_c and K_p are independent of total pressure. Because of the dependence of K_X on pressure, it is rarely employed.

GENERAL APPROACH TO EQUILIBRIUM CALCULATIONS

Numerical calculations involving chemical equilibria vary widely in their degree of difficulty. Nevertheless, all problems can be solved through a relatively simple, general plan of attack. It is essential for each student to become familiar with the principles underlying chemical equilibrium and their application to practical chemical situations; this general plan of attack upon numerical equilibrium problems is a powerful aid in developing such familiarity, and consists of the following four steps.

Step 1. Write a balanced chemical reaction representing the state of equilibrium involved in the problem and, if two or more chemical equilibria occur simultaneously, write the chemical reaction for each.

Step 2. Write the equilibrium-constant expression corresponding to each of the chemical reactions written in Step 1.

Step 3. Write additional mathematical equations from available information and data until the number of mathematical relations, including those of Step 2, equals the number of unknowns contained therein. Each of these equations must be independent of the others, in the sense that no two relationships can be merely rearrangements of each other. One source of information for these equations consists of the data given in the problem, which generally are derived from experimental measurements in practical situations. A second source is the compilation of data in various reference tables and books, particularly the listings of numerical values for equilibrium constants, which are generally based upon research chemists' experimental measurements in combination with theoretical concepts and defined standards. A third source of information for additional equations is the mass-balance relationship; the stoichiometry of the chemical reaction is often useful in establishing such a relationship. If, for example, a $0.100\,M$ solution of silver nitrate is mixed with an equal volume of an aqueous ammonia solution, the total silver ion concentration is $0.050\,M$, but silver ion will exist partly in the form of Ag^+ and partly as the two silver-ammine complexes, $Ag(NH_3)^+$ and $Ag(NH_3)_2^+$, so

$$0.050 = [Ag^+] + [Ag(NH_3)^+] + [Ag(NH_3)_2^+]$$

A fourth source, useful in dealing with ionic equilibrium, is the charge-balance relationship, which states that the sum of negative charges must equal the sum of positive charges in a solution. For example, if a solution contains dissolved potassium chloride and sodium chloride, we can write

$$[K^+] + [Na^+] = [Cl^-]$$

Step 4. Solve these equations for the desired unknown quantity or quantities. As long as Steps 2 and 3 result in as many equations as the number of unknowns, it is possible to manipulate these equations algebraically to obtain a numerical value for any or all of the unknown quantities.

One must pay special attention to the units used in the various equations. Concentrations of substances in solution are normally expressed in terms of moles per liter, because the standard state of solute species is defined with such units. Quantities of gaseous species must be stated in units consistent with the selection of K_p, K_c, or K_x for the equilibrium constant. If data are given or are desired in any other units, such as in grams per liter for a dissolved solute, the necessary conversion factors must be included in the relationships.

Mathematical operations encountered in Step 4 frequently become complex and time-consuming. In order to simplify the mathematical work, it is often possible to make assumptions, in the mathematical solution of the problem, so as to minimize the time and effort involved. It is of the utmost importance to stress, however, that the desire to simplify a calculation is *never* a *sufficient* reason for making such an assumption. Each assumption must be clearly justified or justifiable, either in advance or by subsequent checking, to provide full assurance that the resultant error is fully within the limit of uncertainty that is acceptable in light of the precision of the data and the desired use of the end result of the calculation. Several methods of doing this will be encountered in various places throughout this book.

This four-step approach to the solution of numerical problems involving chemical equilibrium is presented not as a recipe for blind calculations but rather as a set of principles to guide an understanding approach to such problems. Although the range of problems is so wide that no set of guidelines can possibly suffice for solving all of them, these principles will serve as an adequate format for understanding and attacking the various types of problems. We will now apply these principles to several problems, although the four steps will not be specifically identified.

EXAMPLE 14

Calculate the equilibrium constant for the system discussed on pages 1 to 5, in which the *initial* iron(III) concentration was $0.200\,M$, the *initial* iodide concentration was $0.300\,M$, and the *equilibrium* triiodide concentration was $0.0866\,M$; assume that analytical concentrations are identical to effective concentrations.

We may write the pertinent chemical reaction

$$2\,Fe^{+++} + 3\,I^- \rightleftharpoons 2\,Fe^{++} + I_3^-$$

and the corresponding equilibrium expression

$$K = \frac{[Fe^{++}]^2[I_3^-]}{[Fe^{+++}]^2[I^-]^3}$$

Since no iron(II) was originally present, the stoichiometry of the reaction tells us that the equilibrium iron(II) concentration must be twice that of the triiodide ion, two Fe^{++} ions being produced for every triiodide ion. Therefore,

$$[I_3^-] = 0.0866\,M$$

$$[Fe^{++}] = 0.173\,M$$

To obtain the equilibrium concentration of iron(III), it is necessary to use the mass-balance relation for the total iron concentration, which may be written as

$$[Fe^{++}] + [Fe^{+++}] = 0.200\,M$$

$$[Fe^{+++}] = 0.200 - [Fe^{++}]$$

$$[Fe^{+++}] = 0.200 - 0.173 = 0.027\,M$$

Our mass-balance expression for the total iodine concentration must include the stoichiometric relationship that each mole of I_3^- has the same mass as three moles of I^-. Thus,

$$[I^-] + 3[I_3^-] = 0.300\,M$$
$$[I^-] = 0.300 - 3[I_3^-]$$
$$[I^-] = 0.300 - 3(0.0866) = 0.040\,M$$

If we now substitute the values for the concentrations of all four species into the equilibrium expression, the result is

$$K = \frac{(0.173)^2(0.0866)}{(0.027)^2(0.040)^3} = 5.55 \times 10^4$$

EXAMPLE 15

For the dissociation of hydrogen fluoride (HF) gas into the elemental gases, H_2 and F_2, the value of K_c is 1.00×10^{-13} at 1000°C. If 1.00 mole of hydrogen fluoride is allowed to reach dissociation equilibrium in a 2.00-liter container at this temperature, what will be the final molar concentration of fluorine gas?

As a starting point for the solution of this problem, we should write the pertinent reaction

$$2\,HF(g) \rightleftharpoons H_2(g) + F_2(g)$$

along with the equilibrium expression

$$K_c = \frac{[H_2(g)]\,[F_2(g)]}{[HF(g)]^2}$$

Based on the stoichiometry of the reaction which must occur before a state of equilibrium is reached, we can conclude that the final concentrations of hydrogen and fluorine gases must be equal:

$$[H_2(g)] = [F_2(g)]$$

Next, we can formulate the mass-balance relationship

$$[HF(g)] + 2[F_2(g)] = \frac{1.00\ \text{mole}}{2.00\ \text{liters}} = 0.500\,M$$

which states that the *total* concentration of fluorine in both of its forms must be 0.500 M. From this equation it follows that the equilibrium concentration of hydrogen fluoride gas is

$$[HF(g)] = 0.500 - 2[F_2(g)]$$

If the expressions for the concentrations of hydrogen and hydrogen fluoride are inserted into the equilibrium-constant relation, we have

$$K_c = \frac{[F_2(g)]^2}{(0.500 - 2[F_2(g)])^2} = 1.00 \times 10^{-13}$$

This equation can be solved mathematically to obtain a numerical value for the concentration of F_2. However, we can simplify the expression by recognizing that, as a consequence of the very small equilibrium constant, only a small fraction of the HF is dissociated. This means that the concentration of F_2 is far less than the concentration of HF, so the term $2[F_2(g)]$ may be neglected in the denominator, and the last preceding relation may be rewritten as

$$\frac{[F_2(g)]^2}{(0.500)^2} = 1.00 \times 10^{-13}$$

When solved for the fluorine concentration, this equation yields

$$[F_2(g)]^2 = (1.00 \times 10^{-13})(0.250) = 2.50 \times 10^{-14}$$
$$[F_2(g)] = 1.58 \times 10^{-7} M$$

Therefore, the concentration of fluorine gas is $1.58 \times 10^{-7} M$ at equilibrium. It is appropriate here to verify the simplifying assumption which was made — twice $1.58 \times 10^{-7} M$ is indeed much smaller than 0.500 M.

EXAMPLE 16

At a temperature of 760°K the reaction for the gas-phase decomposition of phosphorus pentachloride into phosphorus trichloride and chlorine

$$PCl_5(g) \rightleftharpoons PCl_3(g) + Cl_2(g)$$

has an equilibrium constant (K_c) of 33.3. If 2.00 moles of phosphorus pentachloride are admitted to a previously evacuated

1.00-liter vessel, what will be the equilibrium concentrations of all three species?

Since none of the decomposition products are initially present, it is evident from the stoichiometry of the reaction that equal concentrations of PCl_3 and Cl_2 will be produced. Therefore, when equilibrium prevails

$$[PCl_3] = [Cl_2]$$

Although the original concentration of phosphorus pentachloride is $2.00\,M$, the final equilibrium PCl_5 concentration will be less than this initial value by the concentration of PCl_3 which is formed, inasmuch as the stoichiometry of the process shows that one molecule of PCl_3 arises for every molecule of PCl_5 undergoing decomposition:

$$[PCl_5] = 2.00 - [PCl_3]$$

If we now write the appropriate equilibrium-constant expression

$$K_c = \frac{[PCl_3][Cl_2]}{[PCl_5]} = 33.3$$

and substitute appropriately for the concentrations of chlorine and phosphorus pentachloride, the result is

$$\frac{[PCl_3]^2}{2.00 - [PCl_3]} = 33.3$$

This expression appears similar in form to that encountered in the previous example. However, the reasonably large value for the equilibrium constant indicates that phosphorus pentachloride decomposes to a considerable extent, so it is unrealistic to neglect the $[PCl_3]$ term in the denominator. In other words, the equilibrium concentration of PCl_3 is expected to be comparable in magnitude to $2.00\,M$. If we do not drop the $[PCl_3]$ term, this equation can be rearranged

$$[PCl_3]^2 = 66.6 - 33.3[PCl_3]$$

$$[PCl_3]^2 + 33.3[PCl_3] - 66.6 = 0$$

and solved by means of the quadratic formula:*

---

*An equation of the form $aX^2 + bX + c = 0$ can be solved through the use of the quadratic formula, which is

$$X = \frac{-b \pm \sqrt{b^2 - 4ac}}{2a}$$

$$[PCl_3] = \frac{-33.3 \pm \sqrt{(33.3)^2 - (4)(1)(-66.6)}}{(2)(1)}$$

$$[PCl_3] = 1.89 \, M$$

From earlier relationships, we can conclude that

$$[Cl_2] = [PCl_3] = 1.89 \, M$$

and that

$$[PCl_5] = 2.00 - [PCl_3] = 2.00 - 1.89 = 0.11 \, M$$

EXAMPLE 17

If 0.100 mole of phosphorus pentachloride and 10.0 moles of phosphorus trichloride are introduced into a previously evacuated 2.00-liter chamber at 760°K, and if the equilibrium constant (K_c) for the reaction

$$PCl_5(g) \rightleftharpoons PCl_3(g) + Cl_2(g)$$

is 33.3 at this temperature, calculate the equilibrium concentration of each gaseous species in the system.

As shown in the preceding problem, the equilibrium expression is

$$K_c = \frac{[PCl_3][Cl_2]}{[PCl_5]} = 33.3$$

First, let us calculate the initial concentrations of phosphorus pentachloride and phosphorus trichloride:

$$[PCl_5]_{initial} = \frac{0.100 \text{ mole}}{2.00 \text{ liters}} = 0.050 \, M$$

$$[PCl_3]_{initial} = \frac{10.0 \text{ moles}}{2.00 \text{ liters}} = 5.00 \, M$$

We can state that the *equilibrium* concentration of phosphorus pentachloride is equal to the *initial* concentration minus the concentration of PCl$_5$ which decomposes. We can correctly express this relationship as

$$[PCl_5] = 0.050 - [Cl_2]$$

Notice that the equilibrium concentration of chlorine is a measure of how much phosphorus pentachloride decomposes because PCl_5 is the *only* source of Cl_2. It is incorrect to subtract the PCl_3 concentration from the initial concentration of PCl_5 to obtain the equilibrium concentration of phosphorus pentachloride, as was done in Example 16, because of the fact that a large amount of PCl_3 was added to the system originally. Next, the following expression can be written for the equilibrium concentration of PCl_3:

$$[PCl_3] = 5.00 + [Cl_2]$$

This equation indicates that the final concentration of phosphorus trichloride is larger than its original value of $5.00\,M$ by a term that is equal to the concentration of phosphorus pentachloride which decomposes. However, we have already concluded that the chlorine concentration is equivalent to the concentration of decomposed PCl_5, so the use of $[Cl_2]$ in the last relationship is justified.

When we make appropriate substitutions into the equilibrium expression, the result is

$$K_c = \frac{[PCl_3][Cl_2]}{[PCl_5]} = \frac{(5.00 + [Cl_2])[Cl_2]}{(0.050 - [Cl_2])} = 33.3$$

If all the PCl_5 decomposed, the final concentrations of chlorine and phosphorus trichloride would be 0.050 and $5.05\,M$, respectively. Since the maximal concentration of PCl_3 is not much larger than the original value of $5.00\,M$, we will neglect $[Cl_2]$ which appears in the term $(5.00 + [Cl_2])$ in the preceding equation. This simplification, which corresponds to saying that the equilibrium PCl_3 concentration is essentially $5.00\,M$, leads to

$$\frac{(5.00)[Cl_2]}{(0.050 - [Cl_2])} = 33.3$$

which can be easily solved for the chlorine concentration:

$$5.00[Cl_2] = 1.67 - 33.3[Cl_2]$$
$$38.3[Cl_2] = 1.67$$
$$[Cl_2] = 0.0435\,M$$

Now, when the concentrations of the other two species are calculated, we have

$$[PCl_5] = 0.050 - [Cl_2] = 0.050 - 0.0435 = 0.0065\,M$$
$$[PCl_3] = 5.00 + [Cl_2] = 5.00 + 0.0435 = 5.04\,M$$

Our earlier assumption that the equilibrium concentration of PCl_3 was very close to $5.00\,M$ is seen to be verified, so we can have confidence in the validity of the results.

QUESTIONS AND PROBLEMS

1. The reaction

$$2\,Fe^{+++} + 3\,I^- \rightleftharpoons 2\,Fe^{++} + I_3^-$$

was discussed in an early section of this chapter. If one starts with $0.100\,M$ iron(III) and $0.150\,M$ iodide, and if the equilibrium concentration of triiodide ion is $0.0414\,M$, calculate the equilibrium concentrations of Fe^{+++}, Fe^{++}, and I^-. Neglect activity effects.

2. Assume that one prepares a solution corresponding to the equilibrium state of the preceding problem by mixing solutions of Fe^{+++}, Fe^{++}, I^-, and I_3^- to give the appropriate equilibrium concentrations. If all the iodide ion is initially radioactive, what is the final concentration of radioactive iodide ion after a true state of dynamic equilibrium is established?

3. Suppose the equilibrium-constant expression for the reaction

$$H_2S \rightleftharpoons 2\,H^+ + S^=$$

is to be formulated as a single equation. Assume that the overall process occurs according to the following two steps:

$$H_2S \rightleftharpoons H^+ + HS^-$$
$$HS^- \rightleftharpoons H^+ + S^=$$

Using appropriate symbols for the forward and backward rate constants for each step, write the equations for the rates of the forward and backward reactions for each step. Then, proposing the rates of the forward and backward reactions to be equal at equilibrium, show that the resulting equilibrium-constant expression obtained from the two-step reaction sequence is identical to that which one can write by simple inspection of the overall reaction.

4. Write the equilibrium-constant expression for each of the following reactions:

(a) $H_3PO_4 + PO_4^{\equiv} \rightleftharpoons H_2PO_4^- + HPO_4^{=}$

(b) $N_2(g) + 3\ H_2(g) \rightleftharpoons 2\ NH_3(g)$

(c) $2\ CO_2(g) \rightleftharpoons 2\ CO(g) + O_2(g)$

(d) $H^+ + CO_3^{=} \rightleftharpoons HCO_3^-$

(e) $Ag^+ + 2\ NH_3 \rightleftharpoons Ag(NH_3)_2^+$

(f) $I_2 + 2\ S_2O_3^{=} \rightleftharpoons 2\ I^- + S_4O_6^{=}$

5. For each of the following gas-phase reactions

(a) $2\ HI(g) \rightleftharpoons H_2(g) + I_2(g)$

(b) $PCl_5(g) \rightleftharpoons PCl_3(g) + Cl_2(g)$

(c) $2\ NH_3(g) \rightleftharpoons N_2(g) + 3\ H_2(g)$

predict the direction in which the position of equilibrium will be shifted if the volume of the system is decreased or if the total pressure of the system is decreased.

6. If the reaction

$$Ag^+ + 2\ CN^- \rightleftharpoons Ag(CN)_2^-$$

is at equilibrium, predict the effect of each of the following on the molar concentration of the $Ag(CN)_2^-$ complex: (a) solid silver nitrate is dissolved in the solution; (b) ammonia gas, NH_3, which can form a complex, $Ag(NH_3)_2^+$, with silver ion, is passed into the solution; (c) solid sodium iodide is dissolved in the solution (AgI is insoluble).

7. (a) Using the Debye-Hückel limiting law, calculate the activity of barium ion in an aqueous $0.100\ M$ solution of barium chloride, which is a strong electrolyte.

(b) Repeat the calculation of (a) for $0.00100\ M$ barium chloride solution, and explain the difference in the relative values of activities and analytical concentrations for the two solutions.

8. From each of the indicated values of K_p, calculate the corresponding value of K_c for the following gas-phase equilibria at 85°C:

(a) $N_2(g) + O_2(g) \rightleftharpoons 2\ NO(g);$ $\qquad K_p = 0.0123$

(b) $PCl_3(g) + Cl_2(g) \rightleftharpoons PCl_5(g);$ $\qquad K_p = 1.19$

(c) $2\ NO(g) + Br_2(g) \rightleftharpoons 2\ NOBr(g);$ $\ K_p = 6.43$

9. An equilibrium mixture at 377°C for the all-gas system

$$2\ NH_3(g) \rightleftharpoons N_2(g) + 3\ H_2(g)$$

is found to contain, in one liter, 0.0100 mole of NH_3, 0.100 mole of N_2, and 0.162 mole of H_2. Evaluate K_c and K_p for the reaction.

10. At equilibrium the pressures of NO_2, NO, and O_2 were found to be 0.200, 0.00026, and 0.600 atmosphere, respectively, in a 1.00-liter container at 158°C. Calculate the values of K_p, K_c, and K_X for the reaction

$$2\ NO_2(g) \rightleftharpoons 2\ NO(g) + O_2(g)$$

11. For the gas-phase reaction

$$2\ SO_2(g) + O_2(g) \rightleftharpoons 2\ SO_3(g)$$

the value of K_c is 5800 at 600°C. If 0.150 mole of sulfur dioxide and 6.00 moles of oxygen are admitted to a previously evacuated 6.00-liter chamber at 600°C, what will be the equilibrium concentration of SO_3?

12. If the equilibrium concentrations of sulfur trioxide and sulfur dioxide are equal to each other in the system of the preceding problem, what must be the concentration of O_2 at equilibrium?

13. Given that the reaction

$$N_2O_4(g) \rightleftharpoons 2\ NO_2(g)$$

has an equilibrium constant, K_c, of 0.0510 at 320°K, how many *grams* of NO_2 are present in 5.00 liters of an equilibrium mixture which contains 10.0 *grams* of N_2O_4 gas?

14. Given that the equilibrium constant, K_c, for the dissociation of hydrogen fluoride gas into elemental hydrogen and fluorine

$$2\ HF(g) \rightleftharpoons H_2(g) + F_2(g)$$

is 1.00×10^{-13} at 1000°C, what will be the equilibrium molar concentration of fluorine if 1.00 mole of H_2 and 1.00 mole of F_2 are allowed to reach equilibrium in a 2.00-liter container at this temperature?

15. What is the ionic strength of a 0.00400 M solution of the strong electrolyte lanthanum chloride ($LaCl_3$)?

16. In a 5.00-liter vessel, the equilibrium pressures of hydrogen, iodine, and hydrogen iodide gases were found to be 0.390, 0.114, and 1.50 atmospheres, respectively, at 450°C. Calculate the values of K_p and K_c for the reaction

$$H_2(g) + I_2(g) \rightleftharpoons 2\ HI(g)$$

17. The equilibrium constant K_p for the dissociation of N_2O_4 gas

$$N_2O_4(g) \rightleftharpoons 2\,NO_2(g)$$

is 0.315 atmosphere at 35°C and is 4.87 atmospheres at 75°C. Is the dissociation of N_2O_4 an exothermic or an endothermic process? Explain.

18. At one atmosphere pressure and a temperature of 3000°C, dissociation of carbon dioxide into carbon monoxide and oxygen

$$2\,CO_2(g) \rightleftharpoons 2\,CO(g) + O_2(g)$$

occurs to an extent of 40 per cent. Calculate values for K_p and K_c. (Hint: express the partial pressure of each component as the total pressure multiplied by the mole fraction of that component.)

19. For the reaction

$$H_2(g) + CO_2(g) \rightleftharpoons H_2O(g) + CO(g)$$

the equilibrium constant K_p is 0.24 at a temperature of 527°C and a total pressure of 3.00 atmospheres. If equal amounts of hydrogen and carbon dioxide are mixed at 527°C and 3.00 atmospheres of pressure, what percentage of carbon dioxide will be converted to carbon monoxide after equilibrium is attained? (Hint: express the partial pressure of each component as the total pressure multiplied by the mole fraction of that component.)

20. What is the ionic strength of a solution containing 0.0050 M sodium sulfate, Na_2SO_4, and 0.0030 M lanthanum nitrate, $La(NO_3)_3$?

21. Using the Debye-Hückel limiting law, evaluate the single-ion activity coefficient for iodide ion and the mean activity coefficient for CaI_2 in a 0.0250 M calcium iodide solution at 25°C.

22. Standard enthalpy changes ($\Delta H°$) for the decomposition of nitric oxide (NO) and for the formation of nitrous oxide (N_2O) at 25°C and a total pressure of 1.00 atmosphere are as follows:

(i) $2\,NO(g) \rightleftharpoons O_2(g) + N_2(g)$; $\Delta H° = -43.2$ kilocalories
(ii) $N_2(g) + \frac{1}{2}\,O_2(g) \rightleftharpoons N_2O(g)$; $\Delta H° = +19.5$ kilocalories

Assume that each of these reactions is initially in a state of equilibrium at 25°C and a pressure of 1.00 atmosphere. For each of these two reactions, indicate whether the position of equilibrium will not shift at all, will shift toward the right, or will shift toward the left as each of the following occurs:

(a) At 25°C additional oxygen is added to the equilibrated system, and the total pressure is maintained at one atmosphere.

(b) The temperature is increased to 250°C, and the pressure is kept at one atmosphere.

(c) The pressure is increased to 10 atmospheres, but the temperature is maintained at 25°C.

23. For the following decomposition reaction at 500°K

$$2 \text{ NOCl(g)} \rightleftharpoons 2 \text{ NO(g)} + \text{Cl}_2\text{(g)}; \quad K_p = 0.0192 \text{ atm}$$

what is the equilibrium constant K_c? If 0.200 mole of NOCl and 1.00 mole of Cl_2 are mixed in a 2.00-liter container at 500°K, how many *grams* of the original NOCl will have decomposed when equilibrium is attained?

24. At a temperature of 727°C, the five gas-phase reactions listed below have enthalpy changes and equilibrium constants as indicated.

Reaction	$\Delta H°$, kcal	K_p
(i) $CO_2(g) + CF_4(g) \rightleftharpoons 2 \text{ COF}_2(g)$	+10.4	0.472
(ii) $CO(g) + H_2O(g) \rightleftharpoons CO_2(g) + H_2(g)$	−8.3	1.44
(iii) $2 \text{ NO(g)} + Br_2(g) \rightleftharpoons 2 \text{ NOBr(g)}$	−11.1	1.6×10^{-4}
(iv) $2 \text{ NH}_3(g) \rightleftharpoons 3 \text{ H}_2(g) + N_2(g)$	+26.3	2.9×10^6
(v) $2 \text{ H}_2(g) + S_2(g) \rightleftharpoons 2 \text{ H}_2S(g)$	+43.1	5.0×10^{-5}

(a) Which, if any, of the reactions is (or are) exothermic?

(b) For which, if any, of the reactions is $\Delta G°$ negative?

(c) For which, if any, of the reactions will the value of K_p decrease with decreasing temperature?

(d) For which, if any, of the reactions will K_p and K_c be equal?

(e) For which, if any, of the reactions will reaction proceed toward the right when, with the system initially at equilibrium, the total pressure is decreased by an increase in the volume at constant temperature?

(f) For which, if any, of the reactions will the value of K_p decrease with increasing pressure?

25. Equilibrium-constant data for two reactions involving nitrogen dioxide (NO_2) at 325°C are as follows:

$$2 \text{ NO(g)} + O_2(g) \rightleftharpoons 2 \text{ NO}_2(g): \quad K_p = 1.58 \times 10^2$$
$$2 \text{ NO}_2(g) \rightleftharpoons N_2O_4(g); \quad \quad K_p = 7.50 \times 10^{-5}$$

Suppose that 1.00 mole of oxygen gas and 2.00 moles of nitric oxide (NO) gas were mixed in a reaction chamber and that, when the chamber was heated to 325°C, the total pressure of the gas mixture reached a constant value of 2.00 atmospheres. If the pressure of nitrogen dioxide (NO_2) in the equilibrium gas mixture was 1.54 atmospheres, calculate the pressures of the other three gases present. (Hint: the total pressure is the sum of the partial pressures of the four components.)

26. From the data listed in Table 1-1, compute the standard free-energy change ($\Delta G°$) for each of the following processes:

   (a) $3 O_2(g) \rightleftharpoons 2 O_3(g)$
   (b) $CaCO_3(s) \rightleftharpoons CaO(s) + CO_2(g)$
   (c) $SO_2(g) + \frac{1}{2} O_2(g) \rightleftharpoons SO_3(g)$
   (d) $C_2H_4(g) + H_2(g) \rightleftharpoons C_2H_6(g)$
   (e) $H^+ + OH^- \rightleftharpoons H_2O(g)$
   (f) $2 H_2O(g) + O_2(g) \rightleftharpoons 2 H_2O_2(g)$
   (g) $BaSO_4(s) \rightleftharpoons Ba^{++} + SO_4^{=}$

27. Evaluate the equilibrium constant at 25°C for each of the following reactions using information given in Table 1-1:

   (a) $Ca(OH)_2(s) \rightleftharpoons Ca^{++} + 2 OH^-$
   (b) $3 H_2(g) + N_2(g) \rightleftharpoons 2 NH_3(g)$
   (c) $CO_2(g) + NO(g) \rightleftharpoons CO(g) + NO_2(g)$
   (d) $H_2(g) + Br_2(g) \rightleftharpoons 2 HBr(g)$
   (e) $AgI(s) \rightleftharpoons Ag^+ + I^-$

Chapter 2

EQUILIBRIA IN PRECIPITATION REACTIONS

This chapter is designed to illustrate a variety of typical equilibrium calculations involving solubility. Some of the problems to be described involve acid dissociation or complex formation equilibria in addition to dissolution phenomena. Major attention will be focused upon the equilibria pertaining to the solubility of inorganic compounds in water.

SOLUBILITY, SOLUBILITY PRODUCTS, AND ACTIVITY PRODUCTS

We shall begin our discussion of solubility with a consideration of the dissolution of silver chloride, AgCl, in pure water. In most treatments of the solubility of silver chloride, it is stated that the simple equilibrium

$$AgCl(s) \rightleftharpoons Ag^+ + Cl^-$$

prevails after an aqueous suspension of the solid has been thoroughly shaken. However, one of the interesting features of the behavior of silver chloride is that silver ion and chloride ion may combine to form a soluble, undissociated silver chloride molecule

$$Ag^+ + Cl^- \rightleftharpoons AgCl(aq)$$

which might be regarded as an ion pair. This aqueous, undissociated molecule will be in equilibrium with solid silver chloride, according to the reaction

$$AgCl(s) \rightleftharpoons AgCl(aq)$$

Furthermore, the aqueous, undissociated molecule can react with a chloride ion, originating from silver chloride, to form an anionic complex:

$$AgCl(aq) + Cl^- \rightleftharpoons AgCl_2^-$$

If the chloride ion concentration were high enough, other complexes such as $AgCl^=$ or $AgCl_4^=$ could form. Thus, the solubility behavior of even a simple compound can be extremely complicated. Only through careful investigation can one identify all the reactions which occur. In pure water the concentration of chloride ion is so small that the amounts of the anionic complexes are negligible. However, the solubility of silver chloride should still be considered as the sum of the concentrations of Ag^+ and $AgCl(aq)$.

If we omit the anionic complexes just mentioned, the solubility behavior of silver chloride may be represented in the following way:

$$AgCl(s) \rightleftharpoons AgCl(aq) \rightleftharpoons Ag^+ + Cl^-$$

According to this picture, solid silver chloride dissolves to form the aqueous, undissociated molecule which, in turn, dissociates into silver and chloride ions. It is important to emphasize that all the various equilibria are interrelated. The equilibrium-constant expressions corresponding to this sequence of reactions must be written in terms of activities rather than analytical concentrations, if one is interested in describing the solubility in a completely rigorous manner.

ACTIVITY AND INTRINSIC SOLUBILITY OF A SOLID

For the first step of the solubility reactions discussed in the previous paragraph, the equilibrium-constant expression can be written as

$$\frac{(AgCl(aq))}{(AgCl(s))} = S^\circ$$

where the chemical symbols in parentheses denote activities of the solid and aqueous forms of silver chloride, and where S° is called the **intrinsic solubility** of silver chloride. Let us examine the significance of the terms in this equation. Since the standard state of silver chloride is defined to be the pure solid, we may conclude that

$$(AgCl(s)) = 1$$

if the silver chloride is not contaminated in any way with impurities. Solids which do contain extraneous substances have activities *less* than unity. On the other hand, experimental studies have indicated that the activity of exceedingly small particles of a solid compound is actually *greater* than unity. However, a detailed discussion of this subject would be extremely lengthy and is beyond the scope of the present treatment of solubility. Suffice it to say that particles greater than approximately two microns (2×10^{-4} cm) in diameter exhibit essentially unit activity.

Throughout the remainder of this chapter, the activities of solid phases will always be assumed to be unity, so that for the silver chloride system we may write

$$(\text{AgCl(aq)}) = S°$$

This relation states that the activity of the soluble molecular form of silver chloride is a constant wherever one has an excess of solid AgCl in equilibrium with pure water or any other aqueous solution. Regardless of what other competing reactions occur, the activity of AgCl(aq) remains unchanged. This is why $S°$ is termed the intrinsic solubility of silver chloride.

It is exceedingly difficult to measure experimentally the numerical value of $S°$, because the quantity of AgCl(aq) is almost always small compared to the concentrations of other dissolved silver species. Values for $S°$ reported in the chemical literature vary from 1.0×10^{-7} to $6.2 \times 10^{-7} M$. It seems reasonable to expect that a small concentration of the aqueous, undissociated molecular form of a compound always exists in equilibrium with the solid phase. For AgCl, AgBr, AgI, AgSCN, and $AgIO_3$, the concentration of the molecular species is approximately 0.1 to 1 per cent of the total solubility of the parent compound in water. Dissolution of many metallic hydroxides and sulfides, including $Ni(OH)_2$, $Fe(OH)_3$, $Zn(OH)_2$, HgS, CdS, and CuS, is known to yield a small concentration of the corresponding aqueous molecule.

ACTIVITY PRODUCT

We may consider the second step of the solubility reactions of silver chloride as the dissociation of the aqueous silver chloride molecule (or ion pair) into silver ion and chloride ion:

$$\text{AgCl(aq)} \rightleftharpoons \text{Ag}^+ + \text{Cl}^-$$

As the molecular species is consumed in this reaction, additional solid silver chloride dissolves. The thermodynamic equilibrium-constant expression for the dissociation of AgCl(aq) is

$$\frac{(\text{Ag}^+)(\text{Cl}^-)}{(\text{AgCl(aq)})} = \frac{1}{K_1}$$

Such an apparently unusual representation of this equilibrium constant requires a brief explanation. In some tables of equilibrium constants, the preceding reaction is written as

$$Ag^+ + Cl^- \rightleftharpoons AgCl(aq)$$

and the state of equilibrium is represented by the expression

$$\frac{(AgCl(aq))}{(Ag^+)(Cl^-)} = K_1$$

The equilibrium constant K_1 is called the *first stepwise formation constant* for the silver chloride system because it pertains to the reaction in which silver ion combines with the *first* of several chloride ions. In Chapter 4 the stepwise formation of metal ion complexes will be described in greater detail. Above all, the brief discussion here illustrates the important point that, when we reverse the direction in which a chemical equilibrium is written, the *reciprocal* of the equilibrium constant for the original reaction must be employed.

If we now add the two equilibria

$$AgCl(s) \rightleftharpoons AgCl(aq)$$

and

$$AgCl(aq) \rightleftharpoons Ag^+ + Cl^-$$

the result is

$$AgCl(s) \rightleftharpoons Ag^+ + Cl^-$$

When two reactions are *added* together to obtain a third reaction, the equilibrium constants for these two processes are *multiplied* together to give the equilibrium constant for the third reaction. Therefore,

$$(AgCl(aq)) \cdot \frac{(Ag^+)(Cl^-)}{(AgCl(aq))} = S° \cdot \frac{1}{K_1}$$

or

$$(Ag^+)(Cl^-) = \frac{S°}{K_1}$$

with the activity of solid silver chloride still taken to be unity. Although the individual values of $S°$ and K_1 are not accurately known, the *ratio* of these two quantities can be obtained precisely, since the product of the activities of silver ion and chloride ion is accessible to direct experimental measurement. The product of the activities of silver ion and chloride ion is defined as the **thermodynamic activity product,** K_{ap}:

$$(Ag^+)(Cl^-) = K_{ap}$$

This relation is a statement of the fundamental principle that, in a solution saturated with solid silver chloride, the product of the activities of silver ion and chloride ion is always constant.

Several procedures can be employed for the determination of the thermodynamic activity product, but the most direct method involves measurement of the activities of Ag^+ and Cl^-. Recalling that the activity of an ion is given by the equation

$$a_i = f_i C_i$$

we can formulate the thermodynamic activity-product expression as

$$f_{Ag^+} [Ag^+] f_{Cl^-} [Cl^-] = K_{ap}$$

As pointed out in Chapter 1, the activity coefficient f_i of a single ionic species does not have *experimental* significance because it is impossible to prepare a solution containing just one kind of ion. In the case of the solubility of silver chloride in water, one chloride ion is present for every silver ion. Although it is reasonable to speak of separate activity coefficients having different magnitudes for silver ion and chloride ion, these values cannot be determined experimentally, because each species affects the behavior of the other. Therefore, what one does is to define an activity coefficient for a binary electrolyte, called the mean activity coefficient, $f_\pm$, which is directly measurable and which provides, so to speak, information about the average departure from ideality of either the cation or anion of a salt. For silver chloride the mean activity coefficient is

$$f_\pm^2 = f_{Ag^+} f_{Cl^-}$$

If this relation is substituted into the equation for the thermodynamic activity product, we obtain

$$f_\pm^2 [Ag^+][Cl^-] = K_{ap}$$

Suppose that solid silver chloride is shaken with pure water until solubility equilibrium is attained. After the excess solid is separated from its saturated solution, one can determine by means of titrimetry the analytical concentrations of silver ion and chloride ion. Then, because the solubility of silver chloride is small, one may confidently employ the Debye-Hückel limiting law to evaluate the mean activity coefficient of silver chloride. Finally, the mean activity coefficient and the analytical data are combined to calculate the thermodynamic activity product. Numerous measurements of the solubility of silver chloride at 25°C have been performed, and the results are consistent with the conclusion that

$$(Ag^+)(Cl^-) = K_{ap} = 1.78 \times 10^{-10}$$

SOLUBILITY PRODUCT

In chemical work, we are frequently concerned with the concentration of a species instead of its activity, since the former provides information about the quantity of material present in a particular phase or system. For example, it may be of importance to know the analytical concentration of silver ion in a certain solution. In addition, as discussed in Chapter 1, activity coefficients for ions cannot be reliably calculated for electrolyte solutions other than very dilute ones. Moreover, it should be remembered that equilibrium calculations are often performed for the purpose of predicting information about the behavior of electrolyte solutions which are not extremely dilute. For these reasons, we shall be satisfied to omit the use of activity coefficients throughout most of this book and to write relations involving only analytical concentrations, such as

$$[Ag^+][Cl^-] = K_{sp}$$

This equation is the familiar **solubility-product expression** for silver chloride, and the equilibrium constant is called the **solubility product** or the **solubility-product constant.** For virtually all equilibrium calculations concerned with the solubility of precipitates, we shall use analytical concentrations and we will assume that the activity product K_{ap} and the solubility product K_{sp} are synonymous. Appendix 1 contains a compilation of solubility products.

In the remainder of this chapter, let us consider a series of examples of equilibrium calculations involving the solubilities of inorganic substances. Although we will follow the general four-step procedure presented in Chapter 1 for attacking these problems, the individual steps will not be identified explicitly.

As we encounter these sample problems, it will be noticed that some of the effects which can complicate our picture of the solubility of a compound are ignored—factors such as intrinsic solubility, activity coefficients, the formation of ion pairs, and the existence of other, but very poorly characterized, competing equilibria. Some of these concepts have already been introduced in our discussion of the solubility of silver chloride, first, because it is important to recognize that the dissolution of a compound is not in general a simple process and, second, because the behavior of silver chloride is relatively well understood. However, inclusion of these various complicating factors, if known, would make computations too lengthy and difficult for the present introduction to the subject.

Equilibrium calculations which we perform here should be regarded in most instances as approximate at best. Nevertheless, the results obtained are frequently useful in predicting, for example, whether a certain substance is precipitated quantitatively, or how completely one ion can be separated from another by means of a precipitation process. Such predictions must always be tested in actual experiments, but the fact remains that approximate equilibrium calculations do lead to the design of many successful laboratory procedures.

EXAMPLE 1

Silver chloride dissolves in water to the extent of 1.33×10^{-5} mole per liter of solution; calculate the solubility-product constant of silver chloride. As discussed earlier, we may consider that dissolution of silver chloride takes place according to the reaction

$$AgCl(s) \rightleftharpoons Ag^+ + Cl^-$$

for which the solubility-product expression is

$$K_{sp} = [Ag^+][Cl^-]$$

Inasmuch as 1.33×10^{-5} mole per liter of solid AgCl enters the solution phase as silver ion and chloride ion,

$$[Cl^-] = 1.33 \times 10^{-5}\, M \text{ and } [Ag^+] = 1.33 \times 10^{-5}\, M$$

Combining the three mathematical relations, we obtain

$$K_{sp} = (1.33 \times 10^{-5})(1.33 \times 10^{-5})$$
$$K_{sp} = 1.77 \times 10^{-10}$$

EXAMPLE 2

If the solubility of calcium sulfate in water is 0.191 gram per 100 ml, calculate the solubility-product constant of calcium sulfate. This equilibrium may be represented by the chemical reaction

$$CaSO_4(s) \rightleftharpoons Ca^{++} + SO_4^=$$

and by the solubility-product equation

$$K_{sp} = [Ca^{++}][SO_4^=]$$

in which the concentrations of calcium and sulfate ions are identical, as well as equal to the molar solubility of the solid calcium sulfate. We must next convert the original solubility data into molar concentration by dividing the weight in grams by the formula weight of $CaSO_4$, the latter being 136.2, and by changing from solubility per 100 ml to solubility per liter:

$$[Ca^{++}] = \frac{0.191}{136.2} \times \frac{1000}{100} = 1.40 \times 10^{-2} M$$

$$[SO_4^=] = \frac{0.191}{136.2} \times \frac{1000}{100} = 1.40 \times 10^{-2} M$$

When these relationships are combined, we obtain

$$K_{sp} = (1.40 \times 10^{-2})(1.40 \times 10^{-2})$$
$$K_{sp} = 1.96 \times 10^{-4}$$

EXAMPLE 3

Calculate the solubility-product constant for nickel hydroxide, $Ni(OH)_2$, the solubility of which is 0.00011 gram per liter of water. The simplest possible representation of the dissolution reaction is

$$Ni(OH)_2(s) \rightleftharpoons Ni^{++} + 2\ OH^-$$

and the solubility-product expression is

$$K_{sp} = [Ni^{++}][OH^-]^2$$

As in the preceding example, the molar solubility of nickel hydroxide is obtained if we divide the weight solubility by the formula weight of $Ni(OH)_2$; since one nickel ion is formed for each nickel hydroxide molecule which dissolves, the concentration of nickel ion equals the molar solubility

$$[Ni^{++}] = \frac{0.00011}{92.7} = 1.2 \times 10^{-6} M$$

whereas the hydroxide concentration is seen from the dissolution reaction to be twice that of nickel ion:

$$[OH^-] = 2.4 \times 10^{-6} M$$

It follows that the solubility product is given by

$$K_{sp} = (1.2 \times 10^{-6})(2.4 \times 10^{-6})^2$$
$$K_{sp} = 6.9 \times 10^{-18}$$

It should be mentioned that the solubility behavior of nickel hydroxide is, in fact, much more complicated than this simple calculation suggests, as may be seen in Problem 22 at the end of this chapter.

EXAMPLE 4

Calculate the molar solubility of cadmium hydroxide, for which the solubility equilibrium is

$$Cd(OH)_2(s) \rightleftharpoons Cd^{++} + 2\ OH^-$$

and for which the solubility-product constant is 5.9×10^{-15}. Since one Cd^{++} ion and two OH^- ions are produced from each molecule of cadmium hydroxide which dissolves, it follows that

$$[OH^-] = 2\ [Cd^{++}]$$

Substituting this relationship into the solubility-product expression and solving for $[Cd^{++}]$, we obtain

$$[Cd^{++}]\ (2[Cd^{++}])^2 = 5.9 \times 10^{-15}$$
$$[Cd^{++}] = 1.1 \times 10^{-5} M$$

Thus, the solubility of cadmium hydroxide is $1.1 \times 10^{-5} M$.

EXAMPLE 5

Calculate the weight in grams of silver chromate which will dissolve per liter of water, taking the solubility-product constant to be 2.45×10^{-12}. We may represent the dissolution process by the reaction

$$Ag_2CrO_4(s) \rightleftharpoons 2\ Ag^+ + CrO_4^=$$

for which the equilibrium expression is

$$2.45 \times 10^{-12} = [Ag^+]^2 [CrO_4^=]$$

According to the solubility reaction, there must be twice as many silver ions as chromate ions at equilibrium, so

$$2 [CrO_4^=] = [Ag^+]$$

Combining these relations, we have

$$2.45 \times 10^{-12} = (2[CrO_4^=])^2[CrO_4^=]$$
$$[CrO_4^=] = 8.50 \times 10^{-5} M$$

In order to have a chromate ion concentration of $8.50 \times 10^{-5} M$, the solubility of silver chromate must be exactly the same value. To obtain the solubility in grams per liter, we must multiply the molar solubility by the formula weight of Ag_2CrO_4, the latter being 331.7. Thus, the weight solubility of Ag_2CrO_4 is (8.50×10^{-5}) (331.7) or 0.0282 gram per liter.

DIVERSE ION EFFECT

Although it is convenient and simple to discuss the solubility of a substance in pure water, the formation or dissolution of a precipitate in a practical chemical operation almost invariably occurs in the presence of relatively large concentrations of foreign electrolytes. For example, even in the seemingly simple and straightforward preparation of pure silver chloride, in which one mixes stoichiometric quantities of solutions containing sodium chloride and silver nitrate, the precipitate will be dispersed in a medium containing dissolved sodium nitrate. Therefore, we must be concerned about the solubility behavior of a precipitate in the presence of a foreign electrolyte. However, we will restrict the discussion in this section to chemical systems wherein the desired compound is in equilibrium with a solution which contains no ions common to the precipitate — that is, no ions of which the solid is composed, except for those produced when the precipitate itself dissolves.

Before attempting to predict quantitatively how the solubility of a precipitate such as silver chloride depends on the concentration of foreign electrolyte, we will consider a qualitative picture of the interaction between silver ion and chloride ion. Let us contrast the behavior of silver ion and chloride ion in two environments — pure water and 0.1 M nitric acid. In the nitric acid medium, the positively charged silver ion will exhibit a strong attraction for nitrate anions, whereas chloride ions attract hydrogen ions. Obviously, silver ion and chloride ion have a mutual attraction for each other. However, the concentrations of silver ion and chloride ion should be quite small compared to the quantities of hydrogen ion and nitrate ion, so the ion atmosphere of a silver ion contains nitrate as well as water, and the ion atmosphere of chloride consists predominantly of hydrogen ions and water. The effect of these ion atmospheres is to neutralize partially the charge of a silver ion and of a chloride ion and to decrease their force of attraction for each other. If the force of attraction between Ag^+ and Cl^- is less in nitric acid than in pure water, it follows that the solubility of silver chloride should be larger in the former solvent. This conclusion is in agreement with experimental data; such a simple picture affords a valuable way to predict the effects of foreign electrolytes on chemical equilibria.

Quantitative predictions of the effect of a foreign electrolyte on the solubility of silver chloride can be based upon the equation introduced previously,

$$f_{\pm}^2 \, [Ag^+] \, [Cl^-] = K_{ap}$$

where $f_{\pm}$ is the mean activity coefficient for silver chloride and $[Ag^+]$ and $[Cl^-]$ represent the analytical concentrations of silver ion and chloride ion. Since the molar solubility S of silver chloride is equivalent to the silver ion concentration, and since the concentrations of silver and chloride ions are equal, we may write

$$f_{\pm}^2 \, S^2 = K_{ap}$$

$$S = \frac{(K_{ap})^{1/2}}{f_{\pm}}$$

It is evident from the latter equation that the solubility of silver chloride should increase as the mean activity coefficient decreases; and, of course, the converse is true. Noting the variation of activity coefficients with ionic strength in Figures 1-2 and 1-3, we can conclude that a plot of solubility versus ionic strength will exhibit an initial rise followed by a decrease. It should be recalled that activity coefficients for ions with multiple charges are much more sensitive to variations in ionic strength than those for singly charged species. Consequently, the solubility of precipitates consisting of multicharged ions will change much more drastically with ionic strength than, say, the solubility of silver chloride.

Let us calculate and compare the solubilities of silver chloride in water and in 0.05 M nitric acid. For water, the ionic strength μ is nearly zero because the concentrations of dissolved silver ion and chloride ion are very small. Thus, we shall assume that the mean activity coefficient is essentially unity. Therefore, the molar solubility S of silver chloride is given by the simple relation

$$S = (K_{ap})^{1/2} = (1.78 \times 10^{-10})^{1/2}$$
$$S = 1.33 \times 10^{-5} M$$

Now, a calculation of the solubility of silver chloride in $0.05\ M$ nitric acid requires that we determine the ionic strength of the solution and the mean activity coefficient of silver chloride. Although the ionic strength of a solution depends on the concentrations of all ionic species, the contribution to the ionic strength by dissolved silver chloride is negligible, so

$$\mu = \frac{1}{2}\ [C_{H^+}\ z_{H^+}{}^2 + C_{NO_3^-}\ z_{NO_3^-}{}^2]$$
$$\mu = \frac{1}{2}\ [(0.05)(1)^2 + (0.05)(-1)^2]$$
$$\mu = 0.05$$

We shall use the Debye-Hückel limiting law to obtain the mean activity coefficient, even though the ionic strength is sufficiently large that the limiting law is not highly accurate.

$$-\log f_{\pm} = 0.512\ z_{Ag^+}\ z_{Cl^-} \sqrt{\mu}$$
$$-\log f_{\pm} = 0.512\ (1)\ (1)\ \sqrt{0.05} = 0.114$$
$$f_{\pm} = 0.77$$

If we now combine this result with the equation for the solubility of silver chloride, the value of the molar solubility S can be calculated:

$$S = \frac{(K_{ap})^{1/2}}{f_{\pm}} = \frac{(1.78 \times 10^{-10})^{1/2}}{0.77}$$

$$S = 1.73 \times 10^{-5} M$$

Therefore, the solubility of silver chloride is about 30 per cent higher in $0.05\ M$ nitric acid than in water. It is of interest to note that the experimentally observed solubility of silver chloride in $0.05\ M$ nitric acid is close to $1.60 \times 10^{-5} M$. It is suggested that the student perform a similar calculation with the extended Debye-Hückel equation, taking the average effective diameter of the silver and chloride ions to be $4\ \text{Å}$.

COMMON ION EFFECT

In this section is discussed the solubility behavior of a substance in the presence of a foreign electrolyte which does contain an ion in common with the substance. The influence of an excess of one of the ions comprising a precipitate upon the solubility of that substance is called the

common ion effect. An application of Le Châtelier's principle to the chemical equation representing the state of equilibrium between dissolved and undissolved solute reveals that the excess of common ion represses the solubility of the substance. In general, solubility-product considerations permit us to make predictions about the magnitude of the common ion effect.

Consider the gravimetric determination of silver ion by means of the classical procedure in analytical chemistry in which an excess of chloride ion is added to a solution containing the unknown quantity of silver ion to precipitate silver chloride, the latter then being weighed to establish how much silver was in the original sample. It should be obvious that the accuracy of this determination is influenced by how completely the silver ion is precipitated. If we examine the simple solubility-product expression for silver chloride,

$$K_{sp} = [Ag^+][Cl^-] = 1.78 \times 10^{-10}$$

it appears that any desired completeness of precipitation could be achieved through a suitable adjustment of the chloride concentration. For example, if the chloride ion concentration were $1 \times 10^{-3} M$, the concentration of silver ion should be $1.78 \times 10^{-7} M$, whereas the concentration of silver ion ought to be only $1.78 \times 10^{-9} M$ when the chloride concentration is $0.1 M$. Although it is important to recognize the usefulness of the common ion effect in the prediction of experimental conditions for a desired gravimetric determination, it is equally important to realize that serious errors can result if one places too much confidence in such calculations. It was previously shown that a certain concentration, approximately $2 \times 10^{-7} M$, of aqueous molecular silver chloride exists in equilibrium with the solid and that this concentration is unaffected by the occurrence of other chemical reactions. Therefore, the concentration of AgCl(aq) represents the minimum concentration of dissolved silver chloride that is attainable in an aqueous solution—in spite of the predictions reached on the basis of the common ion effect.

We will now consider several sample problems, in each of which we will calculate the solubility of a substance and demonstrate some aspects of the common ion effect. In each of these calculations we will assume that the data of Appendix 1 are available to us for use as desired.

EXAMPLE 6

Calculate the solubility of lead iodate, $Pb(IO_3)_2$, in pure water and in $0.030 M$ potassium iodate solution. The solubility and solubility-product constant for lead iodate may be written as

$$Pb(IO_3)_2(s) \rightleftharpoons Pb^{++} + 2\ IO_3^-;\ K_{sp} = 2.6 \times 10^{-13}$$

In pure water, each dissolved lead iodate molecule yields one lead ion and two iodate ions. If we represent the solubility of lead iodate by the symbol S, it follows that

$$[Pb^{++}] = S \quad \text{and} \quad [IO_3^-] = 2\ S$$

When these relationships are substituted into the solubility-product expression, we obtain

$$[Pb^{++}][IO_3^-]^2 = (S)(2\ S)^2 = 2.6 \times 10^{-13}$$
$$4\ S^3 = 2.6 \times 10^{-13}$$
$$S = 4.0 \times 10^{-5} M$$

for the solubility of lead iodate in pure water. In the $0.03\ M$ potassium iodate medium, the calculation is slightly more complicated, for there are two sources of iodate ion. At equilibrium the concentration of iodate will be the sum of the contributions from potassium iodate and lead iodate — $0.03\ M$ from potassium iodate and $2\ S$ from lead iodate. As before, the equilibrium concentration of lead ion can be called S, and the appropriate solubility-product expression is

$$(S)(2\ S + 0.03)^2 = 2.6 \times 10^{-13}$$

This relation could be solved in a completely rigorous manner, but the manipulations would involve a third-order equation. Therefore, it is appropriate to consider the feasibility of a suitable simplifying assumption. Since the solubility of lead iodate in pure water is only $4.0 \times 10^{-5} M$ and since the presence of potassium iodate should repress the solubility of lead iodate, we will neglect the $2\ S$ term in the preceding expression:

$$(S)(0.03)^2 = 2.6 \times 10^{-13}$$
$$S = 2.9 \times 10^{-10} M$$

Our neglect of the $2\ S$ term in comparison to $0.03\ M$ was fully justified. Therefore, it is concluded that the solubility of lead iodate is only $2.9 \times 10^{-10} M$ in the presence of $0.030\ M$ potassium iodate, as compared to $4.0 \times 10^{-5} M$ in pure water; the common ion effect is indeed substantial.

EXAMPLE 7

Calculate the weight in grams of magnesium fluoride, MgF_2, which will dissolve in 500 ml of a 0.100 M magnesium nitrate, $Mg(NO_3)_2$, solution. Magnesium fluoride dissolves according to the reaction

$$MgF_2 \rightleftharpoons Mg^{++} + 2\ F^-$$

and has a solubility-product constant of 6.5×10^{-9}:

$$K_{sp} = [Mg^{++}][F^-]^2 = 6.5 \times 10^{-9}$$

Since fluoride is the only ion which is derived exclusively from the dissolution reaction, the molar solubility of magnesium fluoride can be taken as one-half the fluoride ion concentration. However, the concentration of magnesium ion is the sum of that which comes from the magnesium nitrate, 0.100 M, and that which comes from the dissolution of magnesium fluoride, the latter being equal to one-half the fluoride concentration:

$$[Mg^{++}] = 0.100 + \frac{[F^-]}{2}$$

Because the solubility of magnesium fluoride is expected to be relatively small in the presence of magnesium nitrate, it is reasonable to neglect the term $[F^-]/2$ in comparison to the quantity 0.100 M in the previous expression. Combination of the various relationships gives the result

$$0.100\ [F^-]^2 = 6.5 \times 10^{-9}$$
$$[F^-]^2 = 6.5 \times 10^{-8}$$
$$[F^-] = 2.55 \times 10^{-4}\ M$$

Recalling that the solubility S is one-half of the fluoride ion concentration, we have

$$S = 1.28 \times 10^{-4}\ M$$

and recognizing that the formula weight of magnesium fluoride is 62.31 and that the solution volume is only 500 ml, we may write

$$S = 1.28 \times 10^{-4}\ \frac{mole}{liter} \cdot \frac{62.31\ gm}{mole} \cdot \frac{1\ liter}{1000\ ml} \cdot 500\ ml$$

$$S = 3.99 \times 10^{-3}\ gm\ (per\ 500\ ml)$$

COMPLEXATION OF CATION WITH FOREIGN LIGAND

In a preceding section we considered the solubility of a precipitate in the presence of excess diverse ion. In addition, the solubility of a compound can be markedly enhanced if a foreign complexing agent or ligand is available which can react with the cation of the precipitate. An example of the latter kind of system is the increase in the solubility of the silver halides, AgCl, AgBr, and AgI, in ammonia solutions.

If we consider the solubility of silver bromide in aqueous ammonia solutions, it should be evident that the position of equilibrium for the reaction

$$AgBr(s) \rightleftharpoons Ag^+ + Br^-; \qquad K_{sp} = 5.25 \times 10^{-13}$$

will be shifted toward the right because of the formation of stable silver-ammine complexes. Silver ion reacts with ammonia in a stepwise manner, according to the equilibria

$$Ag^+ + NH_3 \rightleftharpoons AgNH_3^+; \qquad K_1 = 2.5 \times 10^3$$

and

$$AgNH_3^+ + NH_3 \rightleftharpoons Ag(NH_3)_2^+; \qquad K_2 = 1.0 \times 10^4$$

EXAMPLE 8

Calculate the solubility of silver bromide in a 0.1 M ammonia solution. On the basis of the preceding reactions, we can conclude that each silver bromide molecule which dissolves will yield one bromide ion and either one Ag^+, one $AgNH_3^+$, or one $Ag(NH_3)_2^+$. Therefore, the solubility S of silver bromide is measured by the concentration of bromide ion or, alternatively, by the sum of the concentrations of all soluble silver species, i.e.,

$$S = [Ag^+] + [AgNH_3^+] + [Ag(NH_3)_2^+] = [Br^-]$$

This relation may be transformed into one equation with a single unknown if we introduce the equilibrium-constant expressions for the silver-ammine species. For the concentration of the silver-monoammine complex, it can be shown that

$$[AgNH_3^+] = K_1 [Ag^+][NH_3]$$

and the concentration of the silver-diammine complex may be

written as

$$[Ag(NH_3)_2^+] = K_2 [AgNH_3^+][NH_3]$$

or

$$[Ag(NH_3)_2^+] = K_1 K_2 [Ag^+][NH_3]^2$$

If we substitute the relations for the concentrations of the two silver-ammine complexes into the solubility equation, the result is

$$S = [Ag^+] + K_1 [Ag^+][NH_3] + K_1 K_2 [Ag^+][NH_3]^2 = [Br^-]$$

Next, we should note that in a solution saturated with silver bromide the solubility-product expression must be obeyed; that is,

$$[Ag^+] = \frac{K_{sp}}{[Br^-]}$$

so it follows that

$$S = \frac{K_{sp}}{[Br^-]} + \frac{K_1 K_{sp}[NH_3]}{[Br^-]} + \frac{K_1 K_2 K_{sp}[NH_3]^2}{[Br^-]}$$

However, since $[Br^-] = S$, we can write

$$S = \frac{K_{sp}}{S} + \frac{K_1 K_{sp}[NH_3]}{S} + \frac{K_1 K_2 K_{sp}[NH_3]^2}{S}$$

Finally, solving for the solubility S, we obtain

$$S^2 = K_{sp} + K_1 K_{sp}[NH_3] + K_1 K_2 K_{sp}[NH_3]^2$$
$$S = K_{sp}^{1/2}(1 + K_1[NH_3] + K_1 K_2 [NH_3]^2)^{1/2}$$

Before we insert numerical values for the ammonia concentration and the various constants into the latter equation, it is interesting to note that this relation is a general one for the solubility of many sparingly soluble silver salts in an ammonia solution. For the solubility of silver bromide in a 0.1 M ammonia solution, we have

$$S = (5.25 \times 10^{-13})^{1/2}$$
$$[1 + (2.5 \times 10^3)(0.1) + (2.5 \times 10^3)(1.0 \times 10^4)(0.1)^2]^{1/2}$$

$$S = 3.6 \times 10^{-4} M$$

In addition, we can calculate the concentration of each soluble silver species. For Ag^+:

$$[Ag^+] = \frac{K_{sp}}{[Br^-]} = \frac{5.25 \times 10^{-13}}{3.6 \times 10^{-4}}$$

$$[Ag^+] = 1.46 \times 10^{-9} M$$

For $AgNH_3^+$:

$$[AgNH_3^+] = K_1[Ag^+][NH_3] = (2.5 \times 10^3)(1.46 \times 10^{-9})(0.1)$$
$$[AgNH_3^+] = 3.6 \times 10^{-7} M$$

For $Ag(NH_3)_2^+$:

$$[Ag(NH_3)_2^+] = K_2[AgNH_3^+][NH_3]$$
$$= (1.0 \times 10^4)(3.6 \times 10^{-7})(0.1)$$

$$[Ag(NH_3)_2^+] = 3.6 \times 10^{-4} M$$

Therefore, the only species which contributes significantly to the solubility of silver bromide in $0.1 M$ ammonia solution is the silver-diammine complex. One of the conceivable complications which we overlooked in solving this problem was the possibility that the formation of silver-ammine complexes might alter the concentration of ammonia. However, it is apparent that the solubility of silver bromide is small enough that neglect of this effect was justified. If the solubility of silver bromide were of a magnitude comparable to the ammonia concentration, it would be necessary to consider the change in the concentration of ammonia.

As another example of the effect of complexation of the cation with a foreign ligand upon the solubility of a compound, consider the dissolution of silver chloride in a sodium thiosulfate solution, where the pertinent equilibria are

$$AgCl(s) \rightleftharpoons Ag^+ + Cl^-; \qquad K_{sp} = 1.78 \times 10^{-10}$$
$$Ag^+ + S_2O_3^= \rightleftharpoons AgS_2O_3^-; \qquad K_1 = 6.6 \times 10^8$$
$$AgS_2O_3^- + S_2O_3^= \rightleftharpoons Ag(S_2O_3)_2^=; \qquad K_2 = 4.4 \times 10^4$$

Every molecule of silver chloride which dissolves must result in the presence in solution of one chloride ion and either one Ag^+ ion, one $AgS_2O_3^-$ ion, or one $Ag(S_2O_3)_2^=$ ion. Accordingly, the molar solubility S can be expressed by means of the relation

$$S = [Ag^+] + [AgS_2O_3^-] + [Ag(S_2O_3)_2^=] = [Cl^-]$$

In a solution which contains several metal complexes, it is often instructive to evaluate the concentration ratios of the various species. For the two complexes involving silver and thiosulfate ions, we can write:

$$\frac{[AgS_2O_3^-]}{[Ag^+]} = K_1[S_2O_3^=] = 6.6 \times 10^8[S_2O_3^=]$$

$$\frac{[Ag(S_2O_3)_2^=]}{[AgS_2O_3^-]} = K_2[S_2O_3^=] = 4.4 \times 10^4[S_2O_3^=]$$

If, for example, the concentration of thiosulfate ion is exactly 1 M at equilibrium, these concentration ratios become

$$\frac{[AgS_2O_3^-]}{[Ag^+]} = 6.6 \times 10^8$$

$$\frac{[Ag(S_2O_3)_2^=]}{[AgS_2O_3^-]} = 4.4 \times 10^4$$

Thus, the concentration of $AgS_2O_3^-$ is 660 million times larger than the Ag^+ concentration, whereas the predominant species is $Ag(S_2O_3)_2^=$, its concentration being a factor of 44,000 greater than that of $AgS_2O_3^-$. Even when the thiosulfate concentration is only 0.001 M, the concentration of $Ag(S_2O_3)_2^=$ is still 44 times greater than that of $AgS_2O_3^-$, and, in turn, the concentration of $AgS_2O_3^-$ exceeds the silver ion concentration by a factor of approximately 660,000. Therefore, in the presence of at least 0.001 M thiosulfate ion, it is permissible to regard $Ag(S_2O_3)_2^=$ as the only important form of dissolved silver and to represent the solubility of silver chloride by the abbreviated expression

$$S = [Ag(S_2O_3)_2^=] = [Cl^-]$$

In addition, the equilibria pertaining to the formation of the thiosulfate complexes of silver ion can be combined to yield

$$Ag^+ + 2 S_2O_3^= \rightleftharpoons Ag(S_2O_3)_2^=; \quad K_1K_2 = 2.9 \times 10^{13}$$

EXAMPLE 9

Calculate the molar solubility of silver chloride in a solution containing *at equilibrium* $1.00 \times 10^{-2} M$ thiosulfate ion. Since the concentration of free thiosulfate ion is sufficiently large, it is apparent that $Ag(S_2O_3)_2^=$ predominates over both $AgS_2O_3^-$ and

Ag^+. Thus, the key equilibria are

$$AgCl(s) \rightleftharpoons Ag^+ + Cl^-$$
$$Ag^+ + 2\ S_2O_3^= \rightleftharpoons Ag(S_2O_3)_2^=$$

the relevant mathematical relationships are

$$[Ag^+][Cl^-] = 1.78 \times 10^{-10}$$

$$\frac{[Ag(S_2O_3)_2^=]}{[Ag^+][S_2O_3^=]^2} = 2.9 \times 10^{13}$$

$$[S_2O_3^=] = 1.00 \times 10^{-2}\ M$$

and, as shown in the preceding discussion,

$$[Ag(S_2O_3)_2^=] = [Cl^-]$$

Since these last four equations contain four unknowns, they may be solved for $[Cl^-]$, which is known to equal the solubility of silver chloride. If we rearrange the first two mathematical relations by solving each for $[Ag^+]$, and then equate the resulting expressions, we have

$$[Ag^+] = \frac{1.78 \times 10^{-10}}{[Cl^-]} = \frac{[Ag(S_2O_3)_2^=]}{2.9 \times 10^{13}[S_2O_3^=]^2}$$

Substituting into this equation the other two relationships, we obtain

$$\frac{1.78 \times 10^{-10}}{[Cl^-]} = \frac{[Cl^-]}{2.9 \times 10^{13}(1.00 \times 10^{-2})^2}$$

Rearranging and solving for $[Cl^-]$, we have

$$[Cl^-]^2 = (1.78 \times 10^{-10})(2.9 \times 10^{13})(1.00 \times 10^{-2})^2 = 0.516$$
$$[Cl^-] = 0.71\ M$$

Thus, the solubility of silver chloride in a solution containing *at equilibrium* $1.00 \times 10^{-2}\ M$ thiosulfate ion is $0.71\ M$. Note that the solubility of silver chloride in pure water is only about $1.33 \times 10^{-5}\ M$, so the solubility is increased over 50,000 times by complexation of silver ion with thiosulfate.

REACTION OF ANION WITH ACID

In certain instances, the anion of a slightly soluble compound undergoes an interaction with one or more of the constituents of the solution phase. In this section, we will discuss the solubilities of two substances, lead sulfate and cadmium sulfide. If the solubility of each of these substances in acid media is investigated, it is found that the solubility is greater in acid than in pure water and that the solubility becomes larger as the concentration of acid increases.

In pure water the solubility of lead sulfate is governed by the equilibrium

$$PbSO_4(s) \rightleftharpoons Pb^{++} + SO_4^=; \quad K_{sp} = 1.6 \times 10^{-8}$$

and, if no other equilibria prevail, the solubility of lead sulfate should essentially be the square root of the solubility product, or approximately $1.3 \times 10^{-4} M$.

If nitric acid is added to the system, the solubility of lead sulfate is increased because sulfate ion reacts with hydrogen ion to form the hydrogen sulfate anion:

$$H^+ + SO_4^= \rightleftharpoons HSO_4^-$$

However, addition of another proton to the hydrogen sulfate anion does not occur to any appreciable extent because sulfuric acid, H_2SO_4, is a very strong acid. Therefore, when a lead sulfate molecule dissolves in nitric acid, one lead ion is formed, but the sulfate ion from the precipitate may be present as either $SO_4^=$ or HSO_4^-. Accordingly, we can express the solubility S of lead sulfate in nitric acid by means of the equation

$$S = [Pb^{++}] = [SO_4^=] + [HSO_4^-]$$

Equilibria involving strong and weak acids will be described in considerable detail in the next chapter. For the present, it is sufficient to point out that a relationship between the concentrations of sulfate ion and hydrogen sulfate ion can be based upon the equilibrium expression for the *second* ionization of sulfuric acid, namely,

$$HSO_4^- \rightleftharpoons H^+ + SO_4^=; \quad K_2 = 1.2 \times 10^{-2}$$

Substituting the latter information into the solubility equation, we obtain

$$S = [Pb^{++}] = [SO_4^=] + \frac{[H^+][SO_4^=]}{K_2}$$

and, utilizing the solubility-product expression for lead sulfate, we can write

$$S = [Pb^{++}] = \frac{K_{sp}}{[Pb^{++}]} + \frac{K_{sp}[H^+]}{K_2[Pb^{++}]}$$

$$[Pb^{++}]^2 = K_{sp} + \frac{K_{sp}[H^+]}{K_2}$$

$$[Pb^{++}] = \left(K_{sp} + \frac{K_{sp}[H^+]}{K_2} \right)^{1/2}$$

Provided that the hydrogen ion concentration is known, we can calculate from the latter relation the concentration of lead ion in equilibrium with solid lead sulfate and, therefore, the solubility of lead sulfate itself.

Suppose that we wish to predict the solubility of lead sulfate in $0.10\,M$ nitric acid. One of the questions that must be answered concerns whether the formation of the hydrogen sulfate anion, through the reaction of $SO_4^=$ with H^+, will consume enough hydrogen ion to change significantly the concentration of the latter. We can either assume that the change will be important — in which case the computations are relatively difficult — or that this change may be neglected as a first approximation. If the second alternative is chosen, it will be necessary to justify the validity of the original assumption after the calculations are completed. Let us assume now that the concentration of hydrogen ion remains essentially constant at $0.1\,M$. Thus, the lead ion concentration is given by the equation

$$[Pb^{++}] = \left(1.6 \times 10^{-8} + \frac{(1.6 \times 10^{-8})(0.1)}{1.2 \times 10^{-2}} \right)^{1/2}$$

which, when solved, yields

$$[Pb^{++}] = 3.9 \times 10^{-4}\,M$$

Therefore, the solubility of lead sulfate in $0.1\,M$ nitric acid is $3.9 \times 10^{-4}\,M$. This value is about three times as great as the solubility we found earlier for lead sulfate in pure water.

To check the validity of the assumption which was made, we may note that the hydrogen ion concentration would be reduced only by 3.9×10^{-4} mole per liter, even if every sulfate ion derived from the dissolution of lead sulfate were converted to hydrogen sulfate anion, which is a negligibly small fraction of the total hydrogen ion concentration. Therefore, by making a simplifying assumption and later justifying its validity, we obtain the desired result in a straightforward way. If, on the other hand, the lead concentration had turned out to be comparable to the original concentration of nitric acid, we should immediately suspect that our assumption was false and return to a more rigorous solution to the problem. It should be stressed that the primary reason for making the assumption was the smallness of the solubility product of lead sulfate compared to the initial nitric acid concentration. It is important for one to be aware of such situations in equilibrium calculations.

Now let us consider the dissolution of cadmium sulfide, CdS, for which the solubility reaction and solubility-product constant are

$$CdS(s) \rightleftharpoons Cd^{++} + S^{=}; \quad K_{sp} = 7.8 \times 10^{-27}$$

Such a small value for the solubility product indicates that cadmium sulfide is indeed of extremely low solubility in water. In acidic media, however, the solubility of cadmium sulfide is increased because sulfide ion is the anion of an exceedingly weak acid, HS^-, which is, in turn, the anion of another weak acid, H_2S. An inspection of the acid dissociation constants for hydrogen sulfide

$$H_2S \rightleftharpoons H^+ + HS^-; \quad K_1 = 9.1 \times 10^{-8}$$
$$HS^- \rightleftharpoons H^+ + S^{=}; \quad K_2 = 1.2 \times 10^{-15}$$

shows the weakly acidic character of H_2S and reveals the tendency of HS^- to ionize so little that free sulfide ion can exist in appreciable concentration only in very strongly alkaline solutions. Thus, sulfide ion produced from the dissolution of cadmium sulfide in an acid medium combines with hydrogen ion to form HS^- as well as H_2S, and as a consequence the solubility of cadmium sulfide is markedly enhanced.

It is often useful to combine the equilibrium expressions corresponding to the two acid dissociation reactions of hydrogen sulfide by multiplying them together to obtain an overall equilibrium relationship:

$$K_1 \times K_2 = \frac{[H^+][HS^-]}{[H_2S]} \times \frac{[H^+][S^=]}{[HS^-]} = (9.1 \times 10^{-8})(1.2 \times 10^{-15})$$

$$K_1 \times K_2 = \frac{[H^+]^2[S^=]}{[H_2S]} = 1.1 \times 10^{-22}$$

It may be seen that the overall equilibrium expression is that which would be written directly for the process

$$H_2S \rightleftharpoons 2 H^+ + S^{=}$$

Although the equilibrium expression for the composite reaction is valid, it is important to realize that the overall dissociation of hydrogen sulfide does take place in two steps, the second of which occurs to a far lesser extent than the first. If one fails to recognize this distinction, he might, for example, erroneously conclude from the balanced chemical reaction that an aqueous solution of hydrogen sulfide contains twice as many hydrogen ions as sulfide ions.

It is common practice in qualitative chemical analysis for one to precipitate cadmium sulfide, as well as other metal sulfides, by first adjusting the hydrogen ion concentration to a predetermined value and then saturating the solution with hydrogen sulfide gas. At room temperature and one atmosphere pressure, the solubility of hydrogen sulfide gas in water is about 0.10 M. Therefore, let us derive an equation for the solubility of cadmium sulfide as a function of the hydrogen ion concentration in a 0.10 M solution of hydrogen sulfide. We may take the solubility S as the molar concentration of cadmium ion, since dissolution of cadmium sulfide is the only source of cadmium ion in solution, and since there is no other reaction to remove cadmium ion from solution. Accordingly,

$$S = [Cd^{++}]$$

or, in terms of the solubility-product constant for cadmium sulfide,

$$S = \frac{K_{sp}}{[S^=]}$$

Rearranging the equilibrium expression for the overall dissociation of hydrogen sulfide by solving it for the sulfide ion concentration,

$$[S^=] = \frac{K_1 K_2 [H_2S]}{[H^+]^2}$$

and substituting this relation into the equation for the solubility of cadmium sulfide, we obtain

$$S = \frac{K_{sp}}{\dfrac{K_1 K_2 [H_2S]}{[H^+]^2}}$$

$$S = \frac{K_{sp}[H^+]^2}{K_1 K_2 [H_2S]}$$

Note that this final relationship has general applicability for the calculation of the solubility of any metal sulfide.

EXAMPLE 10

Calculate the solubility of cadmium sulfide in aqueous media having hydrogen ion concentrations of 0.10 and 0.0010 M. We can solve this problem by substituting the appropriate values into the last preceding equation:

For $[H^+] = 0.10\,M$, $S = \dfrac{(7.8 \times 10^{-27})(0.10)^2}{(1.1 \times 10^{-22})(0.10)}$

$$S = 7.1 \times 10^{-6}\,M$$

For $[H^+] = 0.0010\,M$, $S = \dfrac{(7.8 \times 10^{-27})(0.0010)^2}{(1.1 \times 10^{-22})(0.10)}$

$$S = 7.1 \times 10^{-10}\,M$$

Thus, the molar solubility of cadmium sulfide in an aqueous solution saturated with hydrogen sulfide gas is 10,000-fold greater at a hydrogen ion concentration of $0.10\,M$ than at a hydrogen ion concentration of $0.0010\,M$.

COMPLEXATION BY EXCESS COMMON ION

At the beginning of this chapter, the solubility of silver chloride in water was discussed, and it was suggested that a complete description of the solubility of silver chloride requires detailed knowledge concerning several interrelated equilibria. In particular, it was indicated that certain anionic complexes such as $AgCl_2^-$ and $AgCl_3^=$ may exist to a significant extent when the chloride concentration is relatively large. Accordingly, it is of considerable interest to examine the solubility behavior of silver chloride in the presence of excess chloride ion. In general, we can express the solubility of silver chloride, which we will designate as S, as the sum of the concentrations of all pertinent species:

$$S = [Ag^+] + [AgCl(aq)] + [AgCl_2^-] + [AgCl_3^=] + [AgCl_4^\equiv]$$

The five silver-containing species in this relation account well for the overall solubility behavior of silver chloride over a wide range of chloride ion concentrations.

It is possible to relate the concentrations of these five species to each other through a family of equilibria. First, we can write the solubility-product expression

$$AgCl(s) \rightleftharpoons Ag^+ + Cl^-; \quad K_{sp} = [Ag^+][Cl^-]$$

and the intrinsic solubility relationship

$$AgCl(s) \rightleftharpoons AgCl(aq); \quad S° = [AgCl(aq)]$$

Then, we may formulate the expressions for the stepwise formation of the $AgCl(aq)$, $AgCl_2^-$, $AgCl_3^=$, and $AgCl_4^\equiv$ species.

$$Ag^+ + Cl^- \rightleftharpoons AgCl(aq); \quad K_1 = \frac{[AgCl(aq)]}{[Ag^+][Cl^-]}$$

$$AgCl(aq) + Cl^- \rightleftharpoons AgCl_2^-; \quad K_2 = \frac{[AgCl_2^-]}{[AgCl(aq)][Cl^-]}$$

$$AgCl_2^- + Cl^- \rightleftharpoons AgCl_3^=; \quad K_3 = \frac{[AgCl_3^=]}{[AgCl_2^-][Cl^-]}$$

$$AgCl_3^= + Cl^- \rightleftharpoons AgCl_4^\equiv; \quad K_4 = \frac{[AgCl_4^\equiv]}{[AgCl_3^=][Cl^-]}$$

We are interested here mainly in the solubility of silver chloride as a function of the chloride ion concentration, so it is necessary to express the concentration of each of the individual silver-containing species in terms of the chloride concentration and the various equilibrium constants. When these manipulations are completed, the following results are obtained:

$$[Ag^+] = \frac{K_{sp}}{[Cl^-]}$$

$$[AgCl(aq)] = S° = K_1 K_{sp}$$

$$[AgCl_2^-] = K_1 K_2 K_{sp}[Cl^-]$$

$$[AgCl_3^=] = K_1 K_2 K_3 K_{sp}[Cl^-]^2$$

$$[AgCl_4^\equiv] = K_1 K_2 K_3 K_4 K_{sp}[Cl^-]^3$$

Thus the solubility of silver chloride may be written as

$$S = \frac{K_{sp}}{[Cl^-]} + S° + K_1 K_2 K_{sp}[Cl^-]$$

$$+ K_1 K_2 K_3 K_{sp}[Cl^-]^2 + K_1 K_2 K_3 K_4 K_{sp}[Cl^-]^3$$

This equation looks quite formidable and, in fact, it is inherently difficult to handle. Fortunately, it is possible to make use of the information contained within this equation by relatively simple means. We will describe now a graphical method of representing what the solubility of silver chloride is and what the predominant silver-containing species are for any chosen chloride concentration.

If the expression for the concentration of each silver-containing species is rewritten in logarithmic form, it is found that

$$\log [Ag^+] = \log K_{sp} - \log [Cl^-]$$

$$\log [AgCl(aq)] = \log S° = \log K_1 K_{sp}$$

$$\log [AgCl_2^-] = \log K_1 K_2 K_{sp} + \log [Cl^-]$$

$$\log [AgCl_3^=] = \log K_1 K_2 K_3 K_{sp} + 2 \log [Cl^-]$$

$$\log [AgCl_4^\equiv] = \log K_1 K_2 K_3 K_4 K_{sp} + 3 \log [Cl^-]$$

These equations have been used for the construction of Figure 2-1, in which the logarithm of the concentration of each silver species is plotted

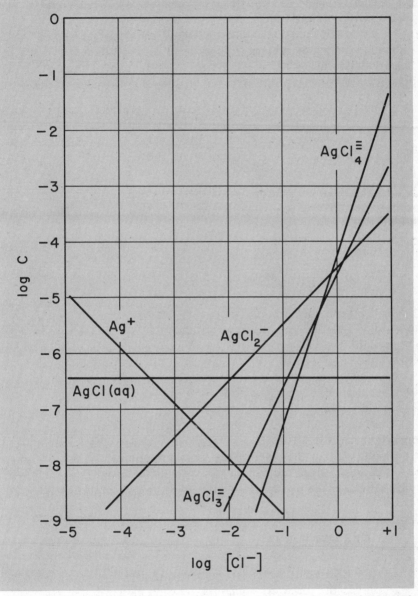

FIGURE 2-1 Logarithm of the concentration of various silver species in equilibrium with solid silver chloride as a function of the logarithm of the chloride concentration at 25°C. (See text for discussion.)

against the logarithm of the chloride concentration. An important and useful feature of this graph is that a straight-line relationship always exists between the logarithm of the concentration of a given species and the logarithm of the chloride concentration. It should be stressed, however, that, in order to construct this figure, one must know the various equilibrium constants, since these parameters actually determine the positions of the straight lines.

Let us calculate the concentration of each species and the total solubility of silver chloride at a chloride ion concentration of $1 \times 10^{-4} M$, that is, when log $[Cl^-] = -4$. From an inspection of Figure 2-1, we obtain the following information for this chloride ion concentration:

$$\log [Ag^+] = -5.9 \quad \text{or} \quad [Ag^+] = 1.3 \times 10^{-6} M$$

$$\log [AgCl(aq)] = -6.4 \quad \text{or} \quad [AgCl(aq)] = 4.0 \times 10^{-7} M$$

$$\log [AgCl_2^-] = -8.5 \quad \text{or} \quad [AgCl_2^-] = 3.2 \times 10^{-9} M$$

Notice that the concentrations of the other two species, $AgCl_3^=$ and $AgCl_4^\equiv$, are far less than $1 \times 10^{-9} M$. Therefore, the total solubility S of silver chloride is essentially

$$S = (1.3 \times 10^{-6}) + (4.0 \times 10^{-7}) + (3.2 \times 10^{-9})$$

$$S = 1.7 \times 10^{-6} M$$

For any other concentration of chloride ion, the concentration of each of the five species and the total solubility of silver chloride may be obtained in a similar manner. It is noteworthy that, at a chloride ion concentration of $1 \times 10^{-4} M$, two species, Ag^+ and $AgCl(aq)$, comprise virtually all of the dissolved silver chloride. At higher chloride concentrations, the anionic complexes become relatively more significant and even predominant.

Since not all of the possible dissolved species are necessarily of importance in every situation, it may be feasible to make meaningful calculations from the appropriate equilibrium-constant data without resorting to the graphical method. Such frequently is the case, as we will illustrate by means of an example involving a different system.

EXAMPLE 11

Calculate the molar solubility of mercuric iodide in water, given the following equilibria between mercuric ion, Hg^{++}, and iodide ion:

$$HgI_2(s) \rightleftharpoons HgI_2(aq); \quad S^\circ = 7.9 \times 10^{-5} = [HgI_2(aq)]$$

$$Hg^{++} + I^- \rightleftharpoons HgI^+; \quad K_1 = 7.4 \times 10^{12} = \frac{[HgI^+]}{[Hg^{++}][I^-]}$$

$$HgI^+ + I^- \rightleftharpoons HgI_2(aq); \quad K_2 = 8.9 \times 10^{10} = \frac{[HgI_2(aq)]}{[HgI^+][I^-]}$$

$$HgI_2(aq) + I^- \rightleftharpoons HgI_3^-; \qquad K_3 = 6.0 \times 10^3 \ = \frac{[HgI_3^-]}{[HgI_2(aq)][I^-]}$$

$$HgI_3^- + I^- \rightleftharpoons HgI_4^=; \qquad K_4 = 1.7 \times 10^2 \ = \frac{[HgI_4^=]}{[HgI_3^-][I^-]}$$

As for silver chloride, the solubility of mercuric iodide is equal to the sum of the concentrations of the five mercury-bearing species in the solution, Hg^{++}, HgI^+, $HgI_2(aq)$, HgI_3^-, and $HgI_4^=$; the minimal solubility must be the intrinsic solubility, $S°$, which is $7.9 \times 10^{-5} M$. We can gain much insight into the solubility behavior of mercuric iodide in water by examining the reactions of $HgI_2(aq)$. This species dissociates to form equal amounts of HgI^+ and I^- ions:

$$HgI_2(aq) \rightleftharpoons HgI^+ + I^-$$

From the value of K_2, it is clear that the position of equilibrium for the reaction just written lies far to the left. In addition, the small quantity of HgI^+ formed in this reaction can undergo further dissociation

$$HgI^+ \rightleftharpoons Hg^{++} + I^-$$

but, in view of the large magnitude of K_1, it is reasonable to assume (subject to later verification) that HgI^+ formed from $HgI_2(aq)$ is exceedingly stable and, therefore, that HgI^+ does not add significantly to the concentration of free iodide ion. Some of the iodide ion resulting from dissociation of $HgI_2(aq)$ can react with other molecules of mercuric iodide to form either HgI_3^- or $HgI_4^=$. However, the numerical values of K_3 and K_4, along with the low concentration of iodide formed from the dissociation of $HgI_2(aq)$ as well as the low intrinsic solubility, indicate that the concentration of HgI_3^- is very small and that of $HgI_4^=$ is even smaller. Based on the assumptions that these higher anion complexes do not contribute significantly to the solubility and that the dissociation of $HgI_2(aq)$ is the only important equilibrium, we may write

$$K_2 = 8.9 \times 10^{10} = \frac{[HgI_2(aq)]}{[HgI^+][I^-]}$$

Since the concentration of $HgI_2(aq)$ is $7.9 \times 10^{-5} M$ and concentrations of HgI^+ and I^- are identical,

$$8.9 \times 10^{10} = \frac{7.9 \times 10^{-5}}{[I^-]^2}$$

$$[I^-]^2 = 8.9 \times 10^{-16}$$

$$[I^-] = 3.0 \times 10^{-8} M \text{ and } [HgI^+] = 3.0 \times 10^{-8} M$$

These results show that the HgI^+ species contributes less than 0.05 per cent as much as does HgI_2(aq) to the total solubility. Any Hg^{++} ion arising from dissociation of HgI^+ would be even less significant, whereas the formation of HgI_3^- and $HgI_4^=$, which requires iodide ion, would likewise be negligible. We conclude, therefore, that the solubility of mercuric iodide in water is essentially equal to its intrinsic solubility, namely $7.9 \times 10^{-5} M$.

If the chemical system of Example 11 were altered by the introduction of another source of either mercuric ion or iodide ion, one or more species other than HgI_2(aq) could be significant in determining the overall solubility.

FORMATION OF PRECIPITATES

Thus far, most of the problems in this chapter have involved calculation of the solubility of a substance under various solution conditions and have dealt with the dissolution of a slightly soluble compound. In many practical situations, however, the state of solubility equilibrium is attained not from partial dissolution of a solid phase but rather by formation of a precipitate from the solution phase. Formation of a precipitate is a physical phenomenon as well as a chemical one. If we are properly to apply the principles of chemical equilibrium to the chemical process, it is necessary to recognize that certain aspects of the physical process may prevent establishment of a state of chemical equilibrium under conditions that would otherwise seem sufficient. In addition, the characteristics of the solid phase are dependent to a large extent upon the physical conditions which prevail at the time of formation of the precipitate.

PRECIPITATION AS A PHYSICAL PROCESS

Two processes, nucleation and crystal growth, comprise the physical reaction in which a precipitate is formed. Nucleation proceeds through the formation within a supersaturated solution of the smallest particles of a precipitate which are capable of spontaneous growth. Crystal growth consists of the deposition of ions (or molecules, if the precipitate is not an ionic one) from the solution upon the surfaces of solid particles which have already been nucleated. The number of particles and, therefore, the particle size of a given mass of precipitate are determined by the number of nuclei formed in the nucleation step.

Generally, the number of nuclei which form is believed to be influenced by the interaction between two factors—first, the extent of supersaturation in the immediate environment where nucleation occurs and, second, the number and effectiveness of sites upon which nuclei may form. Supersaturation is a condition in which a solution phase contains more of the dissolved substance than can be in equilibrium with the solid phase. It is generally a transient condition, particularly when some crystals of the solid phase are present, although certain solutions may remain in the supersaturated state for considerable lengths of time. We may express the extent of supersaturation in terms of the ratio

$$\frac{Q-S}{S}$$

in which Q is the *actual* concentration of solute and S is the *equilibrium* concentration of solute in a saturated solution. Three possible conditions are suggested by the form of this ratio:

(a) If Q is equal to S, the extent of supersaturation is zero, and the solution is saturated. If at least some of the solid phase is present, the system is in a state of chemical equilibrium.

(b) If Q is less than S, the extent of supersaturation is negative, which simply means that the solution is undersaturated. In order for a state of solubility equilibrium to be established, an additional quantity of the solute must be added to the system.

(c) If Q is greater than S, the extent of supersaturation is positive, so the system indeed is in a state of supersaturation, which is a nonequilibrium condition. In order for the system to be in a state of chemical equilibrium, the solution must be saturated, neither supersaturated nor undersaturated.

Even though supersaturation is a transient condition, it is a necessary requirement for the formation of a precipitate. The extent of supersaturation needed for crystal growth may be almost infinitesimally small. However, a considerable amount of supersaturation is required for nucleation to occur. Therefore, the mixing together of reagent solutions in concentrations greater than required to saturate the system does not necessarily result in the formation of a precipitate. Furthermore, the extent of supersaturation at the instant precipitation begins is largely determinative of the particle size and other physical characteristics of the precipitate. In general, the *larger* the extent of supersaturation, the *smaller* will be the size of the individual particles of precipitate.

The initial formation of particles of a precipitate in a supersaturated medium is generally not a spontaneous process. More frequently, the initial clustering of ions is aided by the presence in the solution of some sites which can attract and hold together groups of ions. Possible nucleation sites include tiny solid particles of impurities and of dust, as well as the surfaces of the container. Once some solid particles of the solute substance are present, further precipitation generally occurs on the surfaces of these particles, resulting in crystal growth, rather than nucleation of new particles of precipitate.

Even after a state of solubility equilibrium has been established, the physical process may still be of significance. Precipitation and re-dissolution continually occur, simply because the equilibrium condition is a dynamic one and not a static one. Inasmuch as supersaturation no longer exists, it is highly unlikely that any new particles will form. However, particles which already exist may disappear by dissolution, an equivalent mass of solid phase being added to other particles. In addition, particles which already exist may change outer shape and form, because re-precipitated ions do not necessarily occupy the same sites as do those which dissolve.

CONDITIONS NECESSARY FOR THE FORMATION OF A PRECIPITATE

Some of the most frequently encountered practical applications of solubility-product calculations are in the prediction of conditions necessary for the formation of a precipitate and in the assessment of whether or not a precipitate will form under a given set of circumstances. In general, we can expect a compound to precipitate if the chemical species of which it is comprised are brought together in such a way that the solubility-product constant is exceeded. However, this generalization is not valid if the solution remains supersaturated.

EXAMPLE 12

Calculate the fluoride ion concentration required to begin precipitation of barium fluoride from a solution which is initially $0.00100\,M$ in barium ion. Combination of barium and fluoride ions results in the precipitation of barium fluoride,

$$Ba^{++} + 2\ F^- \rightleftharpoons BaF_2(s)$$

for which the solubility-product expression is

$$K_{sp} = [Ba^{++}][F^-]^2 = 1.7 \times 10^{-6}$$

Inserting the stated value for the initial concentration of barium ion and solving the relation for the fluoride ion concentration, we obtain

$$1.7 \times 10^{-6} = (1.00 \times 10^{-3})[F^-]^2$$

$$[F^-]^2 = 1.7 \times 10^{-3}$$

$$[F^-] = 4.1 \times 10^{-2} M$$

Thus, it would appear on the basis of equilibrium calculations, that a precipitate of barium fluoride will form as soon as the concentration of fluoride ion exceeds $4.1 \times 10^{-2} M$. However, this conclusion is true only apart from the formation of a supersaturated solution.

EXAMPLE 13

Will a precipitate of silver bromide form if one mixes equal volumes of two solutions, one of which is $2.00 \times 10^{-5} M$ in silver ion, and the other $2.00 \times 10^{-5} M$ in bromide ion? If no precipitate formed, the individual concentrations of silver and bromide ions would be $1.00 \times 10^{-5} M$, and the product of these two ion concentrations would be 1.00×10^{-10}. This value is considerably larger than 5.25×10^{-13}, the actual solubility product for silver bromide. Consequently, the solution will be greatly supersaturated unless or until precipitation does occur. Therefore, if we assume that supersaturation to this extent cannot persist, precipitation of silver bromide will proceed and continue until the actual product of the silver and bromide ion concentrations decreases and becomes equal to the solubility-product constant. It is important to note again that supersaturation indeed can and does exist in practical situations, at least temporarily or transiently, and that equilibrium calculations tell us about the conditions at equilibrium but nothing at all about the mechanism or the time involved in reaching the equilibrium state.

EXAMPLE 14

If no state of supersaturation persists, will a precipitate of calcium sulfate be formed when 10.0 ml of a solution $0.0100 M$ in calcium ion is mixed with 20.0 ml of a solution $0.100 M$ in sulfate ion, and when the hydrogen ion concentration in the resulting solution is $0.100 M$? To obtain an answer to this question, we must calculate the product of the concentrations of calcium ion and sulfate ion, and compare the result to the actual solubility product of calcium sulfate.

Since the solution containing calcium ion is diluted from 10 ml to a final volume of 30 ml, it follows that

$$[Ca^{++}] = 0.0100 \cdot \frac{10}{30} = 3.33 \times 10^{-3} M$$

In determining the concentration of sulfate ion, we should recall, from the earlier discussion of the solubility of lead sulfate in nitric acid, that in an acidic medium some of the sulfate will combine with hydrogen ion to yield hydrogen sulfate anion. Thus, the *sum* of the sulfate and hydrogen sulfate concentrations in the final mixture will be the original sulfate ion concentration corrected for the effect of dilution.

$$[SO_4^=] + [HSO_4^-] = 0.100 \cdot \frac{20}{30} = 0.0667 \, M$$

However, the latter two species are in equilibrium with each other according to the reaction

$$HSO_4^- \rightleftharpoons H^+ + SO_4^=; \quad K_2 = \frac{[H^+][SO_4^=]}{[HSO_4^-]} = 1.2 \times 10^{-2}$$

Substituting values for $[H^+]$ and $[HSO_4^-]$ into the preceding relation, and solving the expression for the concentration of sulfate ion, we obtain

$$1.2 \times 10^{-2} = \frac{(0.100)[SO_4^=]}{(0.0667 - [SO_4^=])}$$

$$[SO_4^=] = 7.15 \times 10^{-3} \, M$$

When this concentration of sulfate ion is multiplied by the calcium ion concentration in the final solution, the product is $(7.15 \times 10^{-3})(3.33 \times 10^{-3})$ or 2.38×10^{-5}. In view of the fact that the solubility product for calcium sulfate has a larger magnitude, namely 1.9×10^{-4}, we can conclude that the solution is not saturated and that no precipitation will occur.

COMPLETENESS OF PRECIPITATION

Solubility-product calculations may also be involved in the evaluation of analytical procedures. It is often helpful to predict in advance of an actual laboratory experiment if a precipitation reaction will be quantitatively complete, or if it is feasible to separate two species by means of a precipitation procedure. As pointed out on page 38, a process may be regarded as adequately complete if the quantity of a species which remains unreacted is negligible for the desired purposes. Although the required completeness of reaction may vary drastically from one situation to another, this degree of quantitativeness for a process must be determined or specified for any particular system. For our present purposes, we will state that a reaction is quantitatively complete if the unreacted species comprises no more than 0.1 per cent of the original amount of that substance. Alternatively, we could specify in either mass or concentration units exactly how much of a substance is left unreacted, instead of merely arriving at a "yes" or "no" answer as to whether or not a reaction is complete.

EXAMPLE 15

Is it possible, aside from any supersaturation phenomena, to separate barium ion from calcium ion through precipitation of the former as barium sulfate if the initial concentration of each cation is $0.100\,M$?

From the solubility-product constants for barium sulfate and calcium sulfate

$$BaSO_4(s) \rightleftharpoons Ba^{++} + SO_4^=; \quad K_{sp} = 1.08 \times 10^{-10}$$

$$CaSO_4(s) \rightleftharpoons Ca^{++} + SO_4^=; \quad K_{sp} = 1.9 \times 10^{-4}$$

we can compute the sulfate ion concentration just necessary to start precipitation of these two compounds. In order for barium sulfate to form, the concentration of sulfate must be

$$[SO_4^=] = \frac{K_{sp}}{[Ba^{++}]} = \frac{1.08 \times 10^{-10}}{0.100} = 1.08 \times 10^{-9}\,M \text{ (for } BaSO_4)$$

whereas a much larger sulfate concentration

$$[SO_4^=] = \frac{K_{sp}}{[Ca^{++}]} = \frac{1.9 \times 10^{-4}}{0.100} = 1.9 \times 10^{-3}\,M \text{ (for } CaSO_4)$$

is required to cause formation of calcium sulfate. There is little doubt that barium sulfate will be precipitated first, since a much smaller concentration of sulfate ion is needed. If we now substitute the value of the sulfate ion concentration at which calcium sulfate begins to form, that is, $[SO_4^=] = 1.9 \times 10^{-3}\,M$, into the solubility-product expression for barium sulfate, we can ascertain how much barium ion would remain in solution:

$$[Ba^{++}] = \frac{K_{sp}}{[SO_4^=]} = \frac{1.08 \times 10^{-10}}{1.9 \times 10^{-3}} = 5.7 \times 10^{-8}\,M$$

With the initial barium ion concentration of $0.100\,M$ being reduced to $5.7 \times 10^{-8}\,M$ when calcium sulfate starts to precipitate, the separation may definitely be considered to be quantitatively complete.

EXAMPLE 16

If an acidic solution initially contains $0.100\,M$ zinc ion and $0.0200\,M$ ferric ion, can one separate these two species, through precipitation of one of them as a hydroxide, by adding a concentrated sodium hydroxide solution (so as not to cause dilution of the sample)?

It is necessary to determine from solubility-product data for zinc hydroxide and ferric hydroxide

$$Zn(OH)_2(s) \rightleftharpoons Zn^{++} + 2\,OH^-; \quad K_{sp} = 1.2 \times 10^{-17}$$

$$Fe(OH)_3(s) \rightleftharpoons Fe^{+++} + 3\,OH^-; \quad K_{sp} = 4 \times 10^{-38}$$

which of these two compounds will precipitate first upon addition of sodium hydroxide solution. Let us calculate the hydroxide ion concentration required to cause precipitation of each substance from the respective solubility-product expressions:

$$\text{For } Zn(OH)_2: \ [OH^-]^2 = \frac{K_{sp}}{[Zn^{++}]} = \frac{1.2 \times 10^{-17}}{0.100} = 1.2 \times 10^{-16}$$

$$[OH^-] = 1.1 \times 10^{-8}\,M$$

$$\text{For } Fe(OH)_3: \ [OH^-]^3 = \frac{K_{sp}}{[Fe^{+++}]} = \frac{4 \times 10^{-38}}{0.0200} = 2 \times 10^{-36}$$

$$[OH^-] = 1.3 \times 10^{-12}\,M$$

Since formation of ferric hydroxide occurs at a much smaller $[OH^-]$, it is evident that ferric ion will be precipitated first.

We can predict the effectiveness of the proposed separation of ferric and zinc ions by substituting the hydroxide ion concentration $(1.1 \times 10^{-8}\,M)$ necessary to start precipitation of $Zn(OH)_2$ into the solubility-product relation for $Fe(OH)_3$; such an approach will yield the residual concentration of ferric ion.

$$[Fe^{+++}] = \frac{K_{sp}}{[OH^-]^3} = \frac{4 \times 10^{-38}}{(1.1 \times 10^{-8})^3} = 3 \times 10^{-14}\,M$$

Thus, the ferric ion concentration is decreased theoretically from an original value of $0.0200\,M$ to $3 \times 10^{-14}\,M$ at the point when zinc hydroxide only begins to precipitate, so the separation of the two cations should be feasible. However, there are at least three reasons why this conclusion should be verified experimentally: implicit in the preceding calculations is the assumption that no supersaturation occurs; the gelatinous character of the iron-containing precipitate, with its variable water content, renders calculations with the solubility-product constant for the simple ferric hydroxide only approximate at best; a substance such as zinc hydroxide can frequently precipitate along with another substance (ferric hydroxide in the present example) under conditions for which it would not precipitate by itself.

QUESTIONS AND PROBLEMS

1. Formulate solubility-product expressions for CaF_2, $Fe(OH)_3$, $Ca_3(PO_4)_2$, $MgNH_4PO_4$, and Ag_2CrO_4.

2. Solubility-product relations in which one employs molar concentrations are not completely applicable with solutions containing high concentrations of foreign electrolytes. Explain why, and suggest how the relations can be made more valid in such situations.

3. By means of chemical reactions and the principle of Le Châtelier, predict and explain the effect of
    (a) the magnesium ion concentration upon the solubility of magnesium ammonium phosphate, $MgNH_4PO_4$.
    (b) the hydrogen ion concentration upon the solubility of calcium carbonate, $CaCO_3$.
    (c) the thiosulfate ion concentration upon the solubility of silver chromate, Ag_2CrO_4.

4. Explain why silver chloride is made more soluble by an excess of potassium nitrate but less soluble by an excess of potassium chloride.

5. Under what conditions may a solubility product be exceeded without formation of a precipitate?

6. Suggest two methods by which a solubility-product constant can be determined.

7. The solubility product for barium chromate, $BaCrO_4$, is 2.4×10^{-10}, whereas the solubility product for lead chromate, $PbCrO_4$, is 1.8×10^{-14}. Which compound is more soluble in water?

8. Two compounds with general formulas $A(OH)_2$ and $B(OH)_3$, respectively, have solubility-product constants of the same numerical value. Which compound is more soluble in $0.1\,M$ sodium hydroxide medium?

9. The solubility product for silver chloride is 1.78×10^{-10}, whereas the solubility product for silver chromate is 2.45×10^{-12}. Which compound is more soluble in water?

10. Given the following solubility data in water, evaluate the solubility-product constant for each compound.

    (a) TlCl, 0.32 gram per 100 ml

    (b) $Pb(IO_3)_2$, 3.98×10^{-5} mole per liter

    (c) AgI, 1.40×10^{-6} gram per 500 ml

    (d) $Mg(OH)_2$, 0.0085 gram per liter

11. From the solubility-product constants tabulated in Appendix 1, calculate the solubility of each of the following compounds in moles per liter:

    (a) CdS   (b) BaF_2 (c) $Cu(IO_3)_2$ (d) BiI_3 (e) $SrSO_4$

12. From the solubility-product constants listed in Appendix 1, calculate the solubility of each of the following compounds in grams per 500 ml:

    (a) NiS   (b) SrF_2 (c) $Al(OH)_3$ (d) $PbBr_2$ (e) CuBr

13. Which solution contains a higher concentration of silver ion, a solution saturated with silver iodate or a solution saturated with silver chromate?

14. A solution is saturated with respect to a compound of the general formula AB_2C_3:

$$AB_2C_3(s) \rightleftharpoons A^+ + 2\ B^+ + 3\ C^-$$

If this solution is found to contain ion C^- at a concentration of 0.003 M, evaluate the solubility product of the compound.

15. If the concentration of rubidium ion, Rb^+, is decreased by a factor of 111 when 3.00 moles of lithium perchlorate, $LiClO_4$, are added to 1 liter of a saturated rubidium perchlorate solution, what is the solubility product of $RbClO_4$?

16. The solubility of cerium iodate, $Ce(IO_3)_3$, in pure water is 124 mg per 100 ml of water.

    (a) Calculate the solubility-product constant for cerium iodate, which dissolves according to the reaction

$$Ce(IO_3)_3(s) \rightleftharpoons Ce^{+++} + 3\ IO_3^-$$

    (b) Calculate the solubility in moles per liter of cerium iodate in a 0.050 M potassium iodate solution.

17. What is the maximum concentration of calcium ion that can be present in one liter of solution containing 3.00 moles of fluoride ion?

18. Calculate the weight in grams of cuprous ion remaining in 200 ml of solution after the precipitation of cuprous thiocyanate, CuSCN, if the solution contains an excess of (a) 1.0 mg of thiocyanate ion and (b) 0.10 gm of thiocyanate ion.

19. Calculate the molar concentration of lead ion remaining in solution in the precipitation of lead iodate, $Pb(IO_3)_2$, in the presence of (a) $10^{-4}\ M$ iodate ion and (b) $10^{-2}\ M$ iodate ion.

20. Using information from Figure 2-1, calculate the total molar solubility of silver chloride and the molar concentration of each silver-containing species in solution if the chloride concentration is $0.10\ M$.

21. Calculate the total solubility of zinc hydroxide, $Zn(OH)_2$, in a $0.1\ M$ sodium hydroxide solution, given the following equilibria:

$$Zn(OH)_2(s) \rightleftharpoons Zn^{++} + 2\ OH^-; \quad K_{sp} = 1.2 \times 10^{-17}$$
$$Zn(OH)_2(s) \rightleftharpoons Zn(OH)_2(aq); \quad S° = 10^{-6}$$
$$Zn(OH)_2(s) \rightleftharpoons ZnOH^+ + OH^-; \quad K = 2.4 \times 10^{-13}$$
$$Zn(OH)_2(s) + OH^- \rightleftharpoons Zn(OH)_3^-; \quad K = 2.4 \times 10^{-3}$$
$$Zn(OH)_2(s) + 2\ OH^- \rightleftharpoons Zn(OH)_4^=; \quad K = 2.4 \times 10^{-2}$$

22. The pertinent equilibria for the nickel(II)-hydroxide system are as follows:

$$Ni^{++} + OH^- \rightleftharpoons NiOH^+; \quad K_1 = 2.0 \times 10^3$$
$$NiOH^+ + OH^- \rightleftharpoons Ni(OH)_2(aq); \quad K_2 = 6.3 \times 10^8$$
$$Ni(OH)_2(aq) + OH^- \rightleftharpoons Ni(OH)_3^-; \quad K_3 = 6.3 \times 10^2$$
$$Ni(OH)_2(s) \rightleftharpoons Ni^{++} + 2\ OH^-; \quad K_{sp} = 6.5 \times 10^{-18}$$

(a) Calculate the *intrinsic solubility* $S°$ of $Ni(OH)_2(s)$.
(b) Calculate the *total* solubility of $Ni(OH)_2(s)$, if excess solid nickel hydroxide is shaken with a well-buffered solution of pH 10.00. You may assume that the activity coefficients are unity and that the buffering agent does not undergo any chemical reactions with $Ni(OH)_2(s)$.
(c) What is the predominant nickel(II) species in the solution in (b)?
(d) Explain why the calculation of the solubility of solid nickel hydroxide in pure water would be more difficult than the problem in (b).

23. Calculate the molar solubility of silver iodide in a solution containing an equilibrium cyanide concentration of $0.01\ M$.

24. Calculate the molar solubility of silver iodide in a solution containing an equilibrium ammonia concentration of $0.02\ M$.

25. Calculate the solubility of cuprous iodide in a solution containing an equilibrium ammonia concentration of $0.35\ M$.

$$CuI(s) \rightleftharpoons Cu^+ + I^-; \quad K_{sp} = 5.1 \times 10^{-12}$$
$$Cu^+ + NH_3 \rightleftharpoons CuNH_3^+; \quad K_1 = 8.0 \times 10^5$$
$$CuNH_3^+ + NH_3 \rightleftharpoons Cu(NH_3)_2^+; \quad K_2 = 8.0 \times 10^4$$

26. The equilibria involving the solubilities of lead sulfate

and strontium sulfate and the ionization of sulfuric acid are as follows:

$$PbSO_4(s) \rightleftharpoons Pb^{++} + SO_4^=; \quad K_{sp} = 1.6 \times 10^{-8}$$
$$SrSO_4(s) \rightleftharpoons Sr^{++} + SO_4^=; \quad K_{sp} = 3.8 \times 10^{-7}$$
$$H_2SO_4 \rightleftharpoons H^+ + HSO_4^-; \quad K_1 \gg 1$$
$$HSO_4^- \rightleftharpoons H^+ + SO_4^=; \quad K_2 = 1.2 \times 10^{-2}$$

If an excess of both lead sulfate and strontium sulfate is shaken with a $0.60\,M$ nitric acid solution until equilibrium is attained, what will be the concentrations of Pb^{++}, Sr^{++}, HSO_4^-, and $SO_4^=$?

27. Excess barium sulfate was shaken with $0.25\,M$ sulfuric acid until equilibrium was attained. What was the concentration of barium ion in the solution?

$$BaSO_4(s) \rightleftharpoons Ba^{++} + SO_4^=; \quad K_{sp} = 1.08 \times 10^{-10}$$
$$H_2SO_4 \rightleftharpoons H^+ + HSO_4^-; \quad K_1 \gg 1$$
$$HSO_4^- \rightleftharpoons H^+ + SO_4^=; \quad K_2 = 1.2 \times 10^{-2}$$

28. Excess solid barium sulfate was shaken with $3.6\,M$ hydrochloric acid until equilibrium was attained. Calculate the equilibrium solubility of barium sulfate and the concentrations of $SO_4^=$ and HSO_4^-.

29. Suppose that you wish to dissolve completely 0.0035 mole of solid AgCl in 200 ml of an aqueous ammonia (NH_3) solution. Using the solubility-product constant for silver chloride and assuming an equilibrium constant of 4.0×10^{-8} for the reaction

$$Ag(NH_3)_2^+ \rightleftharpoons Ag^+ + 2\,NH_3$$

calculate what must be the final concentration of ammonia to accomplish this.

30. What hydroxide ion concentration is needed just to begin precipitation of magnesium hydroxide from a $0.01\,M$ solution of magnesium sulfate?

31. What weight of ferric ion must be present in one liter of solution just to begin precipitation of ferric hydroxide if the hydroxide ion concentration is $1.0 \times 10^{-3}\,M$?

32. If 25 mg of magnesium chloride is added to a solution formed by diluting 10 ml of $0.10\,M$ sodium hydroxide solution to 1.0 liter, will a precipitate of magnesium hydroxide be produced?

33. To 150 ml of a solution containing 0.50 gram of Na_2SO_4 is added 50 ml of a solution containing 1.00 gram of $BaCl_2$. Calculate the weight in milligrams of sulfate ion left unprecipitated.

34. What concentration of lead ion remains in solution when strontium sulfate just begins to precipitate from a solution which is $0.0100\,M$ in strontium ion?

35. Calculate the molar concentration of ferric ion left in solution when aluminum hydroxide just begins to precipitate from a solution initially $0.0100\,M$ in both ferric and aluminum ions. Neglect any dilution during the precipitation process.

36. What is the maximal sulfide ion concentration which may exist in order to precipitate cupric sulfide without the formation of a cadmium sulfide precipitate, if the cadmium ion concentration is $0.100\,M$?

37. If 1 liter of a saturated solution of $AgIO_3$ (no solid present) is equilibrated with 3.5×10^{-5} mole of $Pb(IO_3)_2$, what will be the equilibrium concentrations of silver, lead, and iodate ions; and how many milligrams of $AgIO_3$, if any, will precipitate?

$$AgIO_3(s) \rightleftharpoons Ag^+ + IO_3^-; \qquad K_{sp} = 3.0 \times 10^{-8}$$
$$Pb(IO_3)_2(s) \rightleftharpoons Pb^{++} + 2\,IO_3^-; \qquad K_{sp} = 2.6 \times 10^{-13}$$

38. The solubility equilibrium and the solubility-product constant for zinc arsenate are as follows:

$$Zn_3(AsO_4)_2(s) \rightleftharpoons 3\,Zn^{++} + 2\,AsO_4^{\equiv}; \quad K_{sp} = 1.3 \times 10^{-28}$$

Calculate the final concentration of $AsO_4^{\equiv}$ ion required to precipitate all but 0.1 per cent of the Zn^{++} in 250 ml of a solution that originally contains 0.2 gram of $Zn(NO_3)_2$. (Zinc nitrate is very soluble in water.)

39. The solubility of solid barium iodate, $Ba(IO_3)_2$, in a $0.000540\,M$ potassium iodate (KIO_3) solution is 0.000540 mole per liter. What is the solubility-product constant for $Ba(IO_3)_2$?

40. The solubility-product data for lead hydroxide, $Pb(OH)_2$, and chromium hydroxide, $Cr(OH)_3$, are as follows:

$$Pb(OH)_2(s) \rightleftharpoons Pb^{++} + 2\,OH^-; \qquad K_{sp} = 1.2 \times 10^{-15}$$
$$Cr(OH)_3(s) \rightleftharpoons Cr^{+++} + 3\,OH^-; \qquad K_{sp} = 6.0 \times 10^{-31}$$

Suppose that you have an aqueous solution containing $0.030\,M$ Pb^{++} and $0.020\,M$ Cr^{+++}. If concentrated sodium hydroxide solution is slowly added to this mixture (so that volume changes are negligible), which precipitate, $Pb(OH)_2$ or $Cr(OH)_3$, will form *first*? (A guess is unacceptable; justify your answer by calculations.)

41. Solubility-product data for silver chloride ($AgCl$) and silver chromate (Ag_2CrO_4) are as follows:

$$AgCl(s) \rightleftharpoons Ag^+ + Cl^-; \qquad K_{sp} = 1.78 \times 10^{-10}$$
$$Ag_2CrO_4(s) \rightleftharpoons 2\ Ag^+ + CrO_4^=; \qquad K_{sp} = 2.45 \times 10^{-12}$$

(a) Suppose that you have an aqueous solution containing $0.0020\,M$ $CrO_4^=$ and $0.000010\,M$ Cl^-. If *concentrated* silver nitrate solution (so that volume changes may be neglected) is added gradually with good stirring to this solution, which precipitate (Ag_2CrO_4 or $AgCl$) will form first? Justify your conclusion with a calculation.

(b) Eventually, the silver ion concentration should increase enough to cause precipitation of the second ion. What will be the concentration of the *first* ion when the second ion just begins to precipitate?

(c) What *percentage* of the *first* ion is already precipitated when the second ion just begins to precipitate?

42. The solubility-product data for cupric iodate ($Cu(IO_3)_2$), lanthanum iodate ($La(IO_3)_3$), and silver iodate ($AgIO_3$) may be given as follows:

$$Cu(IO_3)_2(s) \rightleftharpoons Cu^{++} + 2\ IO_3^-; \qquad K_{sp} = 7.4 \times 10^{-8}$$
$$La(IO_3)_3(s) \rightleftharpoons La^{+++} + 3\ IO_3^-; \qquad K_{sp} = 6.0 \times 10^{-10}$$
$$AgIO_3(s) \rightleftharpoons Ag^+ + IO_3^-; \qquad K_{sp} = 3.0 \times 10^{-8}$$

Suppose that you prepare a separate saturated solution of each salt in pure water. Calculate the equilibrium concentration of iodate ion, IO_3^-, in each of these three solutions. Neglect activity effects.

43. Calculate the molar concentrations of Hg^{++}, HgI_3^-, and $HgI_4^=$ in the problem of Example 11 in this chapter, and verify that these species do not contribute significantly to the total solubility of $HgI_2(s)$ in pure water.

44. Given the following equilibrium data

$$Ag^+ + 2\ NH_3 \rightleftharpoons Ag(NH_3)_2^+; \qquad K = 2.5 \times 10^7$$
$$AgBr(s) \rightleftharpoons Ag^+ + Br^-; \qquad K_{sp} = 5.25 \times 10^{-13}$$

calculate the concentration of ammonia required to prevent the precipitation of silver bromide from a solution which is $0.025\,M$ in bromide and $0.045\,M$ in $Ag(NH_3)_2^+$.

45. Concentrated potassium iodide (KI) solution is slowly added to a solution that is initially $0.02\,M$ in Pb^{++} and $0.02\,M$ in Ag^+. Which cation will precipitate first? What will be its concentration when the second cation starts to precipitate? Neglect dilution of the sample by the potassium iodide solution added.

Chapter 3

EQUILIBRIA IN ACID-BASE REACTIONS

In this chapter, we shall consider the meanings of the terms *acid* and *base*; the distinctions between strong and weak acids and bases; the significance and use of pH in describing the composition and characteristics of solutions of acids, bases, and salts; and the properties of buffer solutions. Numerous examples of methods for the calculation of the pH of aqueous media containing an acid, a base, a salt, or a mixture of two or more of these components will be discussed in detail.

CONCEPTS OF ACIDITY AND BASICITY

DEFINITIONS OF ACIDS AND BASES

From the point of view of much work in chemistry, one of the most useful definitions of acids and bases was suggested independently in 1923 by Brönsted and by Lowry. A **Brönsted-Lowry acid** is defined as a species having a tendency to lose or donate a proton, whereas a **Brönsted-Lowry base** is a substance which can accept or gain a proton. An important consequence of these definitions is that the loss of a proton by a Brönsted-Lowry acid gives rise to the formation of a corresponding Brönsted-Lowry base, which is generally called the **conjugate base** of the parent acid. Similarly, the addition of a proton to any Brönsted-Lowry base causes the formation of the **conjugate acid** of the original base. This fundamental interrelationship may be indicated most simply by the chemical equilibrium

$$\text{acid} \rightleftharpoons \text{base} + \text{proton}$$

Four typical examples of conjugate acid-base pairs are the following:

$$(1) \quad H_2O \rightleftharpoons OH^- + H^+$$

$$(2) \quad H_3O^+ \rightleftharpoons H_2O + H^+$$

$$(3) \quad NH_4^+ \rightleftharpoons NH_3 + H^+$$

$$(4) \quad HCO_3^- \rightleftharpoons CO_3^= + H^+$$

Notice that H_2O is the conjugate acid of the Brönsted-Lowry base OH^- in reaction 1 as well as the conjugate base of the Brönsted-Lowry acid H_3O^+ in reaction 2.

In the same year that the Brönsted-Lowry concepts were first stated, Lewis proposed a much broader classification of acids and bases which includes substances whose reactions do not necessarily involve the loss or gain of a proton. The basis of the Lewis definition of acids and bases lies in the grouping of electrons in the outer shells of atoms. A **Lewis acid** is a substance that can accept an electron pair from a base in the formation of a covalent chemical bond, and a **Lewis base** is a substance that can donate a pair of electrons to an acid to form a covalent bond. Thus, a Lewis acid has an incomplete outer electron shell, so that it can accept an electron pair from a Lewis base to complete that electron shell. Acids and bases in the Brönsted-Lowry classification are acids and bases in the Lewis sense as well. For example, when the hydroxide ion OH^- reacts with a proton H^+ (the reverse of reaction 1), the hydroxide ion is donating a pair of electrons to a proton to form a covalent bond. On the other hand, there are substances whose reactions involve no protons and do fit into the Lewis classification of acids and bases, but not into the Brönsted-Lowry system of nomenclature. Thus, the reaction between silver ion Ag^+ and two ammonia ($:NH_3$) molecules in an aqueous medium

$$Ag^+ + 2\ NH_3 \rightleftharpoons Ag(NH_3)_2^+$$

is an example of a Lewis acid-base reaction because each ammonia molecule donates a pair of electrons to silver ion to form the largely covalent silver-nitrogen bond.

STRENGTHS OF ACIDS AND BASES

A proton cannot exist in solution by itself, that is, independently of its surrounding environment. In aqueous media the hydrogen ion is combined with one or more molecules of water to form the so-called **hydronium ion**. Although the hydronium ion is usually designated as H_3O^+, it should be recognized that the existence of more highly hydrated states of the proton is almost certain. Furthermore, all other ionic as well as molecular species are hydrated in an aqueous medium.

One of the consequences of the nonexistence of bare protons is that acid-base reactions occur by the transfer of a proton from an acid (proton donor) to a base (proton acceptor). Thus, we should consider the direct proton-transfer reaction between a Brönsted-Lowry acid and base to form the conjugate base of the acid and the conjugate acid of the base, according to the general equation

$$\text{acid } 1 + \text{base } 2 \rightleftharpoons \text{base } 1 + \text{acid } 2$$

Typical acid-base reactions are represented by the following equations:

(1) $\quad HCl + H_2O \rightleftharpoons Cl^- + H_3O^+$

(2) $\quad H_2O + NH_3 \rightleftharpoons OH^- + NH_4^+$

(3) $\quad H_3O^+ + OH^- \rightleftharpoons H_2O + H_2O$

(4) $\quad H_3O^+ + CO_3^= \rightleftharpoons H_2O + HCO_3^-$

The extent to which each reaction proceeds left to right, or its quantitative completeness, is governed by the ease of transferring a proton from acid 1 to base 2, relative to the readiness of proton transfer from acid 2 to base 1. Consider, for example, the reaction of sodium hydroxide with hydrochloric acid in an aqueous solution, as represented by equation 3. This reaction proceeds virtually completely to the right because hydroxide ions (base 2) have a much greater affinity for protons than do water molecules (base 1). Similarly, the reaction shown by equation 4 goes very far toward the right because the carbonate ion is a stronger base than water. However, reaction 4 does not proceed as far as reaction 3 because in water the carbonate ion is a weaker base than the hydroxide ion.

This brief discussion brings up a very important point. It would be advantageous to be able to compare the strengths of various Brönsted-Lowry acids strictly in terms of their intrinsic or absolute tendencies to lose protons. Unfortunately, an acid must be dissolved in some solvent, and this solvent almost always acts as a Brönsted-Lowry base to give the typical kind of acid-base reaction which has just been described. The intrinsic tendency of the acid to lose its proton is inextricably related to the affinity of the solvent for a proton, and, therefore, we find that the solvent is extremely important in determining the apparent strength of an acid. For example, hydrochloric acid in water is a strong acid, so the reaction expressed by equation 1 in the preceding list goes far to the right because water (acting as a Brönsted-Lowry base) has a much stronger affinity for a proton than does chloride ion. However, hydrochloric acid is a weaker acid in methanol (CH_3OH), because methanol molecules do not accept protons as readily as do water molecules. This means that if methanol were substituted for water in equation 1, that is,

$$HCl + CH_3OH \rightleftharpoons Cl^- + CH_3OH_2^+$$

the reaction would not proceed so far to the right. An aqueous solution of ammonia is a weak base because the reaction given by equation 2 does not go far to the right. This is so because the tendency for ammonia to accept a proton from water is significantly, but not tremendously, greater than the tendency for hydroxide ion to accept a proton from the ammonium ion.

AUTOPROTOLYSIS OF WATER

Pure water is slightly ionized, because of the fact that a water molecule is capable of accepting a proton from another water molecule:

$$H_2O + H_2O \rightleftharpoons H_3O^+ + OH^-$$

The phenomenon represented by this equilibrium is called **autoprotolysis**, and the equilibrium expression, written in terms of activities or effective concentrations, is

$$K = \frac{(H_3O^+)(OH^-)}{(H_2O)^2}$$

This equation can be simplified considerably, however, on the basis of the thermodynamic convention that a pure liquid, such as water, is defined as having unit activity, and on the assumption that this definition is valid also for relatively dilute aqueous solutions. Furthermore, if we restrict our consideration to quite dilute aqueous solutions, the activity coefficients for the hydronium and hydroxide ions are essentially unity, and we can replace the activities of H_3O^+ and OH^- by their respective concentrations. Finally, it is convenient to write H^+, instead of the more highly hydrated proton, H_3O^+, in equations dealing with stoichiometry and equilibrium calculations. Making these changes as required, we arrive at the very familiar ion-product-constant expression for water:

$$K_w = [H^+][OH^-]$$

The ion-product constant, which is also known as the autoprotolysis constant, is particularly temperature-dependent, ranging from 1.14×10^{-15} at 0°C through 1.01×10^{-14} at 25°C and 5.47×10^{-14} at 50°C to approximately 5.4×10^{-13} at 100°C. Unless otherwise specified, in all the numerical calculations in this chapter it will be assumed that the solution temperature is 25°C, and the ion-product constant K_w is taken to be 1.00×10^{-14}.

DEFINITION OF pH

In simplest terms the pH of an aqueous solution may be defined as the negative base-ten or decimal logarithm of the hydrogen ion concentration. That is,

$$pH = -\log [H^+]$$

This definition will be employed exclusively throughout the present discussion. Actually, however, the explicit definition of pH is much more complicated. In the final analysis, the pH of a solution is probably more accurately measured by the negative base-ten or decimal logarithm of the hydrogen ion *activity,* a_{H^+}. However, two fundamental problems preclude the establishment of a theoretically rigorous pH scale. One is that the activity coefficient for a single ionic species, such as the hydronium ion, cannot be measured. Another difficulty is related to the fact that in the potentiometric measurement of pH, which is the most direct method of measuring this quantity, there is necessarily present an unknown liquid-junction potential. Although the latter point will not be discussed in detail in this book, it will be encountered briefly in Chapter 5. Suffice it to state here that pH measurements made with a modern electronic pH meter are based upon prior calibration of the particular instrument's electrode system with certain standard buffer solutions, and that the nominal pH values for these standard solutions are specified by the National Bureau of Standards in order to be as close as possible to the relationship $pH = -\log a_{H^+}$.

If we return to the ion-product-constant expression for water,

$$K_w = [H^+][OH^-] = 1.00 \times 10^{-14}$$

and take the negative logarithm of each member of this equation, the result is

$$-\log K_w = -\log [H^+] -\log [OH^-] = 14.00$$

or

$$pK_w = pH + pOH = 14.00$$

where pK_w is the negative logarithm of the ion-product constant for water and pOH is the negative logarithm of the hydroxide ion concentration. This equation provides a simple way to calculate the pOH of a solution if the pH is determined. Conversely, the pH can be obtained if the pOH is known. At 25°C an aqueous solution is said to be *acidic* if the pH is less than 7.00, which is equivalent to saying that the solution is acidic if the concentration of hydrogen ion is greater than $1.00 \times 10^{-7} M$. Similarly, an aqueous solution is *basic* or *alkaline* if the pH is greater than 7.00, that is, the solution is basic if the hydrogen ion concentration is less than $1.00 \times 10^{-7} M$; if the pH of an aqueous medium is precisely 7.00 at 25°C, the solution is *neutral*.

EXAMPLE 1

Calculate the pH of two solutions, the hydrogen ion concentrations of which are 0.0023 and $8.4 \times 10^{-10} M$, respectively.

Since the pH of a solution is, by definition, the negative base-ten logarithm of the hydrogen ion concentration

$$pH = -\log \, [H^+]$$

it follows that, for the first solution,

$$pH = -\log \, (0.0023) = -\log \, (2.3 \times 10^{-3})$$

Recalling that the logarithm of a product is the *sum* of logarithms, we can write

$$pH = -\log \, (2.3 \times 10^{-3}) = -\, [\log \, (2.3) + \log \, (10^{-3})]$$
$$pH = -\, [(0.36) + (-3.00)]$$
$$pH = 2.64$$

For the second solution,

$$pH = -\log \, (8.4 \times 10^{-10}) = -\, [\log \, (8.4) + \log \, (10^{-10})]$$
$$pH = -\, [(0.92) + (-10.00)]$$
$$pH = 9.08$$

EXAMPLE 2

Calculate the hydrogen ion concentration in each of two solutions, the respective pH values of which are 4.76 and 7.28.

If we take the antilogarithm of the relation

$$pH = -\log \, [H^+]$$

or the equivalent expression

$$\log \, [H^+] = -pH$$

the result is

$$[H^+] = 10^{-pH}$$

For the solution with a pH of 4.76, one has

$$[H^+] = 10^{-pH} = 10^{-4.76}$$

When the exponential term is rewritten, we obtain

$$[H^+] = 10^{-4.76} = 10^{0.24-5.00} = 10^{0.24} \times 10^{-5}$$
$$[H^+] = 1.74 \times 10^{-5} M$$

In the case of the second solution,

$$[H^+] = 10^{-7.28} = 10^{0.72-8.00} = 10^{0.72} \times 10^{-8}$$
$$[H^+] = 5.25 \times 10^{-8} M$$

EXAMPLE 3

Calculate the hydrogen ion concentration in a solution whose pOH is 4.57.

Using the relationship previously mentioned, namely

$$pH + pOH = 14.00$$

we can obtain the pH as follows:

$$pH = 14.00 - pOH = 14.00 - 4.57 = 9.43$$

Then,

$$[H^+] = 10^{-9.43} = 10^{0.57} \times 10^{-10} = 3.7 \times 10^{-10} M$$

SOLUTIONS OF STRONG ACIDS OR BASES AND THEIR SALTS

In this and subsequent sections of this chapter, it is assumed, unless specified otherwise, that the solutions are aqueous, at a temperature of 25°C, and that the ion-product constant of water is 1.00×10^{-14}. In addition, molar concentrations of dissolved species will be used in all equilibrium calculations, when, in fact, activities or effective concentrations should be employed. Corrections for the non-ideality of solutions based upon the Debye-Hückel limiting law or one of its modifications could, if it were desired, be made as already discussed.

In simple terms, a strong acid or base is one which is fully ionized in aqueous solution. Moreover, with few exceptions, dissolved salts ionize completely in solution. If the salt is composed of the anion of a strong acid and the cation of a strong base, such as sodium chloride, its ions remain as such in the solution. On the other hand, if the salt is a salt of a weak acid, a weak base, or both, as are sodium acetate and ammonium chloride, one or both of the ions of that salt will react to some extent with any hydrogen or hydroxide ions which may be present. Let us consider first only solutions of strong acids, strong bases, and salts of strong acids and bases.

STRONG ACID SOLUTIONS

For a solution containing a strong monoprotic acid which is fully ionized, the hydrogen ion concentration is equal to the original molar concentration of the acid. Among the familiar strong acids are hydrochloric acid, nitric acid, perchloric acid, and sulfuric acid. For example, a solution prepared by dissolving 0.1 mole of hydrogen chloride in 1 liter of water is $0.1\,M$ in hydrogen (hydronium) ions and $0.1\,M$ in chloride ions. Thus, calculation of the pH of a strong acid solution is essentially the same as encountered in Example 1.

EXAMPLE 4

Calculate the pH of each of the following solutions: (a) $0.00150\,M$ hydrochloric acid and (b) 1.00 liter of solution containing 0.101 gram of HCl.

(a) Noting that the hydrogen ion concentration is 0.00150 or $1.50 \times 10^{-3}\,M$, we can proceed as in Example 1:

$$pH = -\log\,(1.50 \times 10^{-3}) = -[\log\,(1.50) + \log\,(10^{-3})]$$
$$pH = -[(0.18) + (-3.00)]$$
$$pH = 2.82$$

(b) For the second solution, the number of moles of HCl is

$$0.101 \text{ gram} \cdot \frac{1 \text{ mole}}{36.5 \text{ grams}} = 0.00277 \text{ mole}$$

and the concentration of hydrochloric acid is 0.00277 or $2.77 \times 10^{-3}\,M$. Therefore,

$$pH = -\log (2.77 \times 10^{-3}) = -[\log (2.77) + \log (10^{-3})]$$
$$pH = -[(0.44) + (-3.00)]$$
$$pH = 2.56$$

STRONG BASE SOLUTIONS

In a strong base solution, the hydroxide ion concentration is directly related to the original concentration of the base in a manner analogous to the situation for a strong acid solution. The pH may be calculated from the hydroxide ion concentration and the ion-product constant for water.

EXAMPLE 5

Calculate the pH of a 0.0023 M barium hydroxide ($Ba(OH)_2$) solution. It should be noted that two hydroxide ions are formed from the ionization of each molecule of barium hydroxide. Therefore,

$$[OH^-] = 0.0046 \doteq 4.6 \times 10^{-3}\,M$$

Since

$$pOH = -\log [OH^-]$$

we can write

$$pOH = -\log (4.6 \times 10^{-3}) = -[\log (4.6) + \log (10^{-3})]$$
$$pOH = -[(0.66) + (-3.00)] = 2.34$$

Finally,

$$pH = 14.00 - pOH = 14.00 - 2.34$$
$$pH = 11.66$$

SOLUTIONS OF SALTS OF A STRONG ACID AND STRONG BASE

In considering the acidic or basic behavior of any salt, we must first determine whether the salt contributes any hydrogen ions or hydroxide ions to the solution and, second, we must see if the ions of the salt react with any hydrogen ions or hydroxide ions already present. If the salt in question is a salt of a strong acid and a strong base, the answers to both of these queries are necessarily in the negative. Therefore, a salt of this type does not influence the acidity or basicity of a solution (other than its effect on the activity coefficients of hydrogen ion and hydroxide ion, which is being neglected in this discussion). Accordingly, a solution containing no solute other than salts of a strong acid and a strong base has the same pH as the pure solvent alone, and thus the pH of such a solution is 7 at room temperature. Moreover, the addition of such a salt to a solution already containing an acid or base does not change the pH of that acid or base solution.

SOLUTIONS OF WEAK ACIDS OR BASES

A weak acid or base is one which is incompletely ionized in aqueous solution. As a result, the hydrogen ion concentration or the hydroxide ion concentration is always less than the original concentration of the weak acid or weak base. The mathematical expression for the state of equilibrium between the ionized and non-ionized forms of the solute serves as the basis for calculations of the pH of a weak acid or weak base solution.

We may calculate the pH of any solution falling into the present category by direct application of the four-step approach to solving equilibrium problems as introduced in Chapter 1. First, write balanced chemical equations for the one or more pertinent chemical equilibria involved. These reactions must include all sources of hydrogen ions in the solution, such as water or an acid present as solute, and they must include any equilibria involving bases which consume hydrogen ions. There will frequently be only one significant chemical reaction to consider, but two or even more may be involved in other cases. Second, write equilibrium expressions corresponding to each of the separate chemical reactions. Third, the known reference data as well as mass-balance and charge-balance relationships, as available and needed, should be written so that there are as many mathematical equations as there are unknowns contained therein. Fourth, solve these equations for the desired unknown quantity or quantities. These principles will now be considered with reference to aqueous solutions containing weak acids and bases, salts of weak acids or bases, and combinations of these.

SOLUTIONS OF WEAK ACIDS

Let us consider two familiar weak acids, acetic acid and formic acid, as typical examples.

EXAMPLE 6

Calculate the pH of a 0.100 M acetic acid solution. The sources of hydrogen ions in this system are the dissociation of acetic acid which may be represented as

$$CH_3COOH \rightleftharpoons H^+ + CH_3COO^-; \quad K_a = 1.75 \times 10^{-5}$$

and the ionization of water according to the reaction

$$H_2O \rightleftharpoons H^+ + OH^-; \quad K_w = 1.00 \times 10^{-14}$$

Actually, each of these reactions is an abbreviated form of the true acid-base equilibrium which exists. Thus, the ionization reaction for acetic acid should show the transfer of a proton from acetic acid to water, whereas the ionization (autoprotolysis) of water proceeds through the transfer of a proton from one water molecule to another. However, as long as we wish to perform equilibrium calculations involving acid-base reactions in the *same* solvent (water), such abbreviated versions of the acid-base equilibria as well as the corresponding equilibrium expressions can be employed.

Of the two sources of hydrogen ion, acetic acid is such a stronger acid that the ionization of water may be regarded as insignificant. Furthermore, the hydrogen ions from acetic acid will repress the dissociation of water through the common ion effect. It should be pointed out that neglect of the ionization of water may not be justified for extremely dilute acetic acid solutions. For practical situations, however, the ionization of acetic acid is the only important equilibrium:

$$\frac{[H^+][CH_3COO^-]}{[CH_3COOH]} = K_a = 1.75 \times 10^{-5}$$

Each molecule of acetic acid which undergoes ionization produces one hydrogen ion and one acetate ion. Therefore,

$$[H^+] = [CH_3COO^-]$$

At equilibrium the concentration of acetic acid is equal to the initial acid concentration $(0.100\,M)$ minus the amount ionized (which can be expressed by either the concentration of hydrogen ion or the concentration of acetate ion).

$$[CH_3COOH] = 0.100 - [H^+]$$

Substitution of the latter two relations into the equilibrium expression for acetic acid yields

$$\frac{[H^+]^2}{0.100 - [H^+]} = 1.75 \times 10^{-5}$$

There are several ways to solve this equation for the hydrogen ion concentration. First of all, since this relation is a quadratic

equation, the formula for the solution of a quadratic equation*
may be employed, from which the answer is found to be $[H^+] =$
$1.32 \times 10^{-3} M$ or pH $= 2.88$. There is, however, an alternate
procedure which is mathematically much simpler for solving the
previous equation for $[H^+]$.

Let us assume that the equilibrium concentration of acetic
acid is $0.100 M$. This assumption, in effect, says that the
numerical value of $[H^+]$ is a negligible quantity in comparison
to $0.100 M$, or, in other words, that very nearly all the acetic acid
remains as undissociated molecules. Since a weak acid is one
that is only slightly ionized, this assumption should be expected
to be a reasonable one. Ultimately, the validity of this assumption
in any particular case must be demonstrated as indicated below.
On the basis of the approximation that

$$[CH_3COOH] = 0.100 M$$

the equilibrium expression for acetic acid takes the form

$$\frac{[H^+]^2}{0.100} = 1.75 \times 10^{-5}$$

which can be solved as follows:

$$[H^+]^2 = 1.75 \times 10^{-6}$$
$$[H^+] = 1.32 \times 10^{-3} M; \quad pH = 2.88$$

Thus, the results obtained by means of the quadratic formula and
by the second, simple approach are identical.

---

*An equation of the type $aX^2 + bX + c = 0$ may be solved by means of the
quadratic formula, which is

$$X = \frac{-b \pm \sqrt{b^2 - 4ac}}{2a}$$

In the present example, the equilibrium equation may be rearranged to

$$[H^+]^2 + 1.75 \times 10^{-5} [H^+] - 1.75 \times 10^{-6} = 0$$

Applying the quadratic formula, we get

$$[H^+] = \frac{-(1.75 \times 10^{-5}) \pm \sqrt{(1.75 \times 10^{-5})^2 - 4(1)(-1.75 \times 10^{-6})}}{2}$$

$$[H^+] = 1.32 \times 10^{-3} M$$

The other root is negative, which is an impossible situation, so it is discarded.

Notice that the hydrogen ion concentration ($1.32 \times 10^{-3} M$) is only 1.3 per cent of the original concentration of acetic acid ($0.100 M$). Therefore, the actual equilibrium acetic acid concentration would be

$$[CH_3COOH] = 0.100 - 0.00132 = 0.099 M$$

which is not significantly different from the assumed approximate value of $0.100 M$. In general, if the original concentration of weak, monoprotic acid is at least 10,000 times greater than the ionization constant K_a, the approximation will be accurate to within about 1 per cent. Furthermore, if the original acid concentration is only 1000 times larger than K_a, the approximation will still not be in error by much more than 3 per cent, which is a tolerable uncertainty for most practical purposes.

A second assumption, made at the very beginning of this problem, was that the contribution of the ionization of water to the hydrogen ion concentration is negligible. If the hydrogen ion concentration is taken to be $1.32 \times 10^{-3} M$, the value of $[OH^-]$ can be obtained from the relation

$$[OH^-] = \frac{K_w}{[H^+]} = \frac{1.00 \times 10^{-14}}{1.32 \times 10^{-3}} = 7.5 \times 10^{-12} M$$

However, since water is the only source of hydroxide ion in this system and since one hydrogen ion and one hydroxide ion are formed for each water molecule ionized, the $[H^+]$ furnished by water is only $7.5 \times 10^{-12} M$ — an amount which certainly is insignificant in comparison to the $1.32 \times 10^{-3} M$ hydrogen ion furnished by acetic acid.

One other very valuable technique used to solve equilibrium problems is called the **method of successive approximations.** We shall now employ this procedure to consider the ionization of formic acid.

EXAMPLE 7

Calculate the pH of a $0.025 M$ formic acid solution. As in the case of acetic acid, the ionization of the weak acid is the only important source of hydrogen ions.

$$HCOOH \rightleftharpoons H^+ + HCOO^-; \quad K_a = 1.76 \times 10^{-4}$$

Accordingly, we can set the concentrations of hydrogen ion and formate ion equal to each other,

$$[H^+] = [HCOO^-]$$

and the equilibrium concentration of undissociated formic acid is

$$[HCOOH] = 0.0250 - [H^+]$$

The complete equilibrium expression for the ionization of formic acid now takes the form

$$\frac{[H^+][HCOO^-]}{[HCOOH]} = \frac{[H^+]^2}{0.0250 - [H^+]} = 1.76 \times 10^{-4}$$

To solve this equation by the method of successive approximations, we shall first tentatively ignore the $[H^+]$ term in the denominator of the equation (in spite of the fact that the initial formic acid concentration is only about 140 times larger than K_a). Therefore, we obtain

$$\frac{[H^+]^2}{0.0250} = 1.76 \times 10^{-4}$$

$$[H^+]^2 = 4.40 \times 10^{-6}$$

$$[H^+] = 2.10 \times 10^{-3}\, M$$

This hydrogen ion concentration is hardly negligible in comparison to the initial formic acid concentration, but, rather than abandoning this approach and resorting to the quadratic formula, we shall continue. To obtain a closer approximation to the correct formic acid concentration, we could subtract the $[H^+]$ from the original concentration of formic acid, that is,

$$[HCOOH] = 0.0250 - 0.0021 = 0.0229\, M$$

This new value for the concentration of formic acid is now substituted back into the equilibrium expression and the equation is solved once again for $[H^+]$.

$$\frac{[H^+]^2}{0.0229} = 1.76 \times 10^{-4}$$

$$[H^+]^2 = 4.03 \times 10^{-6}$$

$$[H^+] = 2.01 \times 10^{-3}\, M$$

We may repeat the process a third time by using the result of the second approximation ($[H^+] = 0.0020\, M$) to determine the value of $[HCOOH]$ ($0.0250 - 0.0020 = 0.0230\, M$) and by then calculating a third value for the hydrogen ion concentration (which turns out again to be $2.01 \times 10^{-3} M$). Inasmuch as the same hydrogen ion concentration has been obtained in both the second and third approximations, it may safely be considered that this is the correct value. Thus,

$$[H^+] = 2.01 \times 10^{-3} M \quad \text{and} \quad pH = 2.70$$

SOLUTIONS OF WEAK BASES

Equilibrium calculations involving solutions of weak bases are essentially the same as those we have just considered. Ammonia is a typical example of a weak base. We may write the equilibrium between ionized and non-ionized species in an aqueous solution of ammonia as

$$NH_4OH \rightleftharpoons NH_4^+ + OH^-$$

There is good evidence, however, that less than 30 per cent of the dissolved ammonia actually exists as the species NH_4OH. Instead, NH_3 is predominant, so that the chemical equilibrium should be written in the alternative form

$$NH_3 + H_2O \rightleftharpoons NH_4^+ + OH^-$$

In this discussion we need not distinguish between NH_3 and NH_4OH. Rather, we shall use the formula NH_3 to represent the *total* concentration of both species. Taking the activity or effective concentration of water to be unity, the equilibrium expression for each of the two proposed ionization reactions of ammonia is the same and can be represented by the equation

$$\frac{[NH_4^+][OH^-]}{[NH_3]} = K_b = 1.80 \times 10^{-5}$$

The following problem illustrates the use of this relation.

EXAMPLE 8

Calculate the pH of a solution of $0.0100 M$ ammonia. Although ammonia may be classed as a weak base, it is still so much stronger a base than water that we can consider ammonia as the only significant source of hydroxide ions. Neglecting the ionization of water, we may equate the concentrations of ammonium ion and hydroxide ion from the ionization of the ammonia, that is,

$$[NH_4^+] = [OH^-]$$

At equilibrium the concentration of ammonia is given by

$$[NH_3] = 0.0100 - [OH^-]$$

Substitution of these relations into the preceding equilibrium expression gives the result:

$$\frac{[OH^-]^2}{0.0100 - [OH^-]} = 1.80 \times 10^{-5}$$

This equation can be conveniently solved by the method of successive approximations. We shall provisionally assume that the equilibrium concentration of ammonia is $0.0100\,M$ and then solve the expression for $[OH^-]$:

$$\frac{[OH^-]^2}{0.0100} = 1.80 \times 10^{-5}$$

$$[OH^-]^2 = 1.80 \times 10^{-7}$$

$$[OH^-] = 4.24 \times 10^{-4}\,M$$

This calculation indicates that the hydroxide concentration is $4.24 \times 10^{-4}\,M$, and thus the equilibrium concentration of ammonia is closer to

$$[NH_3] = 0.0100 - [OH^-] = 0.0100 - 0.00042 = 0.0096\,M$$

than to $0.0100\,M$. As a second approximation to the equilibrium ammonia concentration, let us substitute the value $0.0096\,M$ into the equilibrium equation and recalculate the hydroxide ion concentration:

$$\frac{[OH^-]^2}{0.0096} = 1.80 \times 10^{-5}$$

$$[OH^-]^2 = 1.73 \times 10^{-7}$$

$$[OH^-] = 4.16 \times 10^{-4}\,M$$

This value for the concentration of hydroxide ion does not differ substantially from the former result. However, the equilibrium concentration of ammonia is indeed very close to $0.0096\,M$, so that $[OH^-] = 4.16 \times 10^{-4}\,M$ is preferable. Noting that the original concentration of ammonia ($0.0100\,M$) was more than 550 times larger than K_b, we might have concluded that it would be acceptable to ignore entirely the correction of the ammonia concentration due to its ionization. It would have been quite acceptable in the present situation, but when doubt exists some mathematical check must be made to ascertain the validity of an assumption. Since we accept the hydroxide ion concentration as being $4.16 \times 10^{-4} M$, the pH of the solution can be obtained as follows:

$$pOH = -\log [OH^-] = 3.38$$
$$pH = 14.00 - pOH = 10.62$$

BUFFER SOLUTIONS

A buffer solution consists of either a weak acid along with a salt of that acid or a weak base plus a salt of the base. Two familiar examples of buffer solutions are a mixture of acetic acid and sodium acetate and a solution containing both ammonia and ammonium chloride. In the first case, equilibrium is established in accordance with the chemical reaction

$$CH_3COOH \rightleftharpoons H^+ + CH_3COO^-$$

This buffer solution differs importantly from a solution of just acetic acid in that the sodium acetate provides an additional and major source of acetate ions. In fact, the salt itself is essentially completely ionized in aqueous solution, the acetate ions thus formed entering into the equilibrium between acetic acid molecules, hydrogen ions, and acetate ions. Calculations of the pH of a buffer solution are carried out as in the case of a solution of either a weak acid or a weak base by itself, with due consideration being given to the influence of the additional ions from the salt.

EXAMPLE 9

Calculate the pH of a solution initially $0.100 M$ in acetic acid and $0.100 M$ in sodium acetate.

A starting point for an attack on this problem is the ionization-constant expression for acetic acid:

$$\frac{[H^+][CH_3COO^-]}{[CH_3COOH]} = 1.75 \times 10^{-5}$$

The fact that acetic acid is a much stronger acid than water, as well as the relatively large amount of acetic acid present, allows us to ignore the ionization of water as a source of hydrogen ions.

To determine the hydrogen ion concentration, and thus the pH, we must derive expressions for the acetate and acetic acid concentrations. Since we have identified acetic acid as the only significant source of hydrogen ions, the acetic acid concentration at equilibrium is

$$[CH_3COOH] = 0.100 - [H^+]$$

On the other hand, the concentration of acetate ion at equilibrium is the sum of the acetate added in the form of sodium acetate $(0.100\,M)$ and the acetate formed from the ionization of acetic acid (given by the hydrogen ion concentration):

$$[CH_3COO^-] = 0.100 + [H^+]$$

Substitution of these relationships into the equilibrium expression gives the following equation:

$$\frac{[H^+](0.100 + [H^+])}{0.100 - [H^+]} = 1.75 \times 10^{-5}$$

In the present problem, it is reasonable to expect that the extent of ionization of acetic acid (represented by $[H^+]$) is small compared to the original acid concentration because the concentration of acetic acid is much larger than K_a and also because the acetate ion furnished by the sodium acetate represses the ionization of acetic acid. Accordingly, the preceding equation can be simplified to

$$\frac{[H^+](0.100)}{0.100} = 1.75 \times 10^{-5}$$

from which it is found that $[H^+] = 1.75 \times 10^{-5}\,M$. The assumption that $[H^+]$ is small in comparison to $0.100\,M$ is well justified. The pH of the solution is 4.76.

EXAMPLE 10

Calculate the pH of 100 ml of a solution containing 0.0100 mole of ammonium chloride and 0.0200 mole of ammonia.

Ammonia, which ionizes in an aqueous medium according to the reaction

$$NH_3 + H_2O \rightleftharpoons NH_4^+ + OH^-$$

is a stronger base than water, so the ionization of water does not contribute appreciably to the hydroxide ion concentration. The equilibrium expression

$$\frac{[NH_4^+][OH^-]}{[NH_3]} = 1.80 \times 10^{-5}$$

can be solved for $[OH^-]$ after appropriate substitutions for $[NH_4^+]$ and $[NH_3]$ are made. From the information given in the statement of the problem, the initial concentrations of ammonium ion and ammonia are $0.100\,M$ and $0.200\,M$, respectively. After equilibrium is established, the ammonium ion concentration is greater than $0.100\,M$ by the amount of NH_4^+ formed by ionization of ammonia (which is measured in this case by $[OH^-]$):

$$[NH_4^+] = 0.100 + [OH^-]$$

The concentration of ammonia at equilibrium is

$$[NH_3] = 0.200 - [OH^-]$$

However, as in the previous example of the acetic acid-sodium acetate buffer, these small corrections to the ammonium ion and ammonia concentrations are insignificant, so the equilibrium expression may be written

$$\frac{(0.100)[OH^-]}{0.200} = 1.80 \times 10^{-5}$$

Therefore, the solution to this problem is as follows:

$$[OH^-] = 3.60 \times 10^{-5}\,M$$
$$pOH = 4.44$$
$$pH = 9.56$$

SOME PROPERTIES OF BUFFER SOLUTIONS

So far no mention has been made of the most important property of a buffer solution — a buffer solution resists pH changes when the solution is diluted (or perhaps concentrated) or when various amounts of acid or base are added.

To illustrate the effect of dilution upon the pH of a buffer solution, let us recall the problem discussed in Example 9, in which the pH of a solution $0.100\,M$ in both acetic acid and sodium acetate was calculated.

In a rigorous manner, we represented the acetic acid concentration at equilibrium as

$$[CH_3COOH] = 0.100 - [H^+]$$

and the acetate ion concentration as

$$[CH_3COO^-] = 0.100 + [H^+]$$

but we assumed and later justified that the term $[H^+]$ in each of these relations was negligibly small, being $1.75 \times 10^{-5} M$. What would happen if the solution were diluted one-hundred-fold, that is, if the original concentrations of acetic acid and sodium acetate each became $0.00100 M$?

At first glance we might conclude that there would be absolutely no change in the pH at all. In this problem, however, the rigorous expressions for the acetic acid and acetate ion concentrations would be as follows:

$$[CH_3COOH] = 0.00100 - [H^+]$$
$$[CH_3COO^-] = 0.00100 + [H^+]$$

If, indeed, the $[H^+]$ term in each relation were negligible compared to $0.00100 M$, we would be correct in the assertion that no pH change would be observed. This statement must be tested. If the hydrogen ion concentration is taken to be $1.75 \times 10^{-5} M$, we discover that the latter rigorous relations yield the results

$$[CH_3COOH] = 0.00100 - 0.00002 = 0.00098 M$$
$$[CH_3COO^-] = 0.00100 + 0.00002 = 0.00102 M$$

provided that we are willing to round off the hydrogen ion concentration to $2 \times 10^{-5} M$ for these calculations. What we can now do is substitute these new values for $[CH_3COOH]$ and $[CH_3COO^-]$ into the general equilibrium expression

$$\frac{[H^+][CH_3COO^-]}{[CH_3COOH]} = 1.75 \times 10^{-5}$$

and calculate a new value for the hydrogen ion concentration:

$$\frac{[H^+](0.00102)}{(0.00098)} = 1.75 \times 10^{-5}$$

$$[H^+] = 1.68 \times 10^{-5} M$$

This result must now be carefully interpreted.

First of all, the calculation is valid because the values of $[CH_3COOH]$ and $[CH_3COO^-]$ are essentially the same (0.00098 and 0.00102 M, respectively) regardless of which hydrogen ion concentration is employed to correct the original concentrations (0.00100 M) of the reagents. However, the difference in the hydrogen ion concentration is significant in two ways. Our calculations have shown that the hydrogen ion concentration in a buffer solution composed of 0.1 M reagents is $1.75 \times 10^{-5} M$ (pH = 4.76) but that dilution by a factor of 100 causes the hydrogen ion concentration to decrease only to $1.68 \times 10^{-5} M$ (pH = 4.78). This result reveals how well a buffer solution does stabilize the pH even upon great dilution. However, the small, but detectable, change in pH does caution against any indiscriminate dilution. The student can probably foresee the great problem which can arise when the constituents of the buffer are so extensively diluted that the concentrations of acetic acid and acetate ion approach the value of K_a.

Next, we shall consider the effects of adding strong acid or strong base to a buffer solution. The present discussion will be restricted to a buffer consisting of a weak acid and a salt of that weak acid, but the general approach that we follow is directly applicable to other types of buffers. The same buffer solution previously discussed (Example 9) will serve as a convenient starting point. Let us assume that we have exactly 100 ml of a buffer solution which is 0.100 M in both acetic acid and sodium acetate. In Example 9, we found that the hydrogen ion concentration was $1.75 \times 10^{-5} M$, corresponding to a pH of 4.76.

EXAMPLE 11

Calculate the pH of the solution which results from the addition of 10.0 ml of 0.100 M HCl to 100 ml of the buffer solution described in Example 9.

First, we note that the position of equilibrium of the ionization reaction

$$CH_3COOH \rightleftharpoons H^+ + CH_3COO^-$$

will be driven toward the left by the addition of the hydrochloric acid. This is the effect desired of a buffer. In this case the large excess of acetate ions can consume the hydrochloric acid through the formation of the much weaker acetic acid. The following calculation will show how effectively the buffer does its job. The relatively large concentrations of reactants with which we are dealing will permit us to ignore the ionization of water.

We will calculate the hydrogen ion concentration from the expression

$$\frac{[H^+][CH_3COO^-]}{[CH_3COOH]} = 1.75 \times 10^{-5}$$

In 100 ml of the buffer solution, there are initially (100)(0.100) or 10.0 millimoles of acetic acid and also 10.0 millimoles of acetate ion. The addition of 10.0 ml of 0.100 M hydrochloric acid is equivalent to 1.00 millimole of strong acid, which we can assume reacts virtually completely with acetate ion to form acetic acid. Therefore, after this reaction, 11.0 millimoles of acetic acid are present and 9.0 millimoles of acetate remain. Accordingly, the concentrations of acetic acid and acetate ion in the solution whose volume is now 110 ml are as follows:

$$[CH_3COOH] = \frac{11.0 \text{ millimoles}}{110 \text{ milliliters}} = 0.100\,M$$

$$[CH_3COO^-] = \frac{9.0 \text{ millimoles}}{110 \text{ milliliters}} = 0.082\,M$$

Substitution of these values into the equilibrium equation yields

$$\frac{[H^+](0.082)}{0.100} = 1.75 \times 10^{-5}$$

from which we calculate that $[H^+] = 2.14 \times 10^{-5}\,M$ and pH = 4.67.

EXAMPLE 12

Calculate the pH of the solution which results from the addition of 10.0 ml of 0.100 M NaOH to 100 ml of the buffer solution described in Example 9.

In this situation the principal equilibrium

$$CH_3COOH \rightleftharpoons H^+ + CH_3COO^-$$

will be shifted toward the right because the addition of a certain amount of strong base (NaOH) will consume or neutralize some of the acetic acid with the formation of an equivalent quantity of acetate ion.

Addition of 10.0 ml of a 0.100 M sodium hydroxide solution to the 100 ml sample of the buffer introduces 1.00 millimole of strong base which reacts with a stoichiometric quantity of acetic acid. Consequently, at equilibrium only 9.0 millimoles of acetic acid remain, whereas a total of 11.0 millimoles of acetate ion is present. The concentrations of acetic acid and acetate ion are

$$[CH_3COOH] = \frac{9.0 \text{ millimoles}}{110 \text{ milliliters}} = 0.082 \, M$$

$$[CH_3COO^-] = \frac{11.0 \text{ millimoles}}{110 \text{ milliliters}} = 0.100 \, M$$

From the equilibrium equation

$$\frac{[H^+][CH_3COO^-]}{[CH_3COOH]} = \frac{[H^+](0.100)}{0.082} = 1.75 \times 10^{-5}$$

the hydrogen ion concentration may be found to be $1.43 \times 10^{-5} \, M$ and the pH is 4.84.

Again, these calculations demonstrate how well a buffer solution can maintain constancy of pH. The pH of the solution, initially 4.76, changed only to 4.67 and to 4.84 by the addition, respectively, of 10 ml of 0.1 M hydrochloric acid and 10 ml of a 0.1 M sodium hydroxide solution.

There is a definite limit to how much acid or base can be added to a given buffer solution before any appreciable change in pH results, and this quantity is designated the *capacity* of the buffer solution. If we are still considering the acetic acid-sodium acetate buffer of the previous examples, the **buffer capacity** is set by the original amounts of the acid and its salt, since one or the other is consumed by reaction with the added strong acid or strong base. In the preceding problem (Example 12), the original buffer solution contained 10 millimoles of acetic acid, the strong base added reacting with this species. Obviously, the addition of 10 millimoles of strong base would have neutralized all of the acetic acid, and no buffering action would have remained. Calculations similar to those of Examples 11 and 12 reveal that the pH changes at a rate which increases more and more rapidly as the limiting buffer capacity is approached.

Another closely related point concerning buffer action is that a specific buffer is useful only in a narrow pH range around pK (that is, the negative logarithm of the equilibrium constant) for the reaction involving the conjugate acid-base pair which comprises the buffer. As an example, for the dissociation of acetic acid, $pK_a = -\log K_a = 4.76$, and the buffering action of an acetic acid-sodium acetate mixture is most effective in a narrow range near pH 4.76. Thus, as shown in Examples 11 and 12, for 100 ml of a buffer initially consisting of 0.100 M concentrations of acetic acid and sodium acetate and having a pH of 4.76, the addition of 1.00 millimole of either strong acid or strong base changed the pH only to 4.67 and 4.84, respectively — a total range which encompasses only about 0.09 pH unit on either side of the pK_a for acetic acid. A formic acid-sodium formate buffer works best in a pH range centered upon 3.75, since pK_a for the dissociation of formic acid has the same numerical value. Similarly, pK_b for the ionization of ammonium hydroxide is 4.74, so a buffer solution containing ammonia and ammonium chloride maintains approximate constancy of pOH near 4.74 or of pH in the vicinity of 9.26.

SOLUTIONS OF SALTS OF WEAK ACIDS AND WEAK BASES

Preceding sections have dealt with solutions of all major types except for those containing a salt whose anion or cation can form a weak acid or base. Although such salts were considered briefly in the previous discussion of buffers, we shall now treat them in detail.

SALT OF A WEAK ACID AND A STRONG BASE

Sodium acetate, which is a salt of this type, ionizes completely in an aqueous medium to give sodium and acetate ions. The only source of hydrogen ions in such a solution is the ionization of water. However, acetate ions will react with hydrogen ions produced by the water ionization and with water itself to form acetic acid molecules. Because of the small concentration of hydrogen ion and the predominance of water, the principal chemical equilibrium which is established is

$$CH_3COO^- + H_2O \rightleftharpoons CH_3COOH + OH^-$$

According to the stoichiometry of this reaction, equal amounts of acetic acid and hydroxide ion are produced. However, since acetic acid is very incompletely ionized and hydroxide ion is a strong base, the solution will definitely contain more hydroxide ions than hydrogen ions. Therefore, a solution of the salt of a weak acid and a strong base is distinctly alkaline. The degree of this alkalinity is determined by the weakness of the acid involved. The weaker the acid which is a product, the higher will be the pH of the solution. This phenomenon can be illustrated by means of the following example:

EXAMPLE 13

Calculate the pH of a solution which is 0.100 M in sodium acetate.

A useful approach to this problem is to consider what reactions can be written which directly involve hydrogen ions. First, a source of hydrogen ions is the ionization of water:

$$H_2O \rightleftharpoons H^+ + OH^-$$

Next, hydrogen ions can be consumed by reaction with acetate ions to form acetic acid:

$$H^+ + CH_3COO^- \rightleftharpoons CH_3COOH$$

From an inspection of these two reactions, we note that one H^+ and one OH^- are formed for each molecule of water which ionizes and that each acetic acid molecule formed results in the consumption of one hydrogen ion. Therefore, the hydrogen ion concentration at equilibrium is given by

$$[H^+] = [OH^-] - [CH_3COOH]$$

Upon rearrangement, this expression becomes

$$[CH_3COOH] = [OH^-] - [H^+]$$

Looking carefully at this last equation, we can conclude that the hydrogen ion concentration is definitely much smaller than $[OH^-]$ because the solution is basic. Hence, we can make the assumption, and later justify it, that the term $[H^+]$ can be neglected. Thus,

$$[CH_3COOH] = [OH^-]$$

Notice that the same conclusion could have been made by considering that the reaction

$$CH_3COO^- + H_2O \rightleftharpoons CH_3COOH + OH^-$$

produces equal quantities of acetic acid and hydroxide ion.

The next step in solving this problem is to formulate the equilibrium-constant equation for the latter main reaction, as follows:

$$\frac{[CH_3COOH][OH^-]}{[CH_3COO^-]} = K_b$$

To evaluate K_b, it is instructive to multiply the numerator and denominator of the left-hand side of this equation by $[H^+]$ so that

$$\frac{[CH_3COOH][OH^-][H^+]}{[CH_3COO^-][H^+]} = K_b$$

It is possible to recognize in this expression the ion-product constant for water

$$[H^+][OH^-] = K_w$$

and the *reciprocal* of the ionization constant for acetic acid

$$\frac{[H^+][CH_3COO^-]}{[CH_3COOH]} = K_a$$

So, we can write the result of this work as follows:

$$\frac{[CH_3COOH][OH^-]}{[CH_3COO^-]} = K_b = \frac{K_w}{K_a} = \frac{1.00 \times 10^{-14}}{1.75 \times 10^{-5}}$$

$$= 5.71 \times 10^{-10}$$

We have already established that, to a good approximation,

$$[CH_3COOH] = [OH^-]$$

The equilibrium concentration of acetate ion is equal to the original acetate concentration ($0.100\,M$) minus that which is converted to acetic acid (expressed by $[OH^-]$):

$$[CH_3COO^-] = 0.100 - [OH^-]$$

However, because the equilibrium constant (K_b) is so small and the initial acetate concentration relatively large, it is permissible to assume that the equilibrium concentration of acetate ion is just $0.100\,M$. Therefore, the equilibrium expression takes the simple form

$$\frac{[OH^-]^2}{0.100} = 5.71 \times 10^{-10}$$

which can be readily solved to give the following results

$$[OH^-]^2 = 5.71 \times 10^{-11}$$

$$[OH^-] = 7.56 \times 10^{-6}\,M$$

$$pOH = 5.12 \quad \text{and} \quad pH = 8.88$$

Before leaving this problem, we should note the validity of the assumptions made in solving the problem: (a) that the hydrogen ion concentration is negligible compared to $[OH^-]$ and (b) that the hydroxide ion concentration is small in comparison to the equilibrium acetate ion concentration. The validity of similar assumptions made for other problems must be carefully assessed. In general, the ability to make meaningful simplifying assumptions depends on one's having a genuine feeling for the chemistry of a particular system.

SALT OF A STRONG ACID AND A WEAK BASE

Equilibrium calculations involving an aqueous solution of the salt of a strong acid and a weak base are analogous to those described in the preceding problem. In fact, the only difference is that the roles played by the hydrogen ion and the hydroxide ion are reversed. For the present example, we shall consider a solution of ammonium chloride. In such a system, there are two sources of hydrogen ions. One is the ionization of water,

$$H_2O \rightleftharpoons H^+ + OH^-$$

and the second, and more significant, is the acid ionization of ammonium ion,

$$NH_4^+ + H_2O \rightleftharpoons NH_3 + H_3O^+$$

which may be written in the abbreviated form

$$NH_4^+ \rightleftharpoons NH_3 + H^+$$

The latter reaction is entirely analogous to the ionization of acetic acid, with NH_4^+ corresponding to CH_3COOH and NH_3 to CH_3COO^-. The equilibrium expression for the ionization of the ammonium ion may be written as

$$K_a = \frac{[H^+][NH_3]}{[NH_4^+]}$$

If the numerator and denominator of the right-hand side of this equation are multiplied by the term $[OH^-]$, the expression becomes

$$K_a = \frac{[H^+][NH_3][OH^-]}{[NH_4^+][OH^-]}$$

and it may be recognized that the numerator now contains the ion-product constant for water, whereas the denominator contains the *basic* dissociation constant for ammonia. Therefore,*

$$K_a = \frac{K_w}{K_b} \quad \text{or} \quad K_a K_b = K_w$$

The basic dissociation constant for ammonia is 1.80×10^{-5}, and the ion product for water is 1.00×10^{-14}; so the acid dissociation constant for ammonium ion is 5.55×10^{-10}.

Of the two sources of hydrogen ions in the solution of ammonium chloride, the dissociation of water yields equal quantities of the strong acid H^+ and the strong base OH^-, and the ionization of ammonium ion

---

*This result (which appears in the discussion and solution of both Examples 13 and 14) is an important, fundamental relationship. Let us consider the *acid* ionization of acetic acid, which may be represented by

$$CH_3COOH \rightleftharpoons H^+ + CH_3COO^-; \quad K_a = \frac{[H^+][CH_3COO^-]}{[CH_3COOH]}$$

and the reaction of water with acetate ion acting as a *base*

$$CH_3COO^- + H_2O \rightleftharpoons CH_3COOH + OH^-$$

with which we can associate the equilibrium expression

$$K_b = \frac{[CH_3COOH][OH^-]}{[CH_3COO^-]}$$

If the expressions for K_a and K_b are multiplied together, the result is

$$K_a \cdot K_b = \frac{[H^+][CH_3COO^-]}{[CH_3COOH]} \cdot \frac{[CH_3COOH][OH^-]}{[CH_3COO^-]} = [H^+][OH^-]$$

and, since the product of the hydrogen ion and hydroxide ion concentrations is the ion-product constant (K_w) for water, we can reach the significant and useful conclusion that

$$K_a K_b = K_w$$

To show that this last expression is indeed a general relation, let us examine briefly the same approach for the system involving ammonium ion and ammonia:

$$NH_4^+ \rightleftharpoons H^+ + NH_3; \quad K_a = \frac{[H^+][NH_3]}{[NH_4^+]}$$

$$NH_3 + H_2O \rightleftharpoons NH_4^+ + OH^-; \quad K_b = \frac{[NH_4^+][OH^-]}{[NH_3]}$$

$$K_a \cdot K_b = \frac{[H^+][NH_3]}{[NH_4^+]} \cdot \frac{[NH_4^+][OH^-]}{[NH_3]} = [H^+][OH^-]$$

$$K_a K_b = K_w$$

Accordingly, whenever we multiply together the dissociation constant (K_a) for an *acid* and the equilibrium constant (K_b) for the reaction between water and the *conjugate base* of that acid, it is a general rule that

$$K_a K_b = K_w$$

liberates equal numbers of the NH_3 and H^+ species. However, the relatively weak base NH_3 from the second reaction in the presence of the strong acid H^+ from the first reaction causes the solution to display definite acidic properties.

EXAMPLE 14

Calculate the pH of a $0.100\,M$ solution of ammonium chloride. A quantity of hydrogen ions equivalent to the quantity of hydroxide ions is formed from water, and the ionization of the ammonium ion produces stoichiometrically equal concentrations of H^+ and NH_3. Therefore, the total concentration of hydrogen ion is

$$[H^+] = [OH^-] + [NH_3]$$

This relation can be rearranged to the more useful form,

$$[NH_3] = [H^+] - [OH^-]$$

and, if we are willing to accept the fact that an ammonium chloride solution is acidic, the $[OH^-]$ can be neglected in comparison to $[H^+]$. In effect, what we are saying is that the ionization of the ammonium ion is the only significant source of hydrogen ions, so that

$$[NH_3] = [H^+]$$

Inserting this relation into the equilibrium expression for the acid ionization of ammonium ion

$$K_a = \frac{[NH_3][H^+]}{[NH_4^+]} = 5.55 \times 10^{-10}$$

we obtain

$$\frac{[H^+]^2}{[NH_4^+]} = 5.55 \times 10^{-10}$$

Because ammonium ion is such a weak acid, we may safely assume that $0.100\,M$ is the equilibrium value for $[NH_4^+]$, so

$$\frac{[H^+]^2}{0.100} = 5.55 \times 10^{-10}$$

$$[H^+]^2 = 5.55 \times 10^{-11}$$

$$[H^+] = 7.45 \times 10^{-6}\,M \quad \text{and} \quad pH = 5.13$$

Notice that even though the ammonium ion is a very weak acid, its ionization constant is still far greater than the ion-product constant for water, so the earlier assumption that the ionization of water does not contribute significantly to the hydrogen ion concentration is a valid one.

SALT OF A WEAK ACID AND A WEAK BASE

As the final example of this section, it is of interest to consider the behavior in an aqueous solution of a salt whose cation is a weak acid and whose anion is a weak base. Ammonium formate is a salt which displays such behavior. It ionizes completely to ammonium ions and formate ions. There are several conceivable acid-base reactions which may occur in this relatively complex system.

The ammonium ion, NH_4^+, can donate a proton to water,

$$NH_4^+ + H_2O \rightleftharpoons NH_3 + H_3O^+$$

or it can donate a proton to the formate ion to yield a formic acid molecule:

$$NH_4^+ + HCOO^- \rightleftharpoons NH_3 + HCOOH$$

In addition, the formate ion, acting as a base, can accept a proton from water,

$$HCOO^- + H_2O \rightleftharpoons HCOOH + OH^-$$

and we have already written the reaction in which formate ion accepts the proton from the ammonium ion.

By evaluation of the equilibrium constants for these reactions, some insight into the relative importance of each equilibrium can be obtained.

From Example 14, the equilibrium constant for the *first* reaction was found to be:

$$K_a = \frac{[NH_3][H_3O^+]}{[NH_4^+]} = \frac{[NH_3][H^+]}{[NH_4^+]} = 5.55 \times 10^{-10}$$

By analogy to Example 13, the equilibrium constant for the *third* reaction can be obtained as follows:

$$\frac{[HCOOH][OH^-]}{[HCOO^-]} = \frac{K_w}{K_a} = \frac{1.00 \times 10^{-14}}{1.76 \times 10^{-4}} = 5.68 \times 10^{-11}$$

The *second* reaction, between NH_4^+ and $HCOO^-$, can be treated as follows:

$$\frac{[NH_3][HCOOH]}{[NH_4^+][HCOO^-]} = K_{eq}$$

The equilibrium constant K_{eq} can be readily evaluated if we multiply the numerator and denominator of the left-hand side of this equation by the term $[H^+]$:

$$\frac{[H^+][NH_3][HCOOH]}{[H^+][NH_4^+][HCOO^-]} = K_{eq}$$

Careful inspection of the terms reveals that K_{eq} is composed of the equilibrium constant for the acid ionization of ammonium ion,

$$NH_4^+ \rightleftharpoons NH_3 + H^+; \quad K_a = 5.55 \times 10^{-10}$$

multiplied by the *reciprocal* of the equilibrium constant for the acid ionization of formic acid,

$$HCOOH \rightleftharpoons H^+ + HCOO^-; \quad K_a = 1.76 \times 10^{-4}$$

Thus, we obtain

$$\frac{[NH_3][HCOOH]}{[NH_4^+][HCOO^-]} = \frac{5.55 \times 10^{-10}}{1.76 \times 10^{-4}} = 3.15 \times 10^{-6}$$

The reaction between NH_4^+ and $HCOO^-$ is far more important than the other two proposed reactions because its equilibrium constant is on the order of 10,000 to 100,000 times greater than the corresponding equilibrium constants for those reactions.

It is now reasonable to focus full attention on the reaction between NH_4^+ and $HCOO^-$. Since the salt solution is originally composed of equal molar quantities of NH_4^+ and $HCOO^-$ and since equal molar amounts of NH_3 and $HCOOH$ must necessarily be formed in the reaction, we can state these relationships at equilibrium:

$$[NH_4^+] = [HCOO^-] \quad \text{and} \quad [NH_3] = [HCOOH]$$

For the purpose of lending some generality to our discussion, we shall rewrite the equilibrium expression as follows:

$$\frac{[NH_3][HCOOH]}{[NH_4^+][HCOO^-]} = \frac{K_w}{K_a K_b} = 3.15 \times 10^{-6}$$

where K_w is the ion-product constant for water, K_a is the acid dissociation constant for formic acid, and K_b is the base constant for ammonia. Substitution of the equalities $[NH_4^+] = [HCOO^-]$ and $[NH_3] = [HCOOH]$ gives us

$$\frac{[HCOOH]^2}{[HCOO^-]^2} = \frac{K_w}{K_a K_b}$$

However, from the dissociation constant for formic acid, we can write

$$\frac{[HCOO^-]^2}{[HCOOH]^2} = \frac{K_a^2}{[H^+]^2} \quad \text{or} \quad \frac{[HCOOH]^2}{[HCOO^-]^2} = \frac{[H^+]^2}{K_a^2}$$

Therefore, further substitution leads to the relations:

$$\frac{[H^+]^2}{K_a^2} = \frac{K_w}{K_a K_b}$$

$$[H^+]^2 = \frac{K_w K_a}{K_b}$$

$$[H^+] = \sqrt{\frac{K_w K_a}{K_b}}$$

This remarkable result shows that the pH of a solution of ammonium formate, and similar salts, is independent of the salt concentration. The independence of $[H^+]$ on the concentration of the salt may fail, however, when the salt concentration is small enough to be of the magnitude of K_a or K_b. Yet, if K_a and K_b are exactly equal, the hydrogen ion concentration is *always* independent of the salt concentration (excepting ionic effects on activity coefficients) and the pH is numerically 7.00. In other words, if K_a and K_b happen to be equal, the tendency of the weak acid to lose a proton is exactly balanced by the affinity of the weak base for a proton, and the salt solution is perfectly neutral. It follows also that the salt solution will be acidic if K_b is less than K_a, and the solution is basic when K_a is less than K_b.

EXAMPLE 15

Calculate the pH of a 0.0100 M ammonium formate solution.
This problem can be solved immediately by application of the preceding equation:

$$[H^+] = \sqrt{\frac{K_w K_a}{K_b}}$$

$$[H^+] = \sqrt{\frac{(1.00 \times 10^{-14})(1.76 \times 10^{-4})}{1.80 \times 10^{-5}}}$$

$$[H^+] = 3.13 \times 10^{-7} M$$

$$pH = 6.50$$

POLYPROTIC ACID SYSTEMS

Thus far in this chapter we have considered only those acids, bases, and salts which are capable of single proton-transfer reactions. However, there is a broad and important class of acids called **polyprotic acids** which have two or more ionizable hydrogen ions. Included in the list of polyprotic acids are phosphoric acid (H_3PO_4), sulfuric acid (H_2SO_4), oxalic acid ($H_2C_2O_4$), and carbonic acid (H_2CO_3). Similarly, salts of these polyprotic acids exist which are capable of acting as bases and accepting two or more protons. Thus, sodium carbonate can react with two protons, and sodium phosphate can accept three hydrogen ions in forming phosphoric acid.

SOLUTIONS OF CARBONIC ACID AND ITS SALTS

Perhaps the most familiar of all polyprotic acid systems is that involving carbonic acid, bicarbonate, and carbonate. Carbonic acid is a diprotic acid which undergoes the following ionization reactions:

$$H_2CO_3 \rightleftharpoons H^+ + HCO_3^-; \quad K_1 = \frac{[H^+][HCO_3^-]}{[H_2CO_3]} = 1.72 \times 10^{-4}$$

$$HCO_3^- \rightleftharpoons H^+ + CO_3^=; \quad K_2 = \frac{[H^+][CO_3^=]}{[HCO_3^-]} = 4.68 \times 10^{-11}$$

Usually, the value given in textbooks for K_1 is 4.47×10^{-7}, but the use of this latter constant overlooks one of the more interesting features of this chemical system, namely, that most of the carbon dioxide dissolved in water exists as molecular CO_2 and not H_2CO_3. We can represent the equilibrium between carbon dioxide and carbonic acid by

$$CO_2(aq) + H_2O \rightleftharpoons H_2CO_3; \quad K_3 = \frac{[H_2CO_3]}{[CO_2(aq)]} = 2.6 \times 10^{-3}$$

Thus, only about 0.26 per cent of the *total* amount of dissolved carbon dioxide really exists as H_2CO_3. As a result, the often-quoted value for K_1 of 4.47×10^{-7} actually pertains to the equilibrium expression

$$\frac{[H^+][HCO_3^-]}{([CO_2(aq)] + [H_2CO_3])} = 4.47 \times 10^{-7}$$

Still another consequence of the very small concentration of H_2CO_3 present in carbonic acid solutions is that H_2CO_3 is approximately a 500-fold stronger acid than is ordinarily assumed. With a K_1 of

1.72×10^{-4}, carbonic acid is almost exactly as strong as formic acid ($K_a = 1.76 \times 10^{-4}$).

For equilibrium calculations it is immaterial which value of K_1 is used, provided that we are careful to specify whether H_2CO_3 or the *sum* of $CO_2(aq)$ and H_2CO_3 is being considered. For practical purposes, however, it is simpler to work with the total analytical concentration of carbon dioxide, i.e., $[CO_2(aq)] + [H_2CO_3]$, and to use the K_1 of 4.47×10^{-7}. Furthermore, for simplicity of writing in all subsequent equilibrium calculations, we will use the designation $[H_2CO_3]$ to represent the *total* analytical concentration of carbon dioxide.

EXAMPLE 16

Calculate the pH of a $0.0250\,M$ solution of carbonic acid in water. In this system there are three potential sources of hydrogen ion—the two successive acid ionizations of carbonic acid and the autoprotolysis of water. However, since the first ionization constant for carbonic acid has a much larger magnitude than either K_2 for carbonic acid or K_w for water, we need only consider the equilibrium expression

$$\frac{[H^+][HCO_3^-]}{[H_2CO_3]} = K_1 = 4.47 \times 10^{-7}$$

where the term $[H_2CO_3]$ is the total concentration of dissolved carbon dioxide. At this point, the problem is essentially identical to the ionization of a weak, monoprotic acid (Example 6). When a state of equilibrium prevails,

$$[H^+] = [HCO_3^-]$$

and

$$[H_2CO_3] = 0.0250 - [H^+]$$

Substitution of these two relationships into the earlier equilibrium expression gives

$$\frac{[H^+]^2}{0.0250 - [H^+]} = 4.47 \times 10^{-7}$$

Because the initial concentration of carbonic acid is very large compared to the value of K_1, the equilibrium concentration of H_2CO_3 may be taken as $0.0250\,M$. Therefore,

$$\frac{[H^+]^2}{0.0250} = 4.47 \times 10^{-7}$$

$$[H^+]^2 = 1.12 \times 10^{-8}$$

$$[H^+] = 1.06 \times 10^{-4} M; \quad pH = 3.97$$

EXAMPLE 17

Calculate the pH of a 0.0500 M sodium bicarbonate solution. This type of problem has not been previously considered in this chapter, because the bicarbonate anion is both an acid and a base. It can undergo an acid ionization

$$HCO_3^- \rightleftharpoons H^+ + CO_3^=$$

and it may accept a proton to form a carbonic acid molecule

$$HCO_3^- + H^+ \rightleftharpoons H_2CO_3$$

A species such as bicarbonate, which is capable of either accepting or donating a proton, is said to be **amphiprotic**. In addition, a second source of protons in this system is the ionization of water

$$H_2O \rightleftharpoons H^+ + OH^-$$

Accordingly, the *total* hydrogen ion concentration is that *produced* by the ionizations of bicarbonate and water minus that *consumed* in the formation of carbonic acid, and hence we may write

$$[H^+] = [CO_3^=] + [OH^-] - [H_2CO_3]$$

This equation can be rewritten in terms of the hydrogen ion concentration, the bicarbonate concentration, and the various equilibrium constants as follows:

$$[H^+] = \frac{K_2[HCO_3^-]}{[H^+]} + \frac{K_w}{[H^+]} - \frac{[H^+][HCO_3^-]}{K_1}$$

Rearranging,

$$[H^+]^2 = K_2[HCO_3^-] + K_w - \frac{[H^+]^2[HCO_3^-]}{K_1}$$

collecting terms,

$$[H^+]^2 \left\{ 1 + \frac{[HCO_3^-]}{K_1} \right\} = K_2[HCO_3^-] + K_w$$

and solving for the hydrogen ion concentration, we obtain

$$[H^+] = \sqrt{\frac{K_2[HCO_3^-] + K_w}{1 + \frac{[HCO_3^-]}{K_1}}}$$

Fortunately, the latter equation may be simplified to a great extent. In most practical situations, $[HCO_3^-]$ is greater than K_1 in the denominator, so the "1" is negligible in comparison to $[HCO_3^-]/K_1$. We can also simplify the numerator of the square-root term. Let us briefly compare the magnitudes of the two terms $K_2[HCO_3^-]$ and K_w for two different values of the bicarbonate concentration. If $[HCO_3^-] = 1.0\,M$, $K_2[HCO_3^-]$ is 4680 times larger than K_w. However, if $[HCO_3^-]$ is only $0.010\,M$, $K_2[HCO_3^-]$ is still 46.8 times greater than K_w. For $[HCO_3^-] = 0.010\,M$, we can neglect the K_w term in the numerator and incur an error of just 1 per cent, which is perfectly acceptable (especially when we intend to convert $[H^+]$ to pH). In conclusion, under the specific condition that the bicarbonate ion concentration is no smaller than $0.010\,M$, the complicated expression for $[H^+]$ becomes

$$[H^+] = \sqrt{K_1 K_2}$$

and the pH of the solution is given by the equation

$$pH = \frac{1}{2}(pK_1 + pK_2) = \frac{1}{2}(6.35 + 10.33) = 8.34$$

It is noteworthy that the pH of a sodium bicarbonate solution is independent of concentration, if this concentration is at least $0.010\,M$ as discussed above.

EXAMPLE 18

Suppose that 5.00 ml of $0.100\,M$ hydrochloric acid is added to 25.00 ml of $0.0500\,M$ sodium carbonate solution. Calculate the pH of the resulting solution.

In attacking this problem, we should notice first that $(5.00)(0.100)$ or 0.500 millimole of hydrochloric acid has been added to $(25.00)(0.0500)$ or 1.25 millimoles of sodium carbonate.

Thus, the principal reaction involves the conversion of carbonate to bicarbonate ion

$$H^+ + CO_3^= \rightleftharpoons HCO_3^-; \quad K = \frac{1}{K_2} = 2.14 \times 10^{10}$$

for which the equilibrium constant is the *reciprocal* of the second ionization constant for carbonic acid. It should be evident, from the size of this constant, that the reaction between carbonate and hydrogen ion has a large driving force and that the position of equilibrium lies quite far toward the right. Therefore, it is reasonable to assert that the addition of 0.500 millimole of strong acid to 1.25 millimoles of sodium carbonate will result in an equilibrium mixture containing 0.500 millimole of bicarbonate and 0.750 millimole of carbonate.

Since the final volume of the solution is 30.00 ml, the concentrations of bicarbonate and carbonate are

$$[HCO_3^-] = \frac{0.500 \text{ millimole}}{30 \text{ ml}} = 0.0167 \, M$$

and

$$[CO_3^=] = \frac{0.750 \text{ millimole}}{30 \text{ ml}} = 0.0250 \, M$$

If we now substitute these values into the equilibrium expression for the principal reaction

$$\frac{[HCO_3^-]}{[H^+][CO_3^=]} = 2.14 \times 10^{10}$$

$$\frac{(0.0167)}{[H^+](0.0250)} = 2.14 \times 10^{10}$$

and solve the relation for the hydrogen ion concentration, we obtain

$$[H^+] = \frac{(0.0167)}{(0.0250)(2.14 \times 10^{10})} = 3.12 \times 10^{-11} \, M$$

$$pH = 10.51$$

EXAMPLE 19

Calculate the pH of the solution resulting from the addition of 15.00 ml of 0.100 M hydrochloric acid to 25.00 ml of 0.0500 M sodium carbonate solution.

Although this situation appears to resemble the preceding example, there is one important difference, namely that the quantity of hydrogen ion is greater than the amount of carbonate ion. To be specific, we have (15.00)(0.100) or 1.50 millimoles of the strong acid, but only (25.00)(0.0500) or 1.25 millimoles of carbonate. Thus, there is more than enough hydrogen ion to neutralize completely the carbonate

$$H^+ + CO_3^= \rightleftharpoons HCO_3^-$$

and the additional amount of acid is available to convert some of the bicarbonate ion which has been formed into carbonic acid

$$H^+ + HCO_3^- \rightleftharpoons H_2CO_3$$

This problem can be most conveniently visualized in a step-wise manner. First, we can conclude that the interaction between hydrogen ion and carbonate ion will produce 1.25 millimoles of bicarbonate, with 0.25 millimole of acid remaining unreacted. Second, the 0.25 millimole of hydrogen ion will combine with 0.25 millimole of bicarbonate, so that at equilibrium we have 0.25 millimole of carbonic acid plus 1.00 millimole of bicarbonate left. Inasmuch as these species are present in 40.00 ml of solution, the final concentrations are

$$[H_2CO_3] = \frac{0.250 \text{ millimole}}{40 \text{ ml}} = 6.25 \times 10^{-3} M$$

$$[HCO_3^-] = \frac{1.00 \text{ millimole}}{40 \text{ ml}} = 2.50 \times 10^{-2} M$$

By substituting the molar concentrations of H_2CO_3 and HCO_3^- into the equilibrium expression for the first ionization of carbonic acid

$$\frac{[H^+][HCO_3^-]}{[H_2CO_3]} = K_1 = 4.47 \times 10^{-7}$$

$$\frac{[H^+](2.50 \times 10^{-2})}{(6.25 \times 10^{-3})} = 4.47 \times 10^{-7}$$

we can compute the hydrogen ion concentration as well as the pH of the solution:

$$[H^+] = 4.47 \times 10^{-7} \frac{(6.25 \times 10^{-3})}{(2.50 \times 10^{-2})} = 1.12 \times 10^{-7} M$$

$$pH = 6.95$$

SOLUTIONS OF PHOSPHORIC ACID AND ITS SALTS

In this section, we shall focus our attention on three aspects of equilibria involving phosphoric acid and its salts. Phosphoric acid is a triprotic acid which can undergo three stepwise ionizations as indicated by the following equilibria:

$$H_3PO_4 \rightleftharpoons H^+ + H_2PO_4^-; \quad K_1 = 7.5 \times 10^{-3}$$
$$H_2PO_4^- \rightleftharpoons H^+ + HPO_4^=; \quad K_2 = 6.2 \times 10^{-8}$$
$$HPO_4^= \rightleftharpoons H^+ + PO_4^\equiv; \quad K_3 = 4.8 \times 10^{-13}$$

From these equilibria, we can see that phosphoric acid itself is a fairly strong acid, being much stronger than acetic or formic acids but not so strong as hydrochloric acid. Dihydrogen phosphate and monohydrogen phosphate ions are increasingly weak acids because the removal of a positively charged proton from a singly and then a doubly negative species is more and more difficult.

EXAMPLE 20

Calculate the pH of a $0.1000\,M$ phosphoric acid solution.

As usual, we must consider the important sources of hydrogen ions in this system. In principle, phosphoric acid can furnish protons from each of its three ionizations, and water is also a potential source of hydrogen ions. However, in view of the comparatively large value of the first dissociation constant of phosphoric acid, it is reasonable to neglect at this point the second and third ionizations as well as the ionization of water. Therefore, this problem is very similar to Examples 6 and 7, which involve weak monoprotic acids. The equilibrium-constant expression for the first ionization of phosphoric acid is

$$\frac{[H^+][H_2PO_4^-]}{[H_3PO_4]} = K_1 = 7.5 \times 10^{-3}$$

At equilibrium, we shall write for this situation

$$[H^+] = [H_2PO_4^-]$$

and

$$[H_3PO_4] = 0.1000 - [H^+]$$

The ionization of phosphoric acid is too extensive for us to neglect the $[H^+]$ term in the preceding relation, so the expression to be solved for $[H^+]$ is:

$$\frac{[H^+]^2}{0.1000 - [H^+]} = 7.5 \times 10^{-3}$$

The last equation is best solved by means of the quadratic formula, and the result is $[H^+] = 2.39 \times 10^{-2}\,M$; so pH = 1.62. Alternatively, the method of successive approximations could have been employed. However, with the ultimate value of $[H^+]$ being such an appreciable part of $0.1000\,M$, three repetitive calculations would be required to obtain an answer with an error of less than one per cent, so relatively little time would be saved.

The next most likely source of hydrogen ions is the ionization of $H_2PO_4^-$. We can show that it and, hence, the other sources of protons, can indeed be neglected. If we provisionally take $[H^+] = 2.39 \times 10^{-2}\,M$ and $[H_2PO_4^-] = 2.39 \times 10^{-2}\,M$, the concentration of $HPO_4^=$ can be calculated from a rearranged form of the second dissociation-constant expression for phosphoric acid. Thus,

$$[HPO_4^=] = K_2 \frac{[H_2PO_4^-]}{[H^+]} = 6.2 \times 10^{-8} \frac{(0.0239)}{(0.0239)} = 6.2 \times 10^{-8}\,M$$

Since the equilibrium concentration of $HPO_4^=$ is so small, it is apparent that an insignificant quantity of $H_2PO_4^-$ has ionized under these conditions. Consequently, our original assumption that the only important source of protons is phosphoric acid is valid, so the pH is 1.62 as calculated.

EXAMPLE 21

Calculate the individual concentrations of all phosphate species in 1.00 liter of solution at pH 8.00 and containing 0.100 mole of phosphate species.

In a solution containing several acidic or basic ions, it is useful to determine the *ratios* of concentrations of the various species. The three ionizations of phosphoric acid allow us to write the following equations:

$$\frac{[H_2PO_4^-]}{[H_3PO_4]} = \frac{K_1}{[H^+]}$$

$$\frac{[HPO_4^=]}{[H_2PO_4^-]} = \frac{K_2}{[H^+]}$$

$$\frac{[PO_4^{\equiv}]}{[HPO_4^{=}]} = \frac{K_3}{[H^+]}$$

If we now substitute $[H^+] = 1.00 \times 10^{-8} M$ and the appropriate values for K_1, K_2, and K_3, the concentration ratios become

$$\frac{[H_2PO_4^-]}{[H_3PO_4]} = \frac{7.5 \times 10^{-3}}{1.00 \times 10^{-8}} = 750,000$$

$$\frac{[HPO_4^{=}]}{[H_2PO_4^-]} = \frac{6.2 \times 10^{-8}}{1.00 \times 10^{-8}} = 6.20$$

$$\frac{[PO_4^{\equiv}]}{[HPO_4^{=}]} = \frac{4.8 \times 10^{-13}}{1.00 \times 10^{-8}} = 0.0000480$$

These ratios show that the concentrations of $HPO_4^{=}$ and $H_2PO_4^-$ are similar in magnitude but that the concentrations of H_3PO_4 and $PO_4^{\equiv}$ are extremely small in comparison. To a very good approximation, therefore, the sum of the $HPO_4^{=}$ and $H_2PO_4^-$ concentrations represents virtually all of the total concentration ($0.100 M$) of phosphate species, i.e.,

$$[H_2PO_4^-] + [HPO_4^{=}] = 0.100 M$$

From the ratio relationships above, we have the result

$$[HPO_4^{=}] = 6.20 [H_2PO_4^-]$$

These last two equations, containing two unknowns, may be solved as follows:

$$[H_2PO_4^-] + 6.20 [H_2PO_4^-] = 7.20 [H_2PO_4^-] = 0.100 M;$$
$$[H_2PO_4^-] = 0.0139 M;$$
$$[HPO_4^{=}] = 0.0861 M.$$

We can now go back again to the ratio relationships to calculate the concentrations of H_3PO_4 and $PO_4^{\equiv}$.

$$[H_3PO_4] = \frac{[H_2PO_4^-]}{750,000} = \frac{1.39 \times 10^{-2}}{7.50 \times 10^5} = 1.85 \times 10^{-8} M$$

$$[PO_4^{\equiv}] = 4.8 \times 10^{-5} [HPO_4^{=}] = 4.8 \times 10^{-5} (0.0861)$$
$$= 4.14 \times 10^{-6} M$$

Our assumption that the $HPO_4^{=}$ and $H_2PO_4^-$ represent essentially all the dissolved phosphate species is correct.

EXAMPLE 22

Calculate the pH of the solution obtained by mixing 500 ml of 0.200 M phosphoric acid with 500 ml of a 0.0800 M trisodium phosphate (Na_3PO_4) solution.

This problem may be solved if we remember that phosphoric acid, a fairly strong acid, can donate a proton to $PO_4^{\equiv}$, which has a marked tendency to accept a hydrogen ion and to form $HPO_4^{=}$:

$$H_3PO_4 + PO_4^{\equiv} \rightleftharpoons H_2PO_4^- + HPO_4^{=}$$

The equilibrium constant for the preceding reaction is K_1/K_3 or 1.56×10^{10}. Since we start with 100 millimoles of H_3PO_4 and 40 millimoles of $PO_4^{\equiv}$, we will have after this reaction is concluded 40 millimoles of $HPO_4^{=}$, 40 millimoles of $H_2PO_4^-$, and 60 millimoles of *unreacted* H_3PO_4.

Now, we must ask whether the strongest acid present (H_3PO_4) can react with the strongest base available ($HPO_4^{=}$). The answer is *yes*, because the equilibrium constant for the reaction

$$H_3PO_4 + HPO_4^{=} \rightleftharpoons 2\ H_2PO_4^-$$

is K_1/K_2 or 1.21×10^5. The reaction of 60 millimoles of H_3PO_4 with 40 millimoles of $HPO_4^{=}$ produces 80 millimoles of $H_2PO_4^-$ to go with the 40 millimoles of $H_2PO_4^-$ formed in the first reaction, and 20 millimoles of H_3PO_4 still remains. As a result of these two reactions, the solution contains 20 millimoles of H_3PO_4 and 120 millimoles of $H_2PO_4^-$ at equilibrium. There can be no further reaction between H_3PO_4 and $H_2PO_4^-$.

The pH of the solution can be calculated simply as if we are dealing with a buffer solution. The hydrogen ion concentration is governed by the equation

$$[H^+] = K_1 \frac{[H_3PO_4]}{[H_2PO_4^-]} = 7.5 \times 10^{-3} \frac{(0.020)}{(0.120)} = 1.25 \times 10^{-3}\ M$$

pH = 2.90

It is important to recognize that, for the most part, these problems really consist of the elements of the simpler calculations considered for monoprotic acids and their salts.

ACID-BASE EQUILIBRIA IN NONAQUEOUS SOLVENTS

Although most of the discussions in this chapter have dealt with aqueous solutions, the general concepts of acidity and basicity which were introduced at the beginning of the chapter are by no means limited to any one solvent. We will conclude this chapter with a brief consideration of other solvent systems and of acid-base equilibria which can exist in them.

CLASSIFICATION OF SOLVENTS

An **amphiprotic solvent** is one that is capable of acting as a Brönsted-Lowry acid or a base. The most familiar example of such a solvent is water itself. The amphiprotic character of water is shown by the reaction between one water molecule (acting as an acid) and a second molecule of water (acting as a base):

$$H_2O + H_2O \rightleftharpoons H_3O^+ + OH^-$$

This reaction is the so-called autoprotolysis of water. Most alcohols, such as ethanol, undergo analogous autoprotolysis reactions and have acid-base properties similar to water:

$$C_2H_5OH + C_2H_5OH \rightleftharpoons C_2H_5OH_2^+ + C_2H_5O^-$$

Glacial acetic acid represents a somewhat different kind of amphiprotic solvent. Although glacial acetic acid does undergo the usual type of autoprotolysis reaction,

$$CH_3COOH + CH_3COOH \rightleftharpoons CH_3COOH_2^+ + CH_3COO^-$$

it is a distinctly more acidic solvent than water; accordingly all bases appear to be stronger in acetic acid than in water. Other solvents such as liquid ammonia

$$NH_3 + NH_3 \rightleftharpoons NH_4^+ + NH_2^-$$

exhibit amphiprotic behavior but, compared to water, they are much more basic and they cause all acids to be stronger.

There is another class of solvents, called **inert** or **aprotic solvents,** which do not show any detectable acid or base properties. Benzene, chloroform, and carbon tetrachloride are typical aprotic solvents, for they have no ionizable protons and they have little or no tendency to accept protons from other substances. It is generally not realistic to propose an autoprotolysis reaction for such a solvent.

Still another group includes those solvents which possess definite basic properties but which are without acidic properties. Consequently, for these solvents no autoprotolysis reaction can be written. Therefore, such solvents are frequently included in the list of aprotic or inert solvents. For example, pyridine (C_5H_5N) can accept a proton from a Brönsted-Lowry acid such as water,

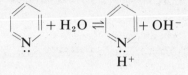

but the acid properties of pyridine are virtually nonexistent. Ethers and ketones are capable of accepting protons from strong Brönsted-Lowry acids such as sulfuric acid, but like pyridine they have no readily ionizable protons.

LEVELING EFFECT AND DIFFERENTIATING ABILITY OF A SOLVENT

In aqueous acid-base chemistry the strongest acids known are the so-called mineral acids—perchloric acid, sulfuric acid, hydrochloric acid, and nitric acid. In water these acids all appear to be equally strong; it is impossible to ascertain whether any real differences in strength exist among these acids. If we study the acid strengths of perchloric acid and hydrochloric acid in water, the following acid-base equilibria are involved:

$$HClO_4 + H_2O \rightleftharpoons ClO_4^- + H_3O^+$$
$$HCl + H_2O \rightleftharpoons Cl^- + H_3O^+$$

Since $HClO_4$ and HCl are both much stronger acids than the hydronium ion, H_3O^+ (or because water is a stronger base than either ClO_4^- or Cl^-), the position of equilibrium in each case lies so far to the right that it is impossible to distinguish experimentally any difference between the two equilibrium positions. Because the strengths of perchloric acid and hydrochloric acid appear to be identical in water, we speak of water as exerting a **leveling effect** on these two acids.

If the same acids, $HClO_4$ and HCl, are compared in glacial acetic acid as solvent, the pertinent acid-base reactions are

$$HClO_4 + CH_3COOH \rightleftharpoons ClO_4^- + CH_3COOH_2^+$$

and

$$HCl + CH_3COOH \rightleftharpoons Cl^- + CH_3COOH_2^+$$

Glacial acetic acid is a much weaker base than water, whereas the protonated acetic acid molecule ($CH_3COOH_2^+$) is a stronger acid than the hydronium ion (H_3O^+). The relative weakness of CH_3COOH as a base and the strength of $CH_3COOH_2^+$ as an acid both act to decrease the extent of the acid-base reactions in glacial acetic acid compared to water. In fact, neither of these acid-base reactions proceeds so far toward the right in acetic acid as in water. However, the greater acid strength of perchloric acid shows up in the fact that its reaction with the glacial acetic acid solvent attains a greater degree of completion than the reaction of hydrochloric acid with the solvent. In the present example, we find that glacial acetic acid possesses the capability to differentiate the acid strengths of $HClO_4$ and HCl. We call it a **differentiating solvent.**

It is very important to recognize that the *leveling* or *differentiating* effect of a solvent depends to a large extent on the acid-base properties of the solvent relative to the dissolved solutes. Thus, although water is a very poor choice of solvent to differentiate the acid strengths of $HClO_4$ and HCl, it is a good solvent to differentiate a mineral acid such as $HClO_4$ or HCl from the much weaker acetic acid. However, a strongly basic solvent such as liquid ammonia would fail to differentiate a mineral acid from acetic acid because the reactions

$$HClO_4 + NH_3 \rightleftharpoons ClO_4^- + NH_4^+$$

and

$$CH_3COOH + NH_3 \rightleftharpoons CH_3COO^- + NH_4^+$$

would both proceed virtually to completion because of the great base strength of NH_3 and the relative weakness of NH_4^+ as an acid.

QUESTIONS AND PROBLEMS

(A comprehensive table of dissociation constants for acids and bases is given in Appendix 2; neglect activity coefficients in each of the problems below.)

1. Compare the Brönsted-Lowry and the Lewis concepts of acids and bases, noting clearly both the similarities and differences between them.

2. List the factors which influence the strength of an acid and explain how each factor affects the acid strength.

3. Distinguish between concentrated and strong acid and base solutions.

4. Convert the following pH values to $[H^+]$: 6.21; 4.37; 11.74; 8.89; 3.18.

5. Convert the following pOH values to $[H^+]$: 3.82; 9.26; 2.65; 12.31; 6.77.

6. Convert the following molar hydrogen ion concentrations to pH values: 0.015; 2.0×10^{-5}; 6.3×10^{-10}; 1.45; 3.9×10^{-6}.

7. Calculate the pH of each of the following solutions:
   (a) 40 ml of 0.100 M hydrochloric acid
   (b) 40 ml of a solution containing 1.00 gram of nitric acid, HNO_3
   (c) 40 ml of a solution containing 12.0 mg of potassium hydroxide, KOH
   (d) 0.0250 M sodium hydroxide solution
   (e) 40 ml of solution containing 2.00 grams of hydrochloric acid and 1.00 gram of sodium chloride
   (f) 0.0100 M potassium nitrate solution
   (g) 0.0100 M acetic acid solution
   (h) 40 ml of solution containing 0.500 gram of acetic acid
   (i) 40 ml of solution containing 0.500 gram of acetic acid and 1.00 gram of sodium acetate
   (j) 500 ml of a 0.100 M aqueous ammonia solution to which 3.00 grams of solid ammonium chloride has been added
   (k) 0.100 M ammonium chloride solution
   (l) 0.100 M sodium acetate solution

8. Calculate the pH of the solution obtained from the addition of 100 ml of water to 100 ml of a solution originally 0.100 M in hydrochloric acid and 0.100 M in sodium chloride.

9. Calculate the pH of the solution obtained from the addition of 100 ml of water to 100 ml of a solution originally 0.100 M in acetic acid and 0.100 M in sodium acetate.

10. In what ratio must acetic acid and sodium acetate be mixed to provide a solution of pH 6.20?

11. In what ratio must ammonia and ammonium chloride be mixed to provide a solution of pH 8.40?

12. Calculate the hydrogen ion concentration and the pH of a solution prepared by adding 0.100 ml of 0.0100 M hydrochloric acid to 10.0 liters of pure water.

13. What is meant by the expression "capacity of a buffer solution"? What limits the capacity of any given buffer solution?

14. Explain with the aid of a generalized equilibrium-constant expression how a buffer solution can maintain a constant pH upon dilution.

15. Consider 100 ml of a 0.100 M acetic acid solution at 25°C.
   (a) Will the addition of 1.00 gram of pure acetic acid cause the extent of ionization of acetic acid to increase, decrease, or remain the same?
   (b) Will the addition of 1.00 gram of sodium acetate cause the pH of the solution to increase, decrease, or remain the same?

(c) Will the addition of 1.00 gram of sodium acetate cause the hydroxide ion concentration to increase, decrease, or remain the same?

16. Consider 50 ml of a 0.100 M aqueous ammonia solution at 25°C.

(a) Will the addition of 1.00 gram of acetic acid cause the pH to increase, decrease, or remain the same?

(b) Will the addition of 1.00 gram of ammonium chloride cause the hydroxide ion concentration to increase, decrease, or remain the same?

(c) Will addition of 10 ml of 0.100 M hydrochloric acid cause pOH to increase, decrease, or remain the same?

17. Calculate the pH and the equilibrium concentration of $HPO_4^=$ in a 0.500 M solution of phosphoric acid, H_3PO_4, in water.

18. Calculate the equilibrium concentrations of H^+, NH_4^+, and NH_3 in a solution prepared by dissolving 0.0400 mole of ammonia in 150 ml of water.

19. Calculate the equilibrium concentrations of NH_4^+ and NH_3 and the pH of the solution obtained from dissolving 0.085 mole of ammonium nitrate and 0.000060 mole of nitric acid in 300 ml of water.

20. Calculate the equilibrium concentrations of H^+, $C_2H_5COO^-$, and C_2H_5COOH in a solution prepared by dissolving 0.0400 mole of propionic acid in 150 ml of water.

21. Calculate the equilibrium concentrations of $C_2H_5COO^-$ and C_2H_5COOH and the pH of the solution obtained by dissolving 0.085 mole of sodium propionate and 0.000050 mole of sodium hydroxide in 250 ml of water.

22. Calculate the pH of a solution prepared by dissolving 0.267 mole of pyridine in 1.00 liter of water.

23. Calculate the pH and the equilibrium concentration of $SO_3^=$ in a 0.300 M solution of sulfurous acid in water.

24. Calculate the equilibrium concentrations of H^+, NO_2^-, and HNO_2 in a solution prepared by dissolving 0.100 mole of nitrous acid in 200 ml of water.

25. Calculate the equilibrium concentrations of NO_2^- and HNO_2 and the pH of the solution prepared by dissolving 0.200 mole of potassium nitrite and 0.00030 mole of potassium hydroxide in 2.00 liters of water.

26. Calculate the equilibrium concentrations of H^+, F^-, and HF in a solution prepared by dissolving 0.100 mole of hydrogen fluoride in 1.00 liter of water.

27. Calculate the equilibrium concentrations of F^- and HF and the pH of the solution prepared by dissolving 0.100 mole of sodium fluoride in 150 ml of water.

28. Calculate the equilibrium concentrations of all ionic and molecular species except water (that is, NH_3, NH_4^+, H^+, and OH^-) in a solution which initially contains 0.00400 mole of ammonia in 150 ml of water.

29. Why is a solution of an acid salt, such as sodium bicarbonate, a convenient pH standard?

30. What will be the pH of a 0.035 M sodium sulfite, Na_2SO_3, solution?

31. If 1.00 mole of pyridine (C_5H_5N) and 0.60 mole of hydrochloric acid are mixed in a liter of aqueous solution, what will be the pH of the resulting solution?

32. If the ionization of a certain weak monoprotic acid occurs to the extent of 20.2 per cent in an originally 0.0100 M aqueous solution of the acid, what will be the extent of ionization in an originally 0.0500 M solution of the acid?

33. A certain nameless acid HZ is known to be a very strong acid (at least as strong as hydrochloric acid) but very insoluble. In fact, the solubility and solubility product for HZ may be represented by

$$HZ(s) \rightleftharpoons H^+ + Z^-; \quad K_{sp} = 1.0 \times 10^{-10}$$

What will be the solubility of HZ in an aqueous solution which is initially 0.100 M in sodium acetate?

34. Magnesium ion (Mg^{++}) and hafnium ion (which exists as HfO^{++} in aqueous media), each initially present at a concentration of 0.10 M, are to be separated. This separation can be accomplished by precipitation of hafnium hydroxide ($HfO(OH)_2$), while Mg^{++} remains in solution, through control of the pH of the solution with an ammonia-ammonium ion buffer. Within what two extremes must the *ratio* $[NH_4^+]/[NH_3]$ be kept so that at least 99.9 per cent of the hafnium ion will be precipitated and none of the magnesium ion will be precipitated? Assume constant solution volume; the solubility products for hafnium hydroxide and magnesium hydroxide are 1.0×10^{-23} and 1.2×10^{-11}, respectively.

35. Calculate the pH of a 0.180 M benzoic acid solution.

36. Calculate the pH of a 0.750 M solution of arsenic acid (H_3AsO_4) in water.

37. Calculate the pH of a 0.250 M solution of sodium dihydrogen phosphate (NaH_2PO_4) in water.

38. Calculate the pH of a 0.0500 M sodium carbonate solution.

39. Calculate the pH of the solution resulting from the addition of 20.00 ml of 0.1000 M hydrochloric acid to 50.00 ml of 0.05000 M sodium carbonate solution.

40. Calculate the pH of the solution resulting from the addition of 45.00 ml of 0.0800 M hydrochloric acid to 50.00 ml of 0.04000 M sodium carbonate solution.

41. Calculate the pH of the solution resulting from the addition of 35.00 ml of 0.5000 M sodium hydroxide solution to 25.00 ml of 0.5000 M phosphoric acid.

42. Calculate the pH of the solution resulting from the addition of 55.00 ml of 0.5000 M sodium hydroxide solution to 25.00 ml of 0.5000 M phosphoric acid.

43. Calculate the pH of the solution resulting from the addition of 32.00 ml of 0.001000 M potassium hydroxide solution to 50.00 ml of 0.001000 M hydrochloric acid.

44. Calculate the pH of the solution resulting from the addition of 17.00 ml of 0.05000 M sodium hydroxide solution to 25.00 ml of 0.05500 M acetic acid solution.

45. Calculate the pH of the solution resulting from the addition of 34.00 ml of 0.1000 M sodium hydroxide solution to 26.00 ml of 0.07500 M acetic acid solution.

46. Calculate the pH of the solution resulting from the addition of 18.00 ml of 0.09000 M hydrochloric acid to 26.00 ml of 0.1200 M ammonia solution.

47. Suppose that 42.00 ml of 0.1000 M sodium hydroxide solution is added to 50.00 ml of a solution containing 0.03000 M hydrochloric acid and 0.07500 M acetic acid. Calculate the pH of the resulting solution.

48. Define or identify clearly each of the following: amphiprotic solvent, aprotic solvent, leveling effect of a solvent, differentiating ability of a solvent, autoprotolysis constant.

49. Which of the following species exhibits amphiprotic character:

$$Cl^-, NH_4^+, H_3O^+, H_2PO_4^-, \text{ and } CH_3COO^-?$$

50. Explain why the mineral acids, such as HNO_3, HCl, $HClO_4$, HBr, and HI, all appear to have about the same strength in water. Explain how you would proceed to establish *experimentally* the *relative* strengths of these mineral acids. Explain why it is not possible to establish the *true* or *intrinsic* strength of any of the mineral acids.

Chapter 4

EQUILIBRIA IN REACTIONS OF COMPLEX IONS

A **complex ion** is a chemical species in which a metal atom or cation is covalently bonded to one or more coordinating groups. Usually, the metal atom or cation is called the **central atom**, whereas the term **ligand** is used to designate the coordinating group. In order for a complex ion to be formed from one or more ligands and a central atom, each ligand must possess at least one unshared pair of electrons, and the central atom must be able to accept an electron pair from each ligand. Thus, the ligand shares a pair of electrons with the central atom in the formation of a covalent bond. This kind of interaction can be represented by the simple chemical reaction

$$M + :L \rightleftharpoons M:L$$

in which M is the central atom and : L is the ligand with its unshared pair of electrons. Any or all of the three species, M, : L, and M : L, may have an electrical charge.

COMPLEX-FORMATION REACTIONS

One example of the formation of a complex ion, which was encountered in Chapter 2, is the reaction between silver ion and ammonia to yield the silver-diammine complex.

$$Ag^+ + 2\ NH_3 \rightleftharpoons Ag(NH_3)_2^+$$

Each ammonia molecule donates an electron pair to the silver ion, and a covalent bond is formed between the two species. It is interesting to

166

note that this process is actually a Lewis acid-base reaction—silver ion is the Lewis acid (electron-pair acceptor) and ammonia is the Lewis base (electron-pair donor). Furthermore, the reaction of ammonia with silver ion is quite analogous to the combination of ammonia with a proton

$$NH_3 + H^+ \rightleftharpoons NH_4^+$$

although the latter is an acid-base reaction in the Brönsted-Lowry classification as well as in the Lewis system of nomenclature.

Let us now discuss several other significant factors pertaining to complex ions by referring to another example, the reaction between the hexaquochromium(III) ion, $Cr(H_2O)_6^{+++}$, and cyanide to form the hexacyanochromate(III) anion:

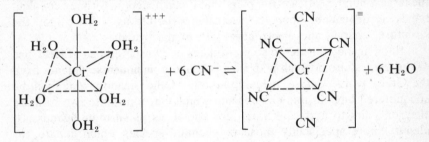

On the left side of this reaction equation, chromium(III) is linked by coordinate covalent bonds to six water molecules, whereas six cyanide ligands are joined to chromium(III) in the complex ion on the right side. Therefore, the ligand in a complex ion may be a neutral molecule, such as water, or it may be an ion, such as cyanide anion. The complex ion itself may be positively charged, as is $Cr(H_2O)_6^{+++}$, or it may be negatively charged, as is $Cr(CN)_6^{\equiv}$. In other instances, however, the complex ion may be a neutral molecule. In the present example, the central atom, chromium, is in the same tripositive oxidation state in both complexes. It is possible for the central atom in a complex ion to be in the zero oxidation state, such as nickel in $Ni(CN)_4^{\equiv}$ or as iron in $Fe(CO)_5$.

Both chromium(III) complexes in the preceding chemical reaction have been drawn in a form which indicates their octahedral geometry. Chromium(III) and four of the ligands lie in a plane, the other two ligands being above and below this plane. In addition, the ligands are symmetrically arranged around the central atom and the six chromium(III)-ligand bond lengths are identical for a given complex ion. A definite kind of geometrical configuration is associated with every complex ion or compound.

Water frequently functions as a ligand in aqueous solutions of metal ions. Nevertheless, for simplicity in the writing of chemical reactions, it is customary to omit water from the formula of a complex ion. For example, it is convenient to represent the hexaquochromium(III) cation as Cr^{+++}, even though it actually exists as an *aquo* complex. Thus, the last preceding chemical reaction is commonly written as

$$Cr^{+++} + 6 \; CN^- \rightleftharpoons Cr(CN)_6^=$$

Such a situation is comparable to the use of H^+ for signifying the hydrated proton in acid-base reactions which occur in aqueous media.

All chromium(III) complexes of the general structure shown in the preceding examples have six ligands, each of which is linked to the central atom by a covalent bond. Accordingly, we can state that the **coordination number** of chromium(III) is 6. On the other hand, the coordination number of silver ion in the silver-diammine complex is 2. For any metal cation, the maximum coordination number, which is simply the largest number of electron pairs that it can accept in forming covalent bonds, is dependent upon its electronic structure as well as upon the structure, charge, and electronegativity of the ligands.

Each ligand considered so far donates one unshared pair of electrons to the central atom. Such a species is called a **monodentate ligand**, from the Greek word *dentate*, meaning "tooth." Other ligands, which will be encountered later in this chapter and which can contribute two or more electron pairs to a central atom, are known as **polydentate ligands**. To identify more specifically those polydentate species which donate, for example, two or three electron pairs to the central atom, we may speak of *bidentate* and *terdentate* ligands, respectively.

Although the position of equilibrium for the chromium(III)-cyanide-water system lies well toward the right for the reaction as written, which demonstrates the relatively high stability of the hexacyanochromate(III) ion, the formation of this complex ion occurs only very slowly at room temperature, particularly in the absence of a large excess of cyanide ion. This slowness of reaction is indicative of the fact that cyanide ions cannot readily displace the water molecules bound to chromium(III). A complex ion which is characterized by a slow rate of ligand exchange is called an inert or **nonlabile** species. Among the metal ions whose complexes frequently display relatively slight reactivity are chromium(III), cobalt(III), and platinum(IV). Likewise, there is another group of metal ions which characteristically form reactive or **labile** complexes, including cobalt(II), copper, lead, bismuth, silver, cadmium, nickel, zinc, mercury, and aluminum. Most complexes of iron(III) and iron(II) are labile, but the cyanide complexes $Fe(CN)_6^\equiv$ and $Fe(CN)_6^\equiv$ are familiar examples of nonlabile species.

STEPWISE AND OVERALL FORMATION CONSTANTS

To describe further the concepts of chemical equilibrium as applied to complex ions, let us consider another example, the interaction between hydrated zinc ion and ammonia. This reaction, as well as others involving monodentate ligands, actually proceeds in a stepwise fashion according to the following equilibria:

$$Zn(H_2O)_4^{++} + NH_3 \rightleftharpoons Zn(NH_3)(H_2O)_3^{++} + H_2O$$
$$Zn(NH_3)(H_2O)_3^{++} + NH_3 \rightleftharpoons Zn(NH_3)_2(H_2O)_2^{++} + H_2O$$
$$Zn(NH_3)_2(H_2O)_2^{++} + NH_3 \rightleftharpoons Zn(NH_3)_3(H_2O)^{++} + H_2O$$
$$Zn(NH_3)_3(H_2O)^{++} + NH_3 \rightleftharpoons Zn(NH_3)_4^{++} + H_2O$$

These equations represent the stepwise formation of the monoammine, diammine, triammine, and tetraammine complexes of zinc, although, as emphasized below, an aqueous solution of zinc ion and ammonia will usually contain at least several of the zinc ammines in equilibrium with each other.

A **stepwise formation constant** is associated with each of these equilibria and is designated by K_n where, in the present example, the subscript n takes an integral value to indicate the addition of the nth ammonia ligand to a complex containing $(n-1)$ ammonia molecules. Thus, the *first stepwise formation constant*, K_1, for the formation of the $Zn(NH_3)(H_2O)_3^{++}$ complex pertains to the equilibrium expression

$$K_1 = \frac{[Zn(NH_3)(H_2O)_3^{++}]}{[Zn(H_2O)_4^{++}][NH_3]}$$

Notice that the concentration (activity) of water does not appear in this relation. If, in addition, the water molecules are omitted from the formula of each complex, the equilibrium-constant expressions for the stepwise formation of the four zinc-ammine complexes may be written in the abbreviated forms:

$$K_1 = \frac{[Zn(NH_3)^{++}]}{[Zn^{++}][NH_3]}$$

$$K_2 = \frac{[Zn(NH_3)_2^{++}]}{[Zn(NH_3)^{++}][NH_3]}$$

$$K_3 = \frac{[Zn(NH_3)_3^{++}]}{[Zn(NH_3)_2^{++}][NH_3]}$$

$$K_4 = \frac{[Zn(NH_3)_4^{++}]}{[Zn(NH_3)_3^{++}][NH_3]}$$

It should be emphasized, however, that the symbols $Zn(NH_3)(H_2O)_3^{++}$ and $Zn(NH_3)^{++}$ both refer to the same species, and similarly for the other zinc-ammine complexes. Numerical values for K_1, K_2, K_3, and K_4 at 25°C are, respectively, 186, 219, 251, and 112.

Sometimes **overall formation constants** are used to characterize the equilibria in systems containing complex ions. Omitting the water molecules from the chemical formulas of all complexes, we can write the equilibria corresponding to the overall reactions for the zinc-ammonia system as follows:

$$Zn^{++} + \quad NH_3 \rightleftharpoons Zn(NH_3)^{++}$$
$$Zn^{++} + 2\ NH_3 \rightleftharpoons Zn(NH_3)_2^{++}$$
$$Zn^{++} + 3\ NH_3 \rightleftharpoons Zn(NH_3)_3^{++}$$
$$Zn^{++} + 4\ NH_3 \rightleftharpoons Zn(NH_3)_4^{++}$$

Overall formation constants are designated by β_n, where the subscript n gives the total number of ligands added to the original aquo-complex ion. For example, the β_n values for the four reactions just listed are

$$\beta_1 = \frac{[Zn(NH_3)^{++}]}{[Zn^{++}][NH_3]}$$

$$\beta_2 = \frac{[Zn(NH_3)_2^{++}]}{[Zn^{++}][NH_3]^2}$$

$$\beta_3 = \frac{[Zn(NH_3)_3^{++}]}{[Zn^{++}][NH_3]^3}$$

$$\beta_4 = \frac{[Zn(NH_3)_4^{++}]}{[Zn^{++}][NH_3]^4}$$

Again note that the concentration of water is absent from the equilibrium expressions and that, in addition, we have omitted the water molecules from the formulas for the complexes even though the coordination number of zinc is four.

There is a definite relationship between the stepwise formation constants and the overall formation constants for any particular system. This may be illustrated if we multiply the numerator and denominator of the equation defining β_3 by the quantity $[Zn(NH_3)^{++}][Zn(NH_3)_2^{++}]$

$$\beta_3 = \frac{[Zn(NH_3)_3^{++}]}{[Zn^{++}][NH_3]^3} \cdot \frac{[Zn(NH_3)^{++}][Zn(NH_3)_2^{++}]}{[Zn(NH_3)^{++}][Zn(NH_3)_2^{++}]}$$

and rearrange the expression as follows:

$$\beta_3 = \frac{[Zn(NH_3)^{++}]}{[Zn^{++}][NH_3]} \cdot \frac{[Zn(NH_3)_2^{++}]}{[Zn(NH_3)][NH_3]} \cdot \frac{[Zn(NH_3)_3^{++}]}{[Zn(NH_3)_2^{++}][NH_3]}$$

Notice that the three terms on the right side of this equation correspond, in order, to K_1, K_2, and K_3. Consequently,

$$\beta_3 = K_1 K_2 K_3$$

In similar fashion it is possible to derive the relationship between each of the overall formation constants and the relevant stepwise formation constants; the results are

$$K_1 = \beta_1$$
$$K_1 K_2 = \beta_2$$
$$K_1 K_2 K_3 = \beta_3$$
$$K_1 K_2 K_3 K_4 = \beta_4$$

It is suggested that the student verify each of these relationships. For the zinc-ammonia system, the overall formation constants have the following numerical values: $\beta_1 = 186$, $\beta_2 = 4.08 \times 10^4$, $\beta_3 = 1.02 \times 10^7$, and $\beta_4 = 1.15 \times 10^9$.

Equilibrium-constant data for a complex ion are sometimes based upon dissociation rather than formation of the complex. For example, the reaction for the overall formation of the zinc-tetraammine complex

$$Zn^{++} + 4\,NH_3 \rightleftharpoons Zn(NH_3)_4^{++}; \quad \beta_4 = \frac{[Zn(NH_3)_4^{++}]}{[Zn^{++}][NH_3]^4}$$

could alternatively be written as a dissociation:

$$Zn(NH_3)_4^{++} \rightleftharpoons Zn^{++} + 4\,NH_3; \quad K = \frac{[Zn^{++}][NH_3]^4}{[Zn(NH_3)_4^{++}]}$$

In the chemical reaction leading to formation of a complex, the complex ion appears as a product, and its concentration is in the numerator of the corresponding equilibrium-constant expression. In the reaction for dissociation of a complex, this species appears as a reactant, and its concentration is in the denominator of the expression for the equilibrium constant. For a given system, the formation constant and the dissociation constant are in reciprocal relationship to each other. However, for convenience the sample problems in this chapter and the tabulations of data in Appendix 3 will involve only formation constants.

Occasionally the term **stability constant** — which is synonymous with formation constant — is encountered with reference to a complex-ion reaction. Regardless of which terminology is employed, the student must recognize that, the larger the numerical value of the formation or stability constant, the more stable is the complex ion. Similarly, the term **instability constant** is often used as a synonym for the dissociation constant — the greater the magnitude of these constants, the lesser the stability of the complex.

CALCULATIONS FOR EQUILIBRIA INVOLVING MONODENTATE LIGANDS

DISTRIBUTION OF METAL AMONG SEVERAL COMPLEX SPECIES

One of the ways in which equilibrium concepts can be applied quantitatively to reactions involving complex ions is in the calculation of the distribution of a metal among several complex species. For most metal ions, and the majority of monodentate ligands, the relative stabilities of the various complexes within a family are such that several complexes are present in a solution for a given concentration of ligand. This situation differs from that encountered in Chapter 3 for polyprotic acids. There we found, for example, that of the four phosphate-bearing substances, H_3PO_4, $H_2PO_4^-$, $HPO_4^=$, and $PO_4^\equiv$, only one or two species are major contributors to the total phosphate concentration at any given pH value. With a sequence of metal-ligand complexes, however, it is not unusual for most or even all of the possible species to be present at the same time in relatively significant quantities.

In Chapter 2, the concentrations of several silver-bearing species in equilibrium with solid silver chloride were evaluated and represented in Figure 2-1 as a function of the chloride ion concentration. We will now consider the relative concentrations of the five zinc-containing ions in the zinc-ammonia system as a function of the ammonia concentration.

EXAMPLE 1

Calculate the molar concentration of each of the species, $Zn(NH_3)^{++}$, $Zn(NH_3)_2^{++}$, $Zn(NH_3)_3^{++}$, and $Zn(NH_3)_4^{++}$, in a solution in which the equilibrium concentrations of ammonia and Zn^{++} ion are 0.0100 and 0.00100 M, respectively.

Information about the concentration of $Zn(NH_3)^{++}$ can be readily obtained if we employ the equilibrium expression for the first overall formation constant, β_1; that is,

$$\frac{[Zn(NH_3)^{++}]}{[Zn^{++}][NH_3]} = \beta_1$$

If we solve this relation for the concentration of $Zn(NH_3)^{++}$ and insert data given in the statement of the problem, along with the numerical value of β_1, we have

$$[Zn(NH_3)^{++}] = \beta_1[Zn^{++}][NH_3]$$
$$[Zn(NH_3)^{++}] = 186(1.00 \times 10^{-3})(1.00 \times 10^{-2})$$
$$[Zn(NH_3)^{++}] = 1.86 \times 10^{-3} M$$

Similar computations may be performed with the second, third, and fourth overall formation constants, as shown below:

$$[Zn(NH_3)_2^{++}] = \beta_2 [Zn^{++}][NH_3]^2$$
$$[Zn(NH_3)_2^{++}] = 4.08 \times 10^4 (1.00 \times 10^{-3}) (1.00 \times 10^{-2})^2$$
$$[Zn(NH_3)_2^{++}] = 4.08 \times 10^{-3} M$$

$$[Zn(NH_3)_3^{++}] = \beta_3 [Zn^{++}][NH_3]^3$$
$$[Zn(NH_3)_3^{++}] = 1.02 \times 10^7 (1.00 \times 10^{-3}) (1.00 \times 10^{-2})^3$$
$$[Zn(NH_3)_3^{++}] = 1.02 \times 10^{-2} M$$

$$[Zn(NH_3)_4^{++}] = \beta_4 [Zn^{++}][NH_3]^4$$
$$[Zn(NH_3)_4^{++}] = 1.15 \times 10^9 (1.00 \times 10^{-3}) (1.00 \times 10^{-2})^4$$
$$[Zn(NH_3)_4^{++}] = 1.15 \times 10^{-2} M$$

To summarize these calculations, we can conclude that the molar concentrations of all zinc-bearing species are as follows: $[Zn^{++}] = 1.00 \times 10^{-3} M$, $[Zn(NH_3)^{++}] = 1.86 \times 10^{-3} M$, $[Zn(NH_3)_2^{++}] = 4.08 \times 10^{-3} M$, $[Zn(NH_3)_3^{++}] = 1.02 \times 10^{-2} M$, $[Zn(NH_3)_4^{++}] = 1.15 \times 10^{-2} M$.

If the preceding concentrations are converted to mole fractions (through division of the concentration of each ion by the *sum* of the concentrations of all five species) and expressed in per cent, it can be shown that there is 3.5 per cent Zn^{++}, 6.5 per cent $Zn(NH_3)^{++}$, 14.2 per cent $Zn(NH_3)_2^{++}$, 35.6 per cent $Zn(NH_3)_3^{++}$, and 40.2 per cent $Zn(NH_3)_4^{++}$ in a solution containing $0.0100 M$ free ammonia. Note that, at least for this particular concentration of ammonia, only two of the species are dominant, although all five forms of zinc(II) are present in very significant amounts.

This same procedure can be used to determine the distribution of zinc(II) among the several ammine and aquo complexes at other specified concentrations of ammonia. Figure 4-1 shows in graphical form the results of many such calculations. In this figure, the areas representing the five zinc-bearing species are bounded by curved solid lines, which can be located in the following way. Using the overall formation constants for the zinc-ammine complexes, one evaluates the mole fractions of all zinc(II) species at each desired ammonia concentration as indicated in the previous example; then these mole fractions are plotted as a function of the logarithm of the ammonia concentration. The order of plotting, from zero mole fraction upwards, begins with the zinc-tetraammine complex, $Zn(NH_3)_4^{++}$, followed in succession by the triammine, diammine, monoammine, and aquo complexes. Points which separate each adjacent pair of complex ions, over the desired range of ammonia concentrations,

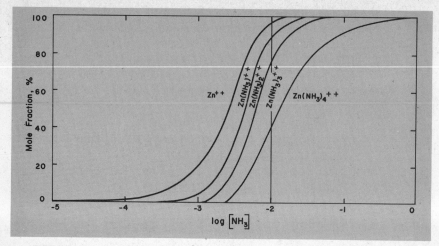

FIGURE 4-1 Distribution diagram showing the percentage mole fractions of the zinc-ammine complexes as a function of the logarithm of the free (uncomplexed) ammonia concentration.

are connected with a solid line to outline the different areas in Figure 4-1. To determine graphically the mole fractions of the five zinc(II) ions for a given concentration of ammonia, it is necessary to draw a vertical line at that ammonia concentration and to measure the length of the line between the curved boundary lines for each species. Thus, a vertical line drawn at log $[NH_3] = -2$ (that is, at $[NH_3] = 0.01\,M$) crosses the regions of Figure 4-1 corresponding to the mole fractions for all five species calculated in Example 1; the length of the line within each region gives the mole per cent of each particular species.

EXAMPLE 2

Calculate the approximate mole fractions of the *major* zinc-containing complexes in a solution, the uncomplexed ammonia concentration of which is $1.0 \times 10^{-3}\,M$. Although rigorous calculations can be performed as in Example 1, we are interested for now in approximate data for the predominant complexes only; therefore, we will simply use Figure 4-1 to obtain the necessary answers. A vertical line drawn at the desired free ammonia concentration, $[NH_3] = 1.0 \times 10^{-3}\,M$ or log $[NH_3] = -3.0$, intersects only the regions representing Zn^{++}, $Zn(NH_3)^{++}$, and $Zn(NH_3)_2^{++}$, so these are the major zinc-containing species. Measurement of the vertical distance within each region gives the mole fractions of these three ions, 80.6 mole per cent Zn^{++}, 15.3 mole per cent $Zn(NH_3)^{++}$, and 4.1 mole per cent $Zn(NH_3)_2^{++}$.

EXAMPLE 3

Calculate the molar concentration at equilibrium of $Zn(NH_3)_4^{++}$ in a solution obtained by mixing together 50.0 ml of a 0.00100 M solution of zinc nitrate with 50.0 ml of a 1.00 M solution of ammonia. We have 0.0500 millimole of zinc(II) in a volume of 100.0 ml, so the total concentration of all zinc-bearing complexes is $5.00 \times 10^{-4} M$; that is,

$$5.00 \times 10^{-4} = [Zn^{++}] + [Zn(NH_3)^{++}] + [Zn(NH_3)_2^{++}] \\ + [Zn(NH_3)_3^{++}] + [Zn(NH_3)_4^{++}]$$

Likewise, the total concentration of ammonia in all of its forms is one-half the initial value, or 0.500 M; so

$$0.500 = [NH_3] + [Zn(NH_3)^{++}] + 2[Zn(NH_3)_2^{++}] \\ + 3[Zn(NH_3)_3^{++}] + 4[Zn(NH_3)_4^{++}]$$

Inasmuch as there is much more ammonia than zinc(II), the concentration of uncomplexed ammonia must be far greater than the sum of all the zinc-ammine complexes. In fact, even if all the zinc ion ($5.00 \times 10^{-4} M$) were present as the tetraammine complex, only $20.0 \times 10^{-4} M$ ammonia would be complexed, leaving well over 99 per cent of the ammonia uncomplexed. Therefore, the mass-balance equation for the ammonia species may be written in the much simpler form:

$$[NH_3] = 0.500 M \quad \text{or} \quad \log [NH_3] = -0.301$$

Figure 4-1 reveals that, at $\log [NH_3] = -0.301$, about 98 per cent of the zinc(II) is in the form of $Zn(NH_3)_4^{++}$. Since the total concentration of all zinc(II) species is $5.00 \times 10^{-4} M$,

$$[Zn(NH_3)_4^{++}] = (5.00 \times 10^{-4})(0.98) \\ [Zn(NH_3)_4^{++}] = 4.90 \times 10^{-4} M$$

We could obtain a more precise answer by using the appropriate overall formation constants, instead of Figure 4-1, along with the same mass-balance equations. This rigorous approach will be examined in the next problem.

EXAMPLE 4

Calculate the concentration of each of the five zinc(II) species in a solution initially containing 0.500 M ammonia and a total zinc(II) concentration of 0.00250 M.

As shown in the preceding example, the mass-balance equation for zinc(II) requires that the sum of the concentrations of all five zinc(II) ions be $0.00250\,M$; that is,

$$0.00250 = [Zn^{++}] + [Zn(NH_3)^{++}] + [Zn(NH_3)_2^{++}] + [Zn(NH_3)_3^{++}] + [Zn(NH_3)_4^{++}]$$

It is possible to express the concentration of each zinc-ammine complex in terms of an appropriate overall formation constant and the equilibrium concentrations of Zn^{++} and NH_3, as in Example 1. When this is done, the latter relation becomes

$$0.00250 = [Zn^{++}] + \beta_1[Zn^{++}][NH_3] + \beta_2[Zn^{++}][NH_3]^2 + \beta_3[Zn^{++}][NH_3]^3 + \beta_4[Zn^{++}][NH_3]^4$$

Since the ammonia concentration is very large compared to the total concentration of zinc(II), we will neglect the decrease in the concentration of ammonia caused by the formation of zinc-ammine complexes and assume that the equilibrium concentration of ammonia is identical to the initial value:

$$[NH_3] = 0.500\,M$$

Now, if we substitute into the second preceding equation the equilibrium ammonia concentration of $0.500\,M$ as well as values for the various overall formation constants, the result is a relation containing only one unknown:

$$\begin{aligned}0.00250 = {}& [Zn^{++}] + (186)(0.500)[Zn^{++}] \\ &+ (4.08 \times 10^4)(0.500)^2[Zn^{++}] \\ &+ (1.02 \times 10^7)(0.500)^3[Zn^{++}] \\ &+ (1.15 \times 10^9)(0.500)^4[Zn^{++}]\end{aligned}$$

$$\begin{aligned}0.00250 = {}& [Zn^{++}] + 93[Zn^{++}] + 1.02 \times 10^4[Zn^{++}] \\ &+ 1.28 \times 10^6[Zn^{++}] + 7.19 \times 10^7[Zn^{++}]\end{aligned}$$

However, only the last two terms on the right side of the latter expression are significant, so we may write, after adding them together,

$$0.00250 = 7.32 \times 10^7[Zn^{++}]$$

which, when solved, yields

$$[Zn^{++}] = \frac{0.00250}{7.32 \times 10^7} = 3.42 \times 10^{-11}\,M$$

Returning to the mass-balance equation for zinc(II), we can see that the last four terms on the right side correspond, in order, to the molar concentrations of $Zn(NH_3)^{++}$, $Zn(NH_3)_2^{++}$, $Zn(NH_3)_3^{++}$, and $Zn(NH_3)_4^{++}$. Therefore,

$$[Zn(NH_3)^{++}] = 93[Zn^{++}] = (93)(3.42 \times 10^{-11})$$
$$= 3.18 \times 10^{-9}\,M$$

$$[Zn(NH_3)_2^{++}] = 1.02 \times 10^4[Zn^{++}]$$
$$= (1.02 \times 10^4)(3.42 \times 10^{-11})$$
$$= 3.49 \times 10^{-7}\,M$$

$$[Zn(NH_3)_3^{++}] = 1.28 \times 10^6[Zn^{++}]$$
$$= (1.28 \times 10^6)(3.42 \times 10^{-11})$$
$$= 4.38 \times 10^{-5}\,M$$

$$[Zn(NH_3)_4^{++}] = 7.19 \times 10^7[Zn^{++}]$$
$$= (7.19 \times 10^7)(3.42 \times 10^{-11})$$
$$= 2.46 \times 10^{-3}\,M$$

EFFECT OF COMPLEX FORMATION ON SOLUBILITY

As described in Chapter 2, the formation of complex ions can have a pronounced effect upon solubility equilibria. For example, in the presence of ammonia, the solubility of silver chloride in water is increased greatly, owing to the formation of silver-monoammine and silver-diammine complexes. Similarly, the dissolution of silver bromide is much greater in a sodium thiosulfate solution than in pure water because of the high stability of the complexes $AgS_2O_3^-$ and $Ag(S_2O_3)_2^\equiv$. In addition, we have seen earlier that chloride ion can react with silver ion to produce the complexes $AgCl_2^-$, $AgCl_3^\equiv$, and $AgCl_4^\equiv$; consequently, for a sufficiently large chloride concentration, the formation of these complexes can overcome the common-ion effect so that the solubility of silver chloride is considerably greater than in water.

Let us now consider another system—one involving the solubility behavior of silver cyanide. In water, the most accurate representation of the dissolution process is

$$Ag[Ag(CN)_2](s) \rightleftharpoons Ag^+ + Ag(CN)_2^-$$

for which the following solubility-product expression may be written:

$$K_{sp} = [Ag^+][Ag(CN)_2^-] = 5.0 \times 10^{-12}$$

Unlike inorganic compounds previously discussed, solid silver cyanide dissolves to yield a silver ion and a metal complex — the dicyanoargentate(I) anion, $Ag(CN)_2^-$. This latter species can be viewed as resulting from the reaction of one silver ion with two cyanide ions

$$Ag^+ + 2\ CN^- \rightleftharpoons Ag(CN)_2^-$$

and the equilibrium expression and overall formation constant are given by

$$\beta_2 = \frac{[Ag(CN)_2^-]}{[Ag^+][CN^-]^2} = 1.26 \times 10^{21}$$

Thus, in a solution containing silver ion and cyanide ion, it is necessary to consider simultaneously both solubility and complex-formation equilibria.

EXAMPLE 5

Calculate the equilibrium concentrations of the three species, Ag^+, CN^-, $Ag(CN)_2^-$, resulting from the mixing of 50.0 ml of 0.200 M sodium cyanide solution with 10.0 ml of 0.100 M silver nitrate solution, and determine whether solid silver cyanide will precipitate.

Prior to the occurrence of any chemical reactions, there are 10.0 millimoles of cyanide and 1.00 millimole of silver ion in 60.0 ml of solution. In view of the large excess of cyanide as well as the stability of the dicyanoargentate(I) anion, let us assume provisionally that essentially all of the silver ion reacts to form the $Ag(CN)_2^-$ complex. Accordingly,

$$[Ag(CN)_2^-] = \frac{1.00 \text{ millimole}}{60.0 \text{ ml}} = 0.0167\ M$$

Since formation of 1.00 millimole of the complex will consume 2.00 millimoles of cyanide ion, only 8.00 millimoles of free CN^- remains, so

$$[CN^-] = \frac{8.00 \text{ millimoles}}{60.0 \text{ ml}} = 0.133\ M$$

Using both of these concentrations and the equilibrium expression for the overall formation of the $Ag(CN)_2^-$ complex, one can calculate the silver ion concentration:

$$\beta_2 = \frac{[Ag(CN)_2^-]}{[Ag^+][CN^-]^2} = 1.26 \times 10^{21}$$

$$\frac{(0.0167)}{[Ag^+](0.133)^2} = 1.26 \times 10^{21}$$

$$[Ag^+] = 7.49 \times 10^{-22}\, M$$

Thus, the equilibrium concentrations of Ag^+, $Ag(CN)_2^-$, and CN^- are 7.49×10^{-22}, 0.0167, and $0.133\, M$, respectively. Our preliminary assumption that essentially all of the silver ion was in the form of the $Ag(CN)_2^-$ complex is valid since the concentration of Ag^+ is indeed far less than that of $Ag(CN)_2^-$. Finally, we can conclude that no precipitation of $Ag[Ag(CN)_2]$ occurs because the product of the Ag^+ and $Ag(CN)_2^-$ concentrations is much smaller than the solubility product.

EXAMPLE 6

Compute the equilibrium concentrations of Ag^+, $Ag(CN)_2^-$, and CN^- resulting from the mixing of 10.0 ml of 0.200 M sodium cyanide solution and 50.0 ml of 0.100 M silver nitrate solution.

Initially, the final solution, whose volume is 60.0 ml, contains 2.00 millimoles of cyanide and 5.00 millimoles of silver ion. Since there is a large excess of silver ion, it may be assumed that virtually all of the cyanide precipitates as $Ag[Ag(CN)_2]$ and that 3.00 millimoles of free silver ion remains, so

$$[Ag^+] = \frac{3.00\ \text{millimoles}}{60.0\ \text{ml}} = 0.0500\, M$$

Next, the concentration of $Ag(CN)_2^-$ can be calculated from the solubility-product expression:

$$K_{sp} = [Ag^+][Ag(CN)_2^-] = 5.0 \times 10^{-12}$$

$$[Ag(CN)_2^-] = \frac{5.0 \times 10^{-12}}{[Ag^+]} = \frac{5.0 \times 10^{-12}}{0.0500} = 1.00 \times 10^{-10}\, M$$

Finally, we may obtain the cyanide concentration from the equilibrium equation for the overall formation of the $Ag(CN)_2^-$ complex:

$$\beta_2 = \frac{[Ag(CN)_2^-]}{[Ag^+][CN^-]^2} = 1.26 \times 10^{21}$$

$$[CN^-]^2 = \frac{1.00 \times 10^{-10}}{(0.0500)(1.26 \times 10^{21})} = 1.59 \times 10^{-30}$$

$$[CN^-] = 1.26 \times 10^{-15} \, M$$

On the basis of these calculations, we have shown that the concentrations of Ag^+, $Ag(CN)_2^-$, and CN^- at equilibrium are, respectively, 0.0500, 1.00×10^{-10}, and $1.26 \times 10^{-15} \, M$. Again, our assumption that essentially all of the cyanide is precipitated should be verified. Of the original 2.00 millimoles of cyanide, the amount of cyanide *not* precipitated is equal to the quantity of free cyanide, $(1.26 \times 10^{-15})(60.0)$ or 7.56×10^{-14} millimole, plus the quantity of cyanide present in the $Ag(CN)_2^-$ complex, $(2)(1.00 \times 10^{-10})$ (60.0) or 1.20×10^{-8} millimole. Indeed the assumption is justified.

One other factor should be mentioned in conjunction with the silver cyanide system. Cyanide is the anion of a very weak acid, hydrocyanic acid, which has an acid dissociation constant of 7.2×10^{-10}. Therefore, the true cyanide ion concentration is smaller than would otherwise be expected, because some of it may combine with hydrogen ion from water:

$$CN^- + H_2O \rightleftharpoons HCN + OH^-$$

Fortunately, the position of this chemical equilibrium lies well to the left under the conditions of both Example 5 and Example 6. If, however, some additional source of protons is introduced, much of the uncomplexed cyanide may exist in the form of hydrogen cyanide, and the effect of this equilibrium must be considered.

EQUILIBRIA INVOLVING POLYDENTATE LIGANDS

A polydentate ligand is one which can donate two or more electron pairs to a central atom in forming a complex. Consider the molecule ethylenediamine, $NH_2CH_2CH_2NH_2$, whose structural formula is

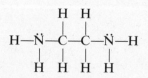

Each of the nitrogen atoms possesses one unshared pair of electrons, so ethylenediamine is an example of a *bidentate* ligand. A copper(II) ion can, for example, be complexed by two ethylenediamine ligands in much the same way as it is complexed by four ammonia molecules:

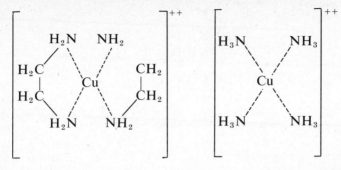

A complex which is composed of a central metal atom and one or more polydentate ligands is called a **chelate**, or chelate compound, after a Greek word meaning "claw." In a manner of speaking, the two or more coordinating groups of the ligand act as a claw in bonding to the central atom.

It is interesting to compare the stabilities of metal complexes involving polydentate ligands to those involving monodentate ligands with the same atoms providing the unshared electron pairs. Consider again the copper(II) complexes with ethylenediamine and with ammonia. Although the overall formation constant for the bis(ethylenediamine) copper(II) complex, which we may abbreviate as $Cu(en)_2^{++}$ by letting *en* represent a molecule of ethylenediamine, is not tabulated in Appendix 3, the two stepwise formation constants are listed. Using the relationship developed earlier in this chapter, we can evaluate the overall formation constant as follows:

$$\beta_2 = \frac{[Cu(en)_2^{++}]}{[Cu^{++}][en]^2} = K_1 K_2 = (3.5 \times 10^{10})(1.1 \times 10^9) = 3.9 \times 10^{19}$$

Similarly, the overall formation constant for the tetraammine complex, $Cu(NH_3)_4^{++}$, can be calculated from the four stepwise formation constants given in Appendix 3:

$$\beta_4 = \frac{[Cu(NH_3)_4^{++}]}{[Cu^{++}][NH_3]^4} = K_1 K_2 K_3 K_4 = (1.3 \times 10^4)(3.2 \times 10^3)(800)(130)$$

$$= 4.3 \times 10^{12}$$

Now, in order that we may directly compare the stabilities of the two complexes, let us assume that [en] and [NH$_3$] are both 0.0100 M, and let us substitute these values into the two overall-formation-constant expressions:

$$\frac{[Cu(en)_2^{++}]}{[Cu^{++}](0.0100)^2} = 3.9 \times 10^{19}$$

$$\frac{[Cu(en)_2^{++}]}{[Cu^{++}]} = 3.9 \times 10^{15}$$

and

$$\frac{[Cu(NH_3)_4^{++}]}{[Cu^{++}](0.0100)^4} = 4.3 \times 10^{12}$$

$$\frac{[Cu(NH_3)_4^{++}]}{[Cu^{++}]} = 4.3 \times 10^4$$

Therefore, the ratio of fully complexed copper(II) to uncomplexed (actually aquo-complexed) copper(II) is 3.9×10^{15} for the bis(ethylenediamine) species and only 4.3×10^4 for the tetraammine species. Although the quantitative ratios vary for other systems, it is generally observed that chelate complexes are much more stable than are complexes with monodentate ligands in which the same atoms are involved. One of the reasons why formation of bis(ethylenediamine)copper(II) is so very favorable compared to the tetraammine complex is the presence of two highly stable five-membered rings in the former species.

A particularly interesting species is the complex of silver ion with ethylenediamine. Typically, silver ion has two coordination sites, as in $Ag(NH_3)_2^+$ and $Ag(CN)_2^-$; each of these ions has a linear structure. If both nitrogen atoms of a single ethylenediamine molecule were to be bonded to silver ion, the resulting complex would be very strained and exceedingly unstable. However, *two* silver ions can be coordinated to *two* ethylenediamine molecules in such a geometrical arrangement that the complex is reasonably stable:

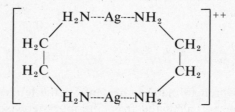

This is an example of a **binuclear** complex, one which contains two atoms or ions of the central element. All of the other complexes considered in this chapter are **mononuclear**.

Ethylenediaminetetraacetic acid, abbreviated as EDTA, is the most important and well-known member of a group of aminopolycarboxylic acids. The structural formula of the EDTA molecule is

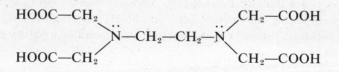

Ethylenediaminetetraacetic acid is a tetraprotic acid. Each of the hydrogen atoms on the carboxyl (—COOH) groups undergoes an acid dissociation. Usually, the parent acid, EDTA, is written as H_4Y in order to show the tetraprotic character of this acid. Ethylenediaminetetraacetate anion, $Y^{\equiv}$, forms very stable, one-to-one complexes with practically every metal ion in the periodic table. This one-to-one nature of metal-EDTA complexes arises from the fact that the $Y^{\equiv}$ ion possesses a total of six functional groups — four carboxyl groups and two amine groups — which can occupy four, five, or six coordination positions around a central atom. One known example of a six-coordinated species is the cobalt(III)-EDTA complex, whose structure is

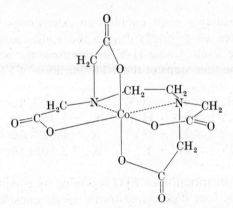

Because of the fact that the ethylenediaminetetraacetate ion coordinates at several positions around a central metal atom, only one-to-one metal to ligand complexes are formed. Consequently, the complicated equilibria encountered in the stepwise reactions between metal ions and monodentate ligands are not encountered with EDTA complexes. Metal-EDTA complexes gain particular stability from the five-membered chelate rings which are formed. In the cobalt(III)-EDTA complex shown above, there are five such five-membered rings. A five-membered ring is an especially stable configuration because the bond angles allow all five atoms in the ring to lie in a plane. Frequently, only four or five of the six functional groups in the EDTA anion are bound to a metal ion, and the remaining positions around the metal may be occupied by monodentate ligands such as water, hydroxide, or ammonia.

We may write the general reaction for the formation of metal-EDTA complexes as

$$M^{+n} + Y^{\equiv} \rightleftharpoons MY^{n-4}$$

where M^{+n} represents an aquated or hydrated metal cation of charge $+n$. In the simplest case, water molecules are displaced by EDTA during the course of the forward reaction. In accordance with the preceding reaction, the equilibrium expression for the formation of metal-EDTA complexes has the form

$$K_{MY} = \frac{[MY^{n-4}]}{[M^{+n}][Y^{\equiv}]}$$

where K_{MY} is the formation constant for the MY^{n-4} complex. In Appendix 3 are listed a number of formation constants for metal-EDTA chelate complexes. Because each of these constants pertains to the formation of a one-to-one complex, so that the terms in the denominator are both first-power, and because the values for the formation constants are extremely large, the metal-EDTA chelates are indeed very stable species.

Before considering some equilibrium calculations involving metal-EDTA complexes, let us briefly discuss the acidic characteristics of the EDTA molecule itself. Using H_4Y to represent the parent compound, we may write the four steps of the acid ionization of EDTA as follows:

$$H_4Y \rightleftharpoons H^+ + H_3Y^-; \quad K_1 = 1.00 \times 10^{-2}$$
$$H_3Y^- \rightleftharpoons H^+ + H_2Y^{=}; \quad K_2 = 2.16 \times 10^{-3}$$
$$H_2Y^{=} \rightleftharpoons H^+ + HY^{\equiv}; \quad K_3 = 6.92 \times 10^{-7}$$
$$HY^{\equiv} \rightleftharpoons H^+ + Y^{\equiv\!\!\!-}; \quad K_4 = 5.50 \times 10^{-11}$$

The partition or distribution of EDTA among its completely undissociated form and its four dissociated forms varies considerably with pH. At any particular pH, the distribution of EDTA species may be calculated from the acid dissociation constants for H_4Y. For example, let us substitute a value for $[H^+]$ of $1.00 \times 10^{-10}\,M$, corresponding to a pH of 10, into each of the four acid ionization equilibrium expressions:

$$\frac{[H_3Y^-]}{[H_4Y]} = \frac{1.00 \times 10^{-2}}{[H^+]} = \frac{1.00 \times 10^{-2}}{1.00 \times 10^{-10}} = 1.00 \times 10^{8}$$

$$\frac{[H_2Y^{=}]}{[H_3Y^-]} = \frac{2.16 \times 10^{-3}}{[H^+]} = \frac{2.16 \times 10^{-3}}{1.00 \times 10^{-10}} = 2.16 \times 10^{7}$$

$$\frac{[HY^{\equiv}]}{[H_2Y^{=}]} = \frac{6.92 \times 10^{-7}}{[H^+]} = \frac{6.92 \times 10^{-7}}{1.00 \times 10^{-10}} = 6.92 \times 10^{3}$$

$$\frac{[Y^{\equiv\!\!\!-}]}{[HY^{\equiv}]} = \frac{5.50 \times 10^{-11}}{[H^+]} = \frac{5.50 \times 10^{-11}}{1.00 \times 10^{-10}} = 5.50 \times 10^{-1}$$

These ratios reveal the following facts. First, the concentration of H_3Y^- is 100 million times greater than that of H_4Y. It is also apparent that the $H_2Y^{=}$ species is almost 22 million times more abundant than H_3Y^-, and, in turn, $HY^{\equiv}$ is approximately 7000 times more abundant than $H_2Y^{=}$. Finally, we see that the ratio of $Y^{\equiv\!\!\!-}$ to $HY^{\equiv}$ is 55/100. What these calculations show is that at pH 10 only $Y^{\equiv\!\!\!-}$ and $HY^{\equiv}$ are present in significant concentrations. The concentrations of the other three species, $H_2Y^{=}$,

TABLE 4-1   FRACTION OF *EDTA* PRESENT AS VARIOUS SPECIES
AS A FUNCTION OF pH*

pH	H_4Y	H_3Y^-	$H_2Y^=$	$HY^{\equiv}$	$Y^{\equiv}$
0	0.990	0.010			
1	0.907	0.091	0.002		
2	0.451	0.451	0.098		
3	0.031	0.307	0.662		
4		0.044	0.949	0.007	
5		0.004	0.931	0.065	
6			0.591	0.409	
7			0.127	0.873	
8			0.014	0.981	0.005
9			0.001	0.947	0.052
10				0.645	0.355
11				0.154	0.846
12				0.018	0.982
13				0.002	0.998
14					1.000

*No entry appears if the fraction of a species present is less than 0.001.

H_3Y^-, and H_4Y, are negligibly small. Therefore, the fraction of EDTA in the $Y^{\equiv}$ form is 55/155 or 0.355, and in the $HY^{\equiv}$ form it is 100/155 or 0.645. The fractions of the other species present are much less than 0.001. In Table 4-1 the fraction of EDTA present as each species at pH values from 0 to 14 is listed. If no entry appears in the table, the fraction is less than 0.001. It is seen from Table 4-1 that H_4Y predominates below pH 2, H_3Y^- between pH 2 and 3, $H_2Y^=$ between pH 3 and 6, $HY^{\equiv}$ between pH 6 and 10, and $Y^{\equiv}$ above pH 10.

EXAMPLE 7

With the aid of Table 4-1, calculate the molar concentration of the H_3Y^- ion in an EDTA solution at pH 4.00 in which the $H_2Y^=$ concentration is 0.125 M.

From Table 4-1, we note that the mole ratio of H_3Y^- to $H_2Y^=$ is 0.044/0.949. Therefore,

$$\frac{[H_3Y^-]}{[H_2Y^=]} = \frac{0.044}{0.949}$$

$$\frac{[H_3Y^-]}{0.125} = \frac{0.044}{0.949}$$

$$[H_3Y^-] = 5.8 \times 10^{-3} M$$

EXAMPLE 8

Calculate the molar concentration of the undissociated acid species H_4Y in an EDTA solution at pH 5.00, in which the total concentration of all EDTA species is 0.0100 M.

Although Table 4-1 reveals that at pH 5.00 the mole fraction of H_4Y is less than 0.001, a specific value is not listed. Therefore, it is necessary to perform calculations with the appropriate equilibrium constants.

Let us begin by writing a relation to show that the sum of the concentrations of all five EDTA species is 0.0100 M; that is,

$$0.0100 = [H_4Y] + [H_3Y^-] + [H_2Y^=] + [HY^\equiv] + [Y^\equiv]$$

In order to solve this equation for $[H_4Y]$, we must express the concentration of the other four species in terms of $[H_4Y]$. If the value for $[H^+]$ of $1.00 \times 10^{-5} M$ is substituted into each of the ionization-constant relationships, as was done on page 184 for a pH value of 10, the results are

$$\frac{[H_3Y^-]}{[H_4Y]} = 1.00 \times 10^3$$

$$\frac{[H_2Y^=]}{[H_3Y^-]} = 2.16 \times 10^2$$

$$\frac{[HY^\equiv]}{[H_2Y^=]} = 6.92 \times 10^{-2}$$

$$\frac{[Y^\equiv]}{[HY^\equiv]} = 5.50 \times 10^{-6}$$

Simple rearrangement of the first expression yields

$$[H_3Y^-] = 1.00 \times 10^3 [H_4Y]$$

and multiplication of the first and second equations gives

$$\frac{[H_3Y^-]}{[H_4Y]} \cdot \frac{[H_2Y^=]}{[H_3Y^-]} = (1.00 \times 10^3)(2.16 \times 10^2)$$

$$\frac{[H_2Y^=]}{[H_4Y]} = 2.16 \times 10^5$$

$$[H_2Y^=] = 2.16 \times 10^5 [H_4Y]$$

If the first, second, and third relations are combined, we have

$$\frac{[H_3Y^-]}{[H_4Y]} \cdot \frac{[H_2Y^=]}{[H_3Y^-]} \cdot \frac{[HY^\equiv]}{[H_2Y^=]}$$

$$= (1.00 \times 10^3)(2.16 \times 10^2)(6.92 \times 10^{-2})$$

$$\frac{[HY^\equiv]}{[H_4Y]} = 1.50 \times 10^4$$

$$[HY^\equiv] = 1.50 \times 10^4 [H_4Y]$$

Finally, when all four equations are multiplied together, one obtains

$$\frac{[H_3Y^-]}{[H_4Y]} \cdot \frac{[H_2Y^=]}{[H_3Y^-]} \cdot \frac{[HY^\equiv]}{[H_2Y^=]} \cdot \frac{[Y^\equiv]}{[HY^\equiv]}$$

$$= (1.00 \times 10^3)(2.16 \times 10^2)(6.92 \times 10^{-2})(5.50 \times 10^{-6})$$

$$\frac{[Y^\equiv]}{[H_4Y]} = 8.23 \times 10^{-2}$$

$$[Y^\equiv] = 8.23 \times 10^{-2}[H_4Y]$$

To summarize the results of these calculations, we have derived four expressions

$$[H_3Y^-] = 1.00 \times 10^3 [H_4Y]$$
$$[H_2Y^=] = 2.16 \times 10^5 [H_4Y]$$
$$[HY^\equiv] = 1.50 \times 10^4 [H_4Y]$$
$$[Y^\equiv] = 8.23 \times 10^{-2} [H_4Y]$$

which give the concentration of each of the ionized forms of EDTA in terms of the concentration of the undissociated acid. Substitution of these relations into the original mass-balance equation for EDTA yields

$$0.0100 = [H_4Y] + 1.00 \times 10^3 [H_4Y] + 2.16 \times 10^5 [H_4Y]$$
$$+ 1.50 \times 10^4 [H_4Y] + 8.23 \times 10^{-2} [H_4Y]$$

When we solve this expression for the desired concentration of H_4Y, we obtain

$$0.0100 = 2.32 \times 10^5 [H_4Y]$$

$$[H_4Y] = \frac{0.0100}{2.32 \times 10^5} = 4.31 \times 10^{-8} M$$

In many practical applications of systems involving metal-EDTA chelates, particularly in analytical chemistry, the reactions occur in neutral or alkaline solutions. This is because metal-EDTA complexes, although generally quite stable, can undergo dissociation in the presence of an acid due to protonation of the $Y^{\equiv}$ ion, as shown, for example, by the reaction

$$MY^{n-4} + 4\,H^+ \rightleftharpoons M^{+n} + H_4Y$$

Accordingly, if MY^{n-4} complexes are formed in neutral or alkaline media, in which the predominant EDTA species are the $H_2Y^{=}$ and $HY^{\equiv}$ ions, we may realistically visualize the net complex-formation reaction as either

$$M^{+n} + H_2Y^{=} \rightleftharpoons MY^{n-4} + 2\,H^+$$

or

$$M^{+n} + HY^{\equiv} \rightleftharpoons MY^{n-4} + H^+$$

depending upon the exact solution pH. If it is desirable that the position of equilibrium for the forward reaction lie far toward the right, as is invariably the case, the solution must be buffered at the appropriate pH value; otherwise, the hydrogen ion formed as a product would cause the pH of the solution to decrease and the forward reaction to cease long before formation of the complex was complete.

Two sample problems which involve the calcium-EDTA chelate are presented in the remaining portion of this chapter. In one of them the chelating ligand is in excess, and in the second the metal ion predominates.

EXAMPLE 9

Calculate the equilibrium concentrations of Ca^{++} and $CaY^{=}$ ions in the solution obtained by mixing 40.0 ml of 0.0100 M calcium chloride solution with 60.0 ml of 0.0100 M EDTA solution, the final pH being 10.0.

From information given in Appendix 3, we can write the reaction and the equilibrium-constant expression for the formation of the calcium-EDTA complex as follows:

$$Ca^{++} + Y^{\equiv} \rightleftharpoons CaY^{=}; \quad K_{CaY} = \frac{[CaY^{=}]}{[Ca^{++}][Y^{\equiv}]} = 5.01 \times 10^{10}$$

Since the total calcium ion concentration is 0.400 millimole in 100 ml, or $4.00 \times 10^{-3}\,M$, and since calcium ion may be present as either of two species, the following mass-balance equation is valid:

$$4.00 \times 10^{-3} = [Ca^{++}] + [CaY^{=}]$$

Inasmuch as the calcium-EDTA complex is quite stable and there is an excess of EDTA (0.600 millimole) over calcium (0.400 millimole), we may assume that essentially all of the calcium is present as the EDTA complex. Therefore, the preceding relation takes the simplified form

$$4.00 \times 10^{-3} = [CaY^=]$$

Referring to the original statement of the problem, we see that the total concentration of all EDTA-containing species is 0.600 millimole per 100 ml, or $6.00 \times 10^{-3} M$. At pH 10, all forms of uncomplexed EDTA except $HY^=$ and $Y^\equiv$ are insignificant, as demonstrated in our calculations on page 184; however, the ethylenediaminetetraacetate ion bound to calcium must not be overlooked. With these facts in mind, we may formulate a mass-balance relation for EDTA as follows:

$$6.00 \times 10^{-3} = [HY^=] + [Y^\equiv] + [CaY^=]$$

From data listed in Table 4-1, it can be shown that at pH 10

$$[HY^=] = 1.82[Y^\equiv]$$

so the mass-balance equation for EDTA becomes

$$6.00 \times 10^{-3} = 2.82[Y^\equiv] + [CaY^=]$$

If we substitute the value for the concentration of the calcium-EDTA complex, namely $4.00 \times 10^{-3} M$, into the latter relation, it becomes

$$6.00 \times 10^{-3} = 2.82[Y^\equiv] + 4.00 \times 10^{-3}$$
$$2.82[Y^\equiv] = 2.00 \times 10^{-3}$$
$$[Y^\equiv] = 7.09 \times 10^{-4} M$$

Finally, if the concentrations of $CaY^=$ and $Y^\equiv$ are inserted into the equilibrium expression for the formation of the calcium-EDTA complex, the calcium ion concentration is obtained:

$$\frac{[CaY^=]}{[Ca^{++}][Y^\equiv]} = 5.01 \times 10^{10}$$

$$\frac{(4.00 \times 10^{-3})}{[Ca^{++}](7.09 \times 10^{-4})} = 5.01 \times 10^{10}$$

$$[Ca^{++}] = 1.13 \times 10^{-10} M$$

Thus, the concentration of uncomplexed Ca^{++} ion is $1.13 \times 10^{-10} M$, whereas the $CaY^=$ concentration is $4.00 \times 10^{-3} M$. Before leaving this problem, we should verify the assumption made in simplifying the calcium mass-balance equation; $[Ca^{++}]$ is indeed negligible in comparison to $[CaY^=]$.

EXAMPLE 10

Calculate the equilibrium concentrations of Ca^{++} and $CaY^=$ ions in a solution prepared by mixing 60.0 ml of 0.0100 M calcium chloride solution with 40.0 ml of 0.0100 M EDTA solution, the final pH being 10.0.

Although the total calcium ion concentration is greater than that of EDTA, the equilibrium expression for the calcium-EDTA complex must still be obeyed. As in the previous problem, mass-balance equations for calcium and for EDTA may be formulated:

$$6.00 \times 10^{-3} = [Ca^{++}] + [CaY^=]$$

and

$$4.00 \times 10^{-3} = [HY^=] + [Y^\equiv] + [CaY^=]$$

However, using the fact that $[HY^=] = 1.82[Y^\equiv]$ at pH 10, we can rewrite the latter relation as

$$4.00 \times 10^{-3} = 2.82[Y^\equiv] + [CaY^=]$$

In addition, this equation may be simplified even more if it is assumed that, with an excess of calcium ion, virtually all of the EDTA is complexed and that $2.82[Y^\equiv]$ is negligibly small in comparison to $[CaY^=]$. On the basis of this assumption, the last preceding relation becomes

$$4.00 \times 10^{-3} = [CaY^=]$$

Substituting this result into the mass-balance expression for calcium, we obtain

$$6.00 \times 10^{-3} = [Ca^{++}] + 4.00 \times 10^{-3}$$
$$[Ca^{++}] = 2.00 \times 10^{-3} M$$

Therefore, the Ca^{++} ion concentration is $2.00 \times 10^{-3} M$ and the $CaY^=$ complex is present at a concentration of $4.00 \times 10^{-3} M$.

Notice that we have not used any equilibrium calculations in solving this problem, other than to recognize that the $CaY^=$ complex is very stable. However, in order to show the validity of the one assumption — that $[Y^\equiv]$ is negligible compared to $[CaY^=]$ — it would be necessary to employ the equilibrium expression for the formation of $CaY^=$ and to calculate the actual value of $[Y^\equiv]$. It is suggested that the student perform this operation.

QUESTIONS AND PROBLEMS

1. Define or identify each of the following terms: labile complex, nonlabile complex, bidentate ligand, stepwise formation constant, overall formation constant, chelate, ammine complex.

2. Write the equilibrium reaction and the equilibrium expression corresponding to the third overall formation constant for the $Cd(NH_3)_3(H_2O)_3^{++}$ complex.

3. Write the equilibrium reaction and the equilibrium expression corresponding to the fourth overall formation constant for the $Ni(NH_3)_4(H_2O)_2^{++}$ complex.

4. Write the equilibrium reaction and the equilibrium expression corresponding to the second stepwise formation constant for the $Ag(S_2O_3)_2^\equiv$ complex.

5. Write the equilibrium reaction and the equilibrium expression corresponding to the third stepwise formation constant for the $Cu(CN)_3^=$ complex.

6. Estimate from Figure 4-1 the mole fractions of the various zinc-ammine complexes, and the mole fraction of the $Zn(H_2O)_4^{++}$ ion, in a solution containing a free ammonia concentration of $0.00316\ M$. If the total concentration of zinc complexes in such a solution is $0.00100\ M$, calculate the concentration of each complex.

7. Calculate the molar concentration of each of the species, $Cu(NH_3)^{++}$, $Cu(NH_3)_2^{++}$, $Cu(NH_3)_3^{++}$, and $Cu(NH_3)_4^{++}$, in a solution in which the equilibrium concentrations of ammonia and Cu^{++} ion are 2.50×10^{-3} and $1.50 \times 10^{-4}\ M$, respectively.

8. What is the free ammonia concentration in a nickel-ammine complex system, if the concentration of $Ni(NH_3)_4^{++}$ is exactly ten times the $Ni(NH_3)_3^{++}$ concentration?

9. Calculate the equilibrium concentrations of $Zn(NH_3)_2^{++}$ and $Zn(NH_3)_3^{++}$ in a solution prepared by mixing 10.0 ml of $0.00200\ M$ zinc nitrate solution with 40.0 ml of $0.200\ M$ ammonia.

10. Calculate the concentration of each of the three silver(I)

species in a solution initially containing 0.400 M ammonia and a total silver(I) concentration of 0.00300 M.

11. Calculate the concentration of each of the seven nickel(II) species in a solution initially containing 0.750 M ammonia and a total nickel(II) concentration of 0.00250 M.

12. Calculate the equilibrium concentrations of the three species, Ag^+, CN^-, and $Ag(CN)_2^-$, resulting from the mixing of 35.0 ml of 0.250 M sodium cyanide solution with 30.0 ml of 0.100 M silver nitrate solution.

13. Calculate the equilibrium concentrations of the three species, Ag^+, CN^-, and $Ag(CN)_2^-$, resulting from the mixing of 50.0 ml of 0.200 M sodium cyanide solution with 70.0 ml of 0.100 M silver nitrate solution.

14. Which has a greater concentration of free silver ion, a solution saturated with AgCl or a solution saturated with $Ag[Ag(CN)_2]$? Assume no source of any ion other than dissolution of the solid phase.

15. Account qualitatively for the high stability of EDTA complexes as compared to other types of complexes with the same cations.

16. In view of the fact that ethylenediaminetetraacetate forms stable complexes with so many cations, discuss how reactions between EDTA and metal ions can be made quite selective.

17. Prepare a graphical presentation of the data listed in Table 4-1. The graph should consist of a plot of mole fraction versus pH for each of the five EDTA species; plot all data on the same graph.

18. Calculate the concentration of $H_2Y^=$ in an EDTA solution of pH 7.00, if the $HY^≡$ concentration is 0.0100 M.

19. Calculate the pH at which an EDTA solution contains equal concentrations of $HY^≡$ and $Y^≡$ ions. Do not merely interpolate from Table 4-1.

20. Calculate the concentrations of each of the five EDTA species in a 0.0250 M EDTA solution of pH 9.50.

21. A solution was prepared by adding 500 ml of a solution 0.0100 M in ethylenediaminetetraacetic acid (H_4Y) to 500 ml of a solution 0.0200 M in sodium ethylenediaminetetraacetate (Na_4Y) and 0.0150 M in sodium hydroxide. Calculate the pH of the resulting solution and the concentrations of all five EDTA species.

22. What is the molar concentration of uncomplexed magnesium ion in a solution prepared by mixing equal volumes of 0.200 M EDTA and 0.100 M magnesium nitrate solutions, assuming that the pH is 9.00?

23. Calculate the concentration of uncomplexed nickel ion in a solution prepared by mixing equal volumes of 0.150 M EDTA solution and 0.100 M nickel nitrate solution. Assume that the solution is buffered at pH 10.50, but that the buffer constituents do not complex nickel(II).

24. If the solution obtained in problem 23 contained ammonia, would the resulting concentration of uncomplexed nickel ion be less than, equal to, or greater than the value found in that problem? Explain.

25. Suppose that a solution is prepared by mixing 50.0 ml of 0.100 M barium chloride solution and 50.0 ml of 0.200 M EDTA solution, and that the final pH of the mixture is buffered at 10.0.

    (a) Calculate the concentration of uncomplexed barium ion.

    (b) Will a precipitate of barium sulfate form if 0.100 millimole of sodium sulfate is dissolved in the solution?

Chapter 5

EQUILIBRIA IN OXIDATION-REDUCTION REACTIONS

Oxidation is the loss of electrons, and **reduction** is the gain of electrons. A substance which is reduced, that is, a substance which causes another chemical species to be oxidized, is an **oxidizing agent** or **oxidant**. Conversely, a substance which causes another species to be reduced, thereby becoming oxidized itself, is a **reducing agent** or **reductant**. Neglecting the formation of chloride complexes of the various metal ion species, consider the relatively simple reaction which occurs when solutions of iron(III) chloride and tin(II) chloride are mixed:

$$2\ Fe^{+++} + Sn^{++} \rightleftharpoons 2\ Fe^{++} + Sn^{++++}$$

In the forward reaction, tin(II) is oxidized and iron(III) is the oxidizing agent. Similarly, iron(III) is reduced and tin(II) is the reducing agent. Oxidation cannot take place without a corresponding reduction, and no substance can be reduced without some other substance simultaneously being oxidized. In this example, there is a direct transfer of electrons between tin(II) and iron(III).

In other situations it is possible for electrons to be transferred from one substance to another through an external connecting wire. Consider, for example, the system depicted in Figure 5-1. One beaker contains a solution of a soluble zinc(II) salt into which is immersed a metallic zinc electrode. A copper(II) solution and a copper metal electrode are placed in the second beaker. Since each beaker contains the oxidized and reduced forms of a single substance, it is called a **half cell**. A **salt bridge,** which connects the two solutions, provides a pathway for the migration of ions (flow of current) from one beaker to the other when an

194

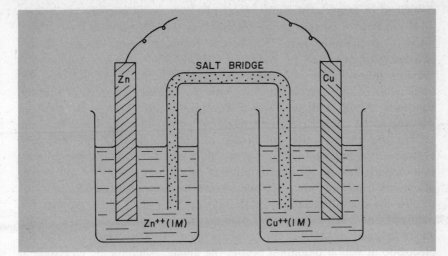

FIGURE 5-1 A simple galvanic cell involving a zinc metal-zinc ion half cell and a cupric ion-copper metal half cell connected by a potassium chloride salt bridge. For this cell the concentration (activity) of each ionic species, Zn^{++} and Cu^{++}, is indicated as unity, although in general any values are possible.

electrical circuit is completed, yet prevents gross mixing of the solutions in the two beakers as well as any direct electron-transfer reaction between one metal electrode and the solution in the opposite beaker. In its simplest form, a salt bridge consists of an inverted U-tube filled with a mixture of potassium chloride solution and agar which form a gel to minimize the leakage of potassium chloride into the two beakers.

If the two metal rods are connected by means of a conducting wire, it can be observed that zinc dissolves according to the reaction

$$Zn \rightleftharpoons Zn^{++} + 2e$$

and that cupric ions are reduced to copper atoms which deposit upon the copper electrode:

$$Cu^{++} + 2e \rightleftharpoons Cu$$

We can represent the net or overall process which occurs as the combination of the two half-cell reactions; that is,

$$Zn + Cu^{++} \rightleftharpoons Zn^{++} + Cu$$

Electrons produced at the zinc electrode, as zinc atoms are oxidized to zinc ions, flow through the external wire to the copper rod, where they are available to combine with the incoming cupric ions to form more copper metal. Although current flowing in the external wire can be described in terms of the movement of electrons, it is more realistic to view the flow of current in the solutions as the migration of ions. It is of interest to mention here that recent research points clearly to the existence of solvated or hydrated electrons in aqueous solution. It remains questionable at present, however, whether free electrons are associated in any important way with the passage of current through solutions. Along with the flow of electrons in the external circuit from the zinc to the copper electrode, negatively charged ions migrate from the copper cell through the salt bridge in the direction of the zinc cell. However, the migration of ions is not all in one direction, for the production of zinc ions and the consumption of cupric ions causes the movement of cations from the zinc electrode toward the copper electrode.

In the overall reaction for the system of Figure 5-1, zinc metal is oxidized and cupric ion is the oxidizing agent. Simultaneously, cupric ion is reduced and zinc is the reducing agent. It is customary to call the electrode at which oxidation occurs the **anode,** whereas the electrode at which the reduction process takes place is the **cathode.** Therefore, the zinc rod is the anode, and the copper rod is the cathode.

Regardless of whether the transfer of electrons in an oxidation-reduction reaction occurs directly or through an external connecting wire, a state of equilibrium can eventually be established. When this condition exists, there is no additional *net* transfer of electrons from one species to another. As with other types of chemical processes, the attainment of equilibrium does not mean that reaction ceases, but rather that the forward and backward reactions continue at equal rates without further change in concentration of any species.

There are two kinds of electrochemical cells, the first of these being called a galvanic cell. A **galvanic cell** may be defined as an electrochemical cell in which the *spontaneous* occurrence of electrode reactions produces electrical energy which can be converted into useful work. Thus, the overall reaction which occurs in the cell of Figure 5-1 is an example of a spontaneous process which, in turn, causes a flow of electrons in an external circuit and makes useful electrical energy available. An **electrolytic cell** is the second type of electrochemical cell. In it, nonspontaneous electrode reactions are forced to proceed when an external voltage is impressed or connected across the two electrodes. In the operation of an electrolytic cell, electrical energy or work must be expended in causing the electrode reactions to occur. In this chapter we will be concerned primarily with galvanic cells, in which chemical reactions occur spontaneously and in which conditions of chemical equilibrium are established, or at least can be established if the spontaneous reaction is permitted to continue long enough. Furthermore, we will restrict our discussion to oxidation-reduction processes occurring in aqueous solutions.

FREE ENERGY AND ELECTROMOTIVE FORCE

In the thermodynamic treatment of chemical equilibrium discussed in Chapter 1, we considered the general chemical reaction

$$a A + b B \rightleftharpoons c C + d D$$

and found that the free-energy change ΔG for such a chemical process is given by

$$\Delta G = \Delta G^\circ + RT \ln \frac{(C)^c (D)^d}{(A)^a (B)^b}$$

where ΔG° is the **standard free-energy change** for the reaction when all the reactants and products are in their standard states and have unit activities. The standard free-energy change is, in turn, related to the equilibrium constant K for the reaction by the equation

$$\Delta G^\circ = -RT \ln K$$

The free-energy change ΔG for any chemical reaction measures the driving force or tendency for reaction. The quantity ΔG also represents the *maximal amount of useful energy* that can be obtained from the process. However, in order for this maximal energy to be actually realized, the chemical process must occur infinitely slowly or with thermodynamic reversibility. A reaction is thermodynamically reversible whenever an infinitesimal force in opposition to the forward reaction can cause the reaction to reverse and proceed in the other direction. If a process occurs rapidly, i.e., at a finite or observable rate, the maximal quantity of useful energy cannot be obtained.

To explore these points further, let us consider the behavior of the system of Figure 5-1. If this cell is discharged infinitely slowly, the current flowing through the external circuit will be infinitesimally small, and the theoretical, maximal amount of useful energy will be obtained (although the *rate* of production of energy would be intolerably slow). However, if we allow the cell to discharge rather rapidly, the quantity of useful energy will be less than before because the flow of a sizable current through the external circuit dissipates some of the energy as heat. No real process occurs infinitely slowly, and so the maximal amount of useful energy, ΔG, can never be obtained. We shall see that a galvanic cell provides a means for studying chemical reactions under conditions which come remarkably close to ideality.

ELECTROMOTIVE FORCE

A quantity which is characteristic of any galvanic cell is E, the electromotive force or emf expressed in volts. The free-energy change for a process which occurs or can be made to occur in a galvanic cell is related to the electromotive force by the equation

$$\Delta G = -nFE$$

where n is the number of faradays of electricity generated by the cell reaction and F is the Faraday constant (96,487 coulombs or 23,060 calories per faraday).

By using a galvanic cell and measuring the electromotive force, we can determine the free-energy change ΔG for a given reaction as well as the equilibrium constant K or the standard free-energy change $\Delta G°$. The unique feature of a galvanic cell is that we can obtain all this information when the reaction virtually does not occur at all, i.e., under conditions very close to thermodynamic reversibility. Let us see how this can be done for the reaction

$$Zn + Cu^{++} \rightleftharpoons Zn^{++} + Cu$$

A galvanic cell in which the desired reaction can occur is shown in Figure 5-1. In setting up a galvanic cell for the measurement of electromotive force, one must specify exactly the concentrations of all ionic and molecular species in solution as well as temperature. If gaseous reactants or products are involved, their partial pressures should be stated. In the cell of Figure 5-1, the concentrations of Zn^{++} and Cu^{++} are both $1 M$. However, the concentration (activity) of each ion could have any value, and the two concentrations need not be the same.

When the zinc and copper electrodes are connected by a conducting wire, there is a flow of electrons from the zinc to the copper electrode. Simultaneously, the zinc electrode dissolves to form zinc ions in the left-hand solution, and cupric ions in the right-hand solution are reduced and plated upon the copper electrode. At the instant the external wire is first connected between the two electrodes, there will be a certain initial value of the electromotive force E. However, the production of zinc ions in the left cell and the consumption of cupric ions in the right cell will change the original concentrations of these ions, thereby diminishing the electromotive force E and the value of ΔG.

It is well known that the concentrations of the ions immediately adjacent to the surfaces of the electrodes affect the driving force for the reaction, so these surface concentrations must be accurately known. The concentrations of the ions away from the electrodes have no effect on the electromotive force. Unfortunately, it is extremely difficult to determine what the surface concentrations of zinc and cupric ions are because they keep changing as current continues to flow through the cell.

At this point, there is a logical question to ask. Why not prevent the flow of current in order to avoid altering the surface concentrations of zinc and cupric ions? Then, we could be confident that the surface concentrations were invariant and equal to the original values of the concentrations, e. g., 1 M. The answer is that this can be done, and, in fact, this is exactly what is done in the measurement of the electromotive force of a galvanic cell.

POTENTIOMETRIC MEASUREMENT OF ELECTROMOTIVE FORCE

A **potentiometer** is an instrument used to determine the electromotive force or emf of a galvanic cell. As a brief introduction to the principles of operation of a potentiometer, let us consider the following simple concepts. Figure 5-2A shows the zinc-copper galvanic cell with an external conducting wire connecting the zinc and copper electrodes. In addition, a current-measuring galvanometer, G, has been inserted into the external circuit.

Suppose that we introduce into the external circuit a source of known emf, as shown in Figure 5-2B, in such a way that the direction of current flowing from it will *oppose* the current flowing from the zinc-copper cell. If the known emf is now varied until the current from the source of known emf (i_{known}) becomes just equal to the current from the zinc-copper cell ($i_{unknown}$), the galvanometer will register a net current of zero. When no net current flows in the circuit, it follows that the emf values of the zinc-copper cell and the known source are identical, and hence the emf of the zinc-copper cell is determined. In practice, an actual potentiometric measurement consists of varying the known emf until the galvanometer indicates zero current.

If the known emf is *less* than that of the zinc-copper cell, the latter will discharge spontaneously as a normal *galvanic* cell according to the reaction

$$Zn + Cu^{++} \rightleftharpoons Zn^{++} + Cu$$

at a rate proportional to the difference in the emf values. On the other hand, if the known emf is *greater* than that of the zinc-copper cell, the latter will behave as an *electrolytic* cell, and the reverse reaction

$$Zn^{++} + Cu \rightleftharpoons Zn + Cu^{++}$$

will occur at a rate governed again by the difference in the emf values. However, at the point of potentiometric balance, where virtually no cur-

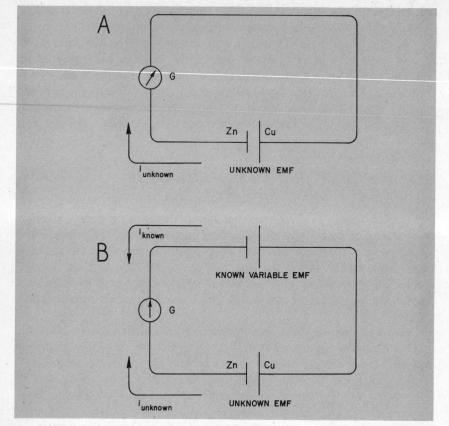

FIGURE 5-2 **Diagram to illustrate the principles of the potentiometric measurement of electromotive force. (See text for discussion.)**

rent flows, the unknown and the known emf values are equal and no net reaction occurs in the zinc-copper cell. Therefore, the major advantages of a potentiometric measurement are that we prevent any electrochemical reaction from occurring in the zinc-copper cell, we avoid disturbing or changing the concentrations of ions at the electrode surfaces, and yet we obtain a highly accurate value for the emf of the zinc-copper cell. It may be added here that with the aid of modern electronic measuring devices, one can easily balance the known and unknown emf values to make the net flow of current no greater than about 10^{-12} ampere (one *pico*ampere). Depending on the direction of current flow, this would correspond, for example, to either an increase or decrease of 5×10^{-18} mole of zinc ions per second in the zinc cell. This result clearly demonstrates how valid the conclusion is that there is no electrochemical reaction occurring in the zinc-copper cell.

The basic design of a simple potentiometer is illustrated in Figure 5-3. First, there must be a source of *known* and *constant* emf, E_{KC}, which

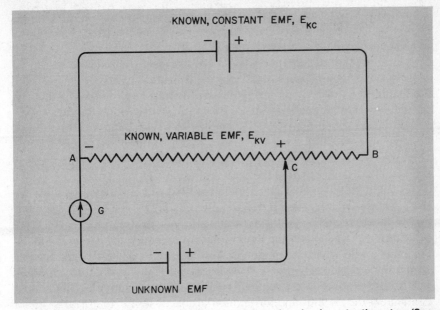

KNOWN, CONSTANT EMF, E_{KC}

KNOWN, VARIABLE EMF, E_{KV}

A

B

C

G

UNKNOWN EMF

FIGURE 5-3 Diagram showing the operation of a simple potentiometer. (See text for discussion.)

could be, for example, an ordinary dry cell or a standard galvanic cell. This known, constant emf is then impressed across the ends of a uniform, precision resistance or slidewire AB. From this arrangement, a *known, variable* emf, E_{KV}, can be obtained. When the position of the sliding contact C coincides with the left end, A, of the slidewire, E_{KV} is zero; when the contact C is moved to the opposite end, B, the variable emf, E_{KV}, is equal to E_{KC}; and when contact C lies between A and B, intermediate values of E_{KV} are obtained. To measure an unknown emf, one simply moves contact C along the slidewire AB until the galvanometer G indicates that potentiometric balance is attained. The value of the unknown emf can be read directly from the final position of contact C.

Notice that the successful potentiometric measurement of an unknown emf requires that the *negative* electrode of the unknown cell be connected to the *negative* side of the known emf so that the known and unknown currents will *oppose* each other as discussed for Figure 5-2B. Although the correct connections can always be established by trial and error, a simple way to decide whether an electrode in a galvanic cell is negative or positive will be described in the section on sign conventions.

SHORTHAND REPRESENTATION OF CELLS

It is both time-consuming and space-consuming to draw a complete diagram of an electrochemical cell—electrodes, salt bridge, solutions, and containers—each time a cell is discussed. As a result, a system for representing cells in a shorthand fashion has been developed. The following set of rules is in widespread use:

1. Conventional chemical symbols are used to indicate the ions, molecules, elements, gases, and electrode materials involved in a cell. Concentrations of ions or molecules are written in parentheses, and the partial pressure of each gaseous species is enclosed in parentheses.

2. A single vertical line | is employed to designate the fact that a boundary between an electrode phase and a solution phase or between two different solution phases exists and that the emf developed across this interface is included in the total emf of the cell.

3. A double vertical line ‖ indicates that the emf developed across the interface between two different solutions is ignored or that it is minimized or eliminated by placing a suitable salt bridge between the two solutions. An emf called the **liquid-junction potential** always originates at the interface between two nonidentical solutions, because charged species —anions and cations—diffuse across this interface at different rates. A salt bridge containing a saturated solution of potassium chloride almost eliminates the liquid-junction potential because of the nearly equal mobilities of potassium and chloride ions.

The following examples will serve to demonstrate the application of these rules:

EXAMPLE 1

The zinc-copper cell depicted in Figure 5-1 may be represented as

$$Zn \mid Zn^{++} \, (1\,M) \parallel Cu^{++} \, (1\,M) \mid Cu$$

This shorthand abbreviation indicates that a zinc electrode in contact with a $1\,M$ solution of zinc ions gives rise to an emf and, similarly, that a $1\,M$ cupric ion solution in contact with a copper electrode produces another emf—the sum of these two emf values being the total emf of the galvanic cell. The double vertical line indicates the presence of a salt bridge and reminds us also that any liquid-junction potential is neglected in considering the overall emf of the cell.

EXAMPLE 2

If, for the zinc-copper cell, we wish to specify $1\,M$ solutions of particular salts, such as $Zn(NO_3)_2$ and $CuSO_4$, and if instead of using a salt bridge we allow the two solutions to contact each other directly through a thin porous membrane (to prevent mixing of the two solutions), the cell would be correctly indicated as

$$Zn \mid Zn(NO_3)_2 \ (1 \ M) \mid CuSO_4 \ (1 \ M) \mid Cu$$

EXAMPLE 3

Suppose that we construct an entirely new galvanic cell. Let one electrode consist of a platinum wire in a mixture of 0.2 M ferric ion and 0.05 M ferrous ion in a 1 M hydrochloric acid medium, and let the other electrode be a second platinum wire immersed in a 2 M hydrochloric acid solution saturated with chlorine gas at a pressure of 0.1 atm. A salt bridge can be used to prevent mixing of the two solutions. The shorthand cell representation would be

$$Pt \mid Fe^{+++} \ (0.2 \ M), Fe^{++} \ (0.05 \ M),$$
$$HCl \ (1 \ M) \parallel HCl \ (2 \ M) \mid Cl_2 \ (0.1 \ atm), Pt$$

This example brings up two other significant points. First, when several soluble species are present in the same solution, no special order of listing these is needed. Second, although electron transfer between chloride ion and chlorine molecules occurs with species dissolved in solution, it is customary to indicate gaseous substances as part of the electrode phase along with the electrode material, e.g., platinum metal.

Mention should be made of one additional point; that is, the relative orientation of any cell on paper can be reversed just as the relative position of the actual physical cell can be changed by turning it around on a table top. Thus, the cell described in Example 2 could have been written

$$Cu \mid CuSO_4 \ (1 \ M) \mid Zn(NO_3)_2 \ (1 \ M) \mid Zn$$

However, once a given shorthand cell representation has been set down, certain conventions must be followed subsequently in making thermodynamic and electrochemical predictions on the basis of this representation.

THERMODYNAMIC AND ELECTROCHEMICAL SIGN CONVENTIONS

It was previously stated in this chapter that determination of the electromotive force of a galvanic cell is a powerful means for the evaluation of ΔG, which, in turn, measures the driving force for chemical reaction. We shall now explore some of the relationships between thermodynamics and electrochemistry.

Let us discuss the galvanic cell shown in Figure 5-4. In the left-hand compartment is a platinum electrode dipped into a hydrochloric acid solution of *unit activity* and bathed with hydrogen gas at a pressure of 1 atm. For convenience, the platinum electrode can be sealed into an inverted tube, with an enlarged open bottom to admit the hydrochloric acid solution and with exit ports for the hydrogen gas to escape. Hydrogen gas at 1 atm pressure enters through a side-arm tube. It is important that the hydrogen gas come into intimate contact with the platinum electrode. This requirement can be fulfilled if the platinum electrode is coated prior to its use with a thin layer of finely divided, spongy platinum metal (so-called **platinum black**). A platinum-black electrode is easily prepared if one cathodically polarizes a shiny platinum electrode in a dilute solution of $PtCl_6^=$. With platinum black on the electrode surface, hydrogen gas permeates and virtually dissolves in the spongy platinum, and electron transfer between hydrogen ions and hydrogen molecules (or atoms) is greatly facilitated. This special combination of a platinum-black electrode, hydrochloric acid of unit activity, and hydrogen gas at 1 atm pressure is called the **standard hydrogen electrode** or the **normal hydrogen electrode** (NHE).

In the right-hand compartment is a silver electrode coated with a layer of silver chloride and placed into a hydrochloric acid solution of unit activity. The hydrochloric acid solution must be saturated with respect to silver chloride. Although excess solid AgCl could simply be

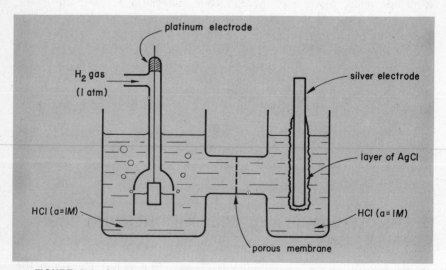

FIGURE 5-4 A galvanic cell consisting of a standard or normal hydrogen electrode (NHE) and a silver-silver chloride electrode.

added to the compartment, the thin coating of silver chloride on the electrode provides an especially convenient source of AgCl. In addition, the layer of silver chloride serves as a source of silver ions in contact with the metallic silver electrode, and so electron transfer between elemental silver and silver ions can occur readily and reversibly.

It is possible, although not necessary, to insert a porous membrane between the two compartments of the cell as a means of preventing direct mixing of the solutions. However, the liquid-junction potential for this cell is virtually zero because the solutions on each side of the membrane are nearly identical in terms of their ionic compositions; the very slight solubility of silver chloride in hydrochloric acid means that both solutions contain essentially hydrochloric acid at unit activity. Cells of this general type, sometimes called *galvanic cells without liquid-junction potentials*, have been used extensively in the precise determination and definition of the pH scale at the National Bureau of Standards.

The word and picture description of this cell can be portrayed by means of the shorthand cell representation, as described earlier in this chapter:

$$\text{Pt, H}_2 \text{ (1 atm)} \mid \text{HCl } (a = 1 \; M), \text{ AgCl(s)} \mid \text{Ag}$$

Once the shorthand cell representation has been written, it is useful to consider the overall electrochemical reaction which will occur when the electrodes are connected by an external conducting wire. To write this cell reaction, we must adopt a definite rule or convention which must *always* be obeyed. This rule may be stated as follows:

Looking at the shorthand cell representation, we combine as *reactants* the reductant (reducing agent) of the left-hand electrode and the oxidant (oxidizing agent) of the right-hand electrode. As *products* we obtain the oxidant of the left-hand electrode and the reductant of the right-hand electrode.

If we now apply this rule, hydrogen gas (reductant of the left-hand electrode) reacts with silver chloride (oxidant of the right-hand electrode) to yield hydrogen ions (oxidant of the left-hand electrode) and elemental silver (reductant of the right-hand electrode). Chloride ions, freed by the reduction of silver chloride, are also formed as a reaction product. The cell reaction is

$$\text{H}_2 + 2 \text{ AgCl} \rightleftharpoons 2 \text{ H}^+ + 2 \text{ Ag} + 2 \text{ Cl}^-$$

The value of ΔG, the free-energy change for this process, provides us with information about the tendency for this cell reaction to occur as written. According to thermodynamic conventions, the cell reaction will be spontaneous if ΔG is a negative quantity. However, if ΔG is positive, the reaction is nonspontaneous and, in fact, will proceed in the reverse direction. In the event that ΔG is zero, the system is at equilibrium and no net cell reaction will occur, the rates of the forward and backward reactions being equal. From the relationship between free-energy change ΔG and electromotive force E,

$$\Delta G = -nFE$$

it can be seen that E is positive for spontaneous processes, negative for nonspontaneous reactions, and zero for systems at equilibrium. Therefore, by measuring the electromotive force for a galvanic cell, we can determine the direction of the electrochemical reaction along with the free-energy change or driving force for that reaction.

The electromotive force for the cell must be measured potentiometrically as described in a previous section of this chapter. When this measurement is performed, it is found that the emf of the cell has an absolute magnitude of 0.2222 v. In addition, the cell reaction proceeds from left to right as written; this fact can be demonstrated if we connect the electrodes by a conducting wire and examine their behavior. To indicate that the cell reaction is a spontaneous process and that the driving force for this reaction is 0.2222 v, we can write

$$H_2 + 2\,AgCl \rightleftharpoons 2\,H^+ + 2\,Ag + 2\,Cl^-; \quad E = +0.2222\,v$$

Let us now focus our attention more closely on the galvanic cell itself. In the potentiometric measurement of a cell emf, no electrochemical reaction occurs because no net current flows through the cell. However, we do measure the tendency for the reaction to proceed when the electrodes are connected by an external wire. Since the cell reaction should proceed spontaneously ($E = +0.2222$ v) from left to right, we can conclude that there is a tendency for hydrogen gas to be oxidized to hydrogen ions and a tendency for silver chloride to be reduced to silver metal. Therefore, the hydrogen gas-hydrogen ion electrode is the *anode*, and the silver-silver chloride electrode functions as the *cathode*. Likewise, there is a tendency for an excess of electrons to accumulate at the left-hand electrode and for a deficiency of electrons to exist at the right-hand electrode. Note that we can speak only of a tendency because, under the conditions of an ideal potentiometric emf measurement, there is no flow of electrons. An excess of electrons at the hydrogen gas-hydrogen ion electrode causes the anode to be the *negative* electrode of the galvanic cell, and a deficiency of electrons at the silver-silver chloride electrode means that the cathode is the *positive* electrode. The signs of the electrodes are often indicated on the shorthand cell representation as follows:

$$-Pt, H_2\ (1\ atm)\ |\ HCl\ (a = 1\ M),\ AgCl(s)\ |\ Ag+$$

We come now to one of the most important and fundamental conclusions of this discussion:

There is no direct relationship between the sign of the electromotive force (emf) for a cell reaction and the signs (+ or −) of the electrodes of the cell. The sign of an emf is a *thermodynamic* concept; it may be positive (+) when a process occurs spontaneously or it may be negative (−) when a process is nonspontaneous. On the other hand, the sign of any particular electrode of a galvanic cell is an *electrochemical* concept and is completely invariant.

To illustrate the significance of these statements, the following galvanic cell may be considered:

$$Ag \mid AgCl(s), HCl \ (a = 1 \ M) \mid H_2(1 \ atm), Pt$$

Notice that this is the same galvanic cell we have been discussing, except for the fact that we are viewing it from the other side of the bench top. According to our rule for writing the electrochemical reaction corresponding to a shorthand cell representation, we combine the reductant of the left-hand electrode and the oxidant of the right-hand electrode to yield the oxidant of the left-hand electrode and the reductant of the right-hand electrode:

$$2 \ H^+ + 2 \ Ag + 2 \ Cl^- \rightleftharpoons H_2 + 2 \ AgCl$$

This reaction is exactly the reverse of the process we considered earlier, and so it follows that the present reaction is nonspontaneous and that the sign of the electromotive force is negative (−). However, since the galvanic cell is the same as before, the absolute magnitude of the emf is identical to the previous value. To indicate these facts, we may write

$$2 \ H^+ + 2 \ Ag + 2 \ Cl^- \rightleftharpoons H_2 + 2 \ AgCl; \quad E = -0.2222 \ v$$

In *thermodynamics,* whenever we reverse the direction of a process, the magnitude of the emf remains the same, whereas the sign of the emf is changed to denote whether the process is spontaneous or nonspontaneous. This rule carries over to all kinds of thermodynamic calculations, such as those involving energies of chemical bonds, heats of formation, and heats of combustion.

The sign of the electromotive force ($E = -0.2222 \ v$) reveals that the reaction is nonspontaneous as written, *that it actually would proceed from right to left if the electrodes were short-circuited.* There is a tendency for hydrogen gas to be oxidized to hydrogen ions and for silver chloride to be reduced to silver metal. Thus, the *electrochemical* conclusions made previously about the galvanic cell,

$$-Pt, H_2 \ (1 \ atm) \mid HCl \ (a = 1 \ M), AgCl(s) \mid Ag+$$

are completely valid for the cell

$$+\text{Ag} \mid \text{AgCl(s)}, \text{HCl} \ (a = 1 \ M) \mid \text{H}_2 \ (1 \ \text{atm}), \text{Pt}-$$

The hydrogen gas-hydrogen ion electrode is the *anode* and the *negative* electrode, whereas the silver-silver chloride electrode is the *cathode* and the *positive* electrode.

There is a useful correlation between the sign of the emf of the cell reaction and the sign of the right-hand electrode of the shorthand cell representation — *these signs are identical when the reaction corresponding to a shorthand representation is written in accord with the rule stated earlier.*

STANDARD POTENTIALS AND HALF-REACTIONS

It is convenient and customary to consider every overall cell reaction as being composed of two separate half-reactions. A **half-reaction** is a balanced chemical equation showing the transfer of electrons between two different oxidation states of the same element. We have already written half-reactions in our discussion of the zinc-copper cell. Each half-reaction must represent as accurately as possible one of the two individual electrode processes which occur in a galvanic cell. As a familiar example, for the cell

$$-\text{Pt}, \text{H}_2 \ (1 \ \text{atm}) \mid \text{HCl} \ (a = 1 \ M), \text{AgCl(s)} \mid \text{Ag}+$$

the overall cell reaction is

$$\text{H}_2 + 2 \ \text{AgCl} \rightleftharpoons 2 \ \text{H}^+ + 2 \ \text{Ag} + 2 \ \text{Cl}^-$$

and the two half-reactions are

$$\text{H}_2 \rightleftharpoons 2 \ \text{H}^+ + 2 \ \text{e}$$

and

$$2 \ \text{AgCl} + 2 \ \text{e} \rightleftharpoons 2 \ \text{Ag} + 2 \ \text{Cl}^-$$

Notice that each half-reaction contains the same number of electrons, so when these half-reactions are added together the electrons cancel and the overall cell reaction is obtained. It is important to recognize that the overall cell reaction could have been correctly written as

$$\tfrac{1}{2} \ \text{H}_2 + \text{AgCl} \rightleftharpoons \text{H}^+ + \text{Ag} + \text{Cl}^-$$

and the half-reactions as

$$\tfrac{1}{2} \ \text{H}_2 \rightleftharpoons \text{H}^+ + \text{e}$$

and

$$AgCl + e \rightleftharpoons Ag + Cl^-$$

The electromotive force for an overall reaction or for an individual half-reaction is *independent* of how much reaction occurs. For example, the emf for the reaction

$$H_2 + 2\,AgCl \rightleftharpoons 2\,H^+ + 2\,Ag + 2\,Cl^-$$

has exactly the same sign and magnitude as that for the process

$$\tfrac{1}{2}\,H_2 + AgCl \rightleftharpoons H^+ + Ag + Cl^-$$

in spite of the fact that the former reaction involves twice as many units of the reactant and product species as the latter. In other words, electromotive force or emf does not depend on the quantity of reaction— electromotive force is a measure of reaction intensity. This fact becomes apparent when we realize that a common 1.5 v dry cell has the same emf regardless of its physical size. Clearly, a large dry cell can supply more electrical energy than a small cell, simply because it contains more chemical ingredients, but the emf values are identical.

DEFINITION AND DETERMINATION OF STANDARD POTENTIALS

It is logical to expect that the electromotive force for the overall cell reaction

$$H_2 + 2\,AgCl \rightleftharpoons 2\,H^+ + 2\,Ag + 2\,Cl^-$$

or

$$\tfrac{1}{2}\,H_2 + AgCl \rightleftharpoons H^+ + Ag + Cl^-$$

can be regarded as the sum of two emf values, one being associated with the half-reaction occurring at each electrode of the cell. Unfortunately, it is theoretically impossible either to measure or to calculate the *absolute* value for the emf of any single half-reaction because the activity of a single ionic species, such as hydrogen ion or chloride ion, can never be known exactly. In order to make further progress, it is necessary to define arbitrarily the value for the electromotive force of some half-reaction chosen as a reference; then, the emf values for all other half-reactions can be quoted *relative* to this standard.

The hydrogen electrode has been adopted as the standard. This electrode involves the hydrogen ion-hydrogen gas half-reaction with hydrogen ion and hydrogen gas in their standard states of unit activity and

1 atm pressure, respectively. Under these specific conditions, the electro-motive force for this half-reaction is assigned the value of *zero* at all temperatures and is called the *standard potential, E°, for the hydrogen ion-hydrogen gas couple.*

$$2\,H^+ + 2\,e \rightleftharpoons H_2; \quad E° = 0.0000\ v$$

The standard potential for any other half-reaction *relative to the standard hydrogen electrode* can be determined if a suitable galvanic cell is constructed in which one electrode is the standard hydrogen electrode and the second electrode involves the unknown half-reaction.

Let us use this approach to determine the standard potential for the silver chloride-silver metal half-reaction. The galvanic cell to be used for this measurement is the same one discussed on the preceding several pages:

$$-Pt,\ H_2\ (1\ atm)\ |\ HCl\ (a = 1\ M),\ AgCl(s)\ |\ Ag+$$

Notice that the hydrogen ion-hydrogen gas electrode actually is the standard hydrogen electrode because all species are present in their standard states. In addition, the substances which comprise the silver chloride-silver metal electrode are in their standard states. Chloride ion is present at unit activity, and silver chloride and silver metal are in their standard states as solids. Although $E°$ for the standard hydrogen electrode is *defined* to be independent of temperature, standard potentials for all other half-reactions do vary with temperature. By convention, standard potentials are always determined at 25°C. The conditions which are necessary for the successful measurement of a standard potential are included in the basic definition of this quantity:

The *standard potential* for any redox couple is the emf or potential **(sign and magnitude) of an electrode consisting of that redox couple under standard-state conditions measured in a galvanic cell against the standard hydrogen electrode at 25°C.**

Since the galvanic cell just described fulfills all requirements of the definition of standard potential, we can anticipate that the potentiometric measurement of the emf of this cell will provide us with information about $E°$ for the silver chloride-silver metal electrode.

Let us carefully examine the results of this emf measurement in the light of the previous discussion of thermodynamic and electrochemical sign conventions. First, we discover that the magnitude of the emf of the galvanic cell is 0.2222 v. Second, we find that the silver chloride-silver metal electrode is always the positive electrode regardless of the bench-top orientation of the cell. Therefore, we can conclude correctly that *the standard potential, E°, of the silver chloride-silver metal electrode is +0.2222 v* (relative to the standard hydrogen electrode).

The standard potential for any other electrode can be determined in an analogous manner if one constructs a galvanic cell which consists of the standard hydrogen electrode and an electrode involving the unknown half-reaction under standard-state conditions. Although the hydrogen electrode is the universal standard, it is seldom used in practice because it is cumbersome as well as hazardous. Instead of the hydrogen electrode, secondary standard electrodes (whose standard potentials have been previously measured against the hydrogen electrode) are employed. It is a very simple matter to relate the potential of an unknown electrode, measured against a secondary standard electrode, to the standard hydrogen electrode itself. The saturated calomel electrode and the silver chloride-silver metal electrode are two especially good secondary standards because they are easy to prepare and handle and because they are exceptionally stable and reproducible.

TABLE OF STANDARD POTENTIALS

Table 5-1 presents a selected list of standard potentials along with the half-reaction to which each pertains. It should be noted that all the half-reactions are written as *reductions*. This practice follows the recommendation set down by the International Union of Pure and Applied Chemistry (IUPAC) in 1953. The rationale of such a convention may be explained as follows:

1. Although only half-reactions appear in the table, standard potentials are always derived from a galvanic cell which consists of a standard hydrogen electrode and an electrode involving the desired half-reaction under standard-state conditions.

2. Each half-reaction in a table of standard potentials automatically implies an overall cell reaction in which the half-reaction of interest (written as a reduction) is combined with the *hydrogen gas-hydrogen ion* half-reaction,

$$\tfrac{1}{2} H_2 \rightleftharpoons H^+ + e$$

or its equivalent. For example, the half-reaction

$$AgCl + e \rightleftharpoons Ag + Cl^-$$

should be thought of as the overall reaction

$$\tfrac{1}{2} H_2 + AgCl \rightleftharpoons H^+ + Ag + Cl^-$$

Similarly, the entry

$$Zn^{++} + 2\,e \rightleftharpoons Zn$$

TABLE 5-1 STANDARD AND FORMAL POTENTIALS

$E°$	Half-reaction
2.87	$F_2 + 2\,e = 2\,F^-$
2.07	$O_3 + 2\,H^+ + 2\,e = O_2 + H_2O$
2.01	$S_2O_8^= + 2\,e = 2\,SO_4^=$
1.927	$Ag^{++} + e = Ag^+ \;(4\,F\,HNO_3)$
1.842	$Co^{+++} + e = Co^{++}$
1.77	$H_2O_2 + 2\,H^+ + 2\,e = 2\,H_2O$
1.70	$Ce^{++++} + e = Ce^{+++} \;(1\,F\,HClO_4)$
1.695	$MnO_4^- + 4\,H^+ + 3\,e = MnO_2 + 2\,H_2O$
1.685	$PbO_2 + SO_4^= + 4\,H^+ + 2\,e = PbSO_4 + 2\,H_2O$
1.68	$NiO_2 + 4\,H^+ + 2\,e = Ni^{++} + 2\,H_2O$
1.61	$Ce^{+++} + e = Ce^{+++} \;(1\,F\,HNO_3)$
1.52	$2\,BrO_3^- + 12\,H^+ + 10\,e = Br_2 + 6\,H_2O$
1.51	$MnO_4^- + 8\,H^+ + 5\,e = Mn^{++} + 4\,H_2O$
1.50	$Au^{+++} + 3\,e = Au$
1.47	$2\,ClO_3^- + 12\,H^+ + 10\,e = Cl_2 + 6\,H_2O$
1.455	$PbO_2 + 4\,H^+ + 2\,e = Pb^{++} + 2\,H_2O$
1.44	$Ce^{++++} + e = Ce^{+++} \;(1\,F\,H_2SO_4)$
1.41	$Au^{+++} + 2\,e = Au^+$
1.3595	$Cl_2 + 2\,e = 2\,Cl^-$
1.33	$Cr_2O_7^= + 14\,H^+ + 6\,e = 2\,Cr^{+++} + 7\,H_2O$
1.288	$PdCl_6^= + 2\,e = PdCl_4^= + 2\,Cl^-$
1.25	$Tl^{+++} + 2\,e = Tl^+$
1.23	$MnO_2 + 4\,H^+ + 2\,e = Mn^{++} + 2\,H_2O$
1.229	$O_2 + 4\,H^+ + 4\,e = 2\,H_2O$
1.20	$2\,IO_3^- + 12\,H^+ + 10\,e = I_2 + 6\,H_2O$
1.15	$ClO_3^- + 2\,H^+ + e = ClO_2 + H_2O$
1.15	$NpO_2^{++} + e = NpO_2^+$
1.15	$PuO_2^+ + 4\,H^+ + e = Pu^{++++} + 2\,H_2O$
1.15	$SeO_4^= + 4\,H^+ + 2\,e = H_2SeO_3 + H_2O$
1.087	$Br_2(aq) + 2\,e = 2\,Br^-$
1.07	$NO_2 + H^+ + e = HNO_2$
1.067	$PuO_2^{++} + 4\,H^+ + 2\,e = Pu^{++++} + 2\,H_2O$
1.065	$Br_2(l) + 2\,e = 2\,Br^-$
1.05	$Br_3^- + 2\,e = 3\,Br^-$
1.03	$NO_2 + 2\,H^+ + 2\,e = NO + H_2O$
1.00	$HNO_2 + H^+ + e = NO + H_2O$
1.000	$VO_2^+ + 2\,H^+ + e = VO^{++} + H_2O$
0.987	$Pd^{++} + 2\,e = Pd$
0.97	$Pu^{++++} + e = Pu^{+++}$
0.96	$NO_3^- + 4\,H^+ + 3\,e = NO + 2\,H_2O$
0.94	$NO_3^- + 3\,H^+ + 2\,e = HNO_2 + H_2O$
0.93	$PuO_2^{++} + e = PuO_2^+$
0.920	$2\,Hg^{++} + 2\,e = Hg_2^{++}$
0.88	$H_2O_2 + 2\,e = 2\,OH^-$
0.86	$Cu^{++} + I^- + e = CuI$
0.854	$Hg^{++} + 2\,e = Hg$
0.85	$OsO_4 + 8\,H^+ + 8\,e = Os + 4\,H_2O$
0.80	$NO_3^- + 2\,H^+ + e = NO_2 + H_2O$
0.7995	$Ag^+ + e = Ag$
0.789	$Hg_2^{++} + 2\,e = 2\,Hg$
0.771	$Fe^{+++} + e = Fe^{++}$
0.75	$NpO_2^+ + 4\,H^+ + e = Np^{++++} + 2\,H_2O$
0.740	$H_2SeO_3 + 4\,H^+ + 4\,e = Se + 3\,H_2O$
0.71	$Fe(CN)_6^= + e = Fe(CN)_6^\equiv \;(1\,F\,HCl\ or\ HClO_4)$
0.70	$Fe^{+++} + e = Fe^{++} \;(1\,F\,HCl)$
0.6994	$C_6H_4O_2 + 2\,H^+ + 2\,e = C_6H_4(OH)_2$ (quinhydrone electrode)

TABLE 5-1 STANDARD AND FORMAL POTENTIALS *(Continued)*

$E°$	Half-reaction
0.682	$O_2 + 2 H^+ + 2 e = H_2O_2$
0.68	$Fe^{+++} + e = Fe^{++} (1\ F\ H_2SO_4)$
0.68	$PtCl_6^= + 2 e = PtCl_4^= + 2 Cl^-$
0.62	$UO_2^+ + 4 H^+ + e = U^{++++} + 2 H_2O$
0.6197	$I_2(aq) + 2 e = 2 I^-$
0.6151	$Hg_2SO_4 + 2 e = 2 Hg + SO_4^=$
0.61	$Fe^{+++} + e = Fe^{++} (0.5\ F\ H_3PO_4 \text{-} 1\ F\ H_2SO_4)$
0.581	$Sb_2O_5 + 6 H^+ + 4 e = 2 SbO^+ + 3 H_2O$
0.564	$MnO_4^- + e = MnO_4^=$
0.559	$H_3AsO_4 + 2 H^+ + 2 e = HAsO_2 + 2 H_2O$
0.5355	$I_3^- + 2 e = 3 I^-$
0.5345	$I_2(s) + 2 e = 2 I^-$
0.53	$Mo^{+6} + e = Mo^{+5} (2\ F\ HCl)$
0.48	$HgCl_4^= + 2 e = Hg + 4 Cl^-$
0.361	$VO^{++} + 2 H^+ + e = V^{+++} + H_2O$
0.36	$Fe(CN)_6^= + e = Fe(CN)_6^{\equiv}$
0.337	$Cu^{++} + 2 e = Cu$
0.334	$Hg_2Cl_2(s) + 2 e = 2 Hg + 2 Cl^- (0.1\ F\ KCl)$
0.334	$UO_2^{++} + 4 H^+ + 2 e = U^{++++} + 2 H_2O$
0.280	$Hg_2Cl_2(s) + 2 e = 2 Hg + 2 Cl^- (1\ F\ KCl)$
0.26	$W^{+6} + e = W^{+5} (12\ F\ HCl)$
0.2415	$Hg_2Cl_2(s) + 2 K^+ + 2 e = 2 Hg + 2 KCl(s)$ (saturated calomel electrode)
0.2222	$AgCl + e = Ag + Cl^-$
0.17	$SO_4^= + 4 H^+ + 2 e = H_2SO_3 + H_2O$
0.16	$BiCl_4^- + 3 e = Bi + 4 Cl^-$
0.154	$Sn^{++++} + 2 e = Sn^{++}$
0.153	$Cu^{++} + e = Cu^+$
0.147	$Np^{++++} + e = Np^{+++}$
0.141	$S + 2 H^+ + 2 e = H_2S$
0.14	$SnCl_6^= + 2 e = SnCl_4^= + 2 Cl^- (1\ F\ HCl)$
0.10	$TiO^{++} + 2 H^+ + e = Ti^{+++} + H_2O$
0.08	$S_4O_6^= + 2 e = 2 S_2O_3^=$
0.073	$AgBr + e = Ag + Br^-$
0.05	$UO_2^{++} + e = UO_2^+$
0.0000	$2 H^+ + 2 e = H_2$
−0.126	$Pb^{++} + 2 e = Pb$
−0.136	$Sn^{++} + 2 e = Sn$
−0.151	$AgI + e = Ag + I^-$
−0.23	$N_2 + 5 H^+ + 4 e = N_2H_5^+$
−0.24	$Ni^{++} + 2 e = Ni$
−0.255	$V^{+++} + e = V^{++}$
−0.277	$Co^{++} + 2 e = Co$
−0.3363	$Tl^+ + e = Tl$
−0.3563	$PbSO_4 + 2 e = Pb + SO_4^=$
−0.37	$Ti^{+++} + e = Ti^{++}$
−0.403	$Cd^{++} + 2 e = Cd$
−0.41	$Cr^{+++} + e = Cr^{++}$
−0.440	$Fe^{++} + 2 e = Fe$
−0.49	$2 CO_2 + 2 H^+ + 2 e = H_2C_2O_4$
−0.61	$U^{++++} + e = U^{+++}$
−0.763	$Zn^{++} + 2 e = Zn$
−0.828	$2 H_2O + 2 e = H_2 + 2 OH^-$
−0.91	$Cr^{++} + 2 e = Cr$
−0.93	$Sn(OH)_6^= + 2 e = HSnO_2^- + H_2O + 3 OH^-$
−1.04	$Zn(NH_3)_4^{++} + 2 e = Zn + 4 NH_3$

Table continues on following page.

TABLE 5-1 STANDARD AND FORMAL POTENTIALS *(Continued)*

$E°$	Half-reaction
−1.09	$Cd(CN)_4^= + 2 e = Cd + 4 CN^-$
−1.18	$Mn^{++} + 2 e = Mn$
−1.18	$V^{++} + 2 e = V$
−1.66	$Al^{+++} + 3 e = Al$
−1.85	$Be^{++} + 2 e = Be$
−2.35	$Al(OH)_4^- + 3 e = Al + 4 OH^-$
−2.37	$Mg^{++} + 2 e = Mg$
−2.714	$Na^+ + e = Na$
−2.87	$Ca^{++} + 2 e = Ca$
−2.89	$Sr^{++} + 2 e = Sr$
−2.90	$Ba^{++} + 2 e = Ba$
−2.92	$Cs^+ + e = Cs$
−2.925	$K^+ + e = K$
−2.925	$Rb^+ + e = Rb$
−3.045	$Li^+ + e = Li$

in the table may be considered as

$$H_2 + Zn^{++} \rightleftharpoons 2 H^+ + Zn$$

3. In turn, the first of these overall reactions occurs in a galvanic cell whose shorthand representation is

$$-Pt, H_2 (1 \text{ atm}) \mid HCl (a = 1 M), AgCl(s) \mid Ag+$$

and the second reaction occurs in the galvanic cell

$$+Pt, H_2 (1 \text{ atm}) \mid H^+ (a = 1 M) \parallel Zn^{++} (a = 1 M) \mid Zn-$$

4. As stated previously, a positive electromotive force or emf for any chemical process (such as a cell reaction or a half-reaction) indicates that this process is a spontaneous one, whereas a negative emf denotes a nonspontaneous process. The electromotive force for the first galvanic cell has an absolute magnitude of 0.2222 v. Furthermore, the cell reaction

$$\tfrac{1}{2} H_2 + AgCl \rightleftharpoons H^+ + Ag + Cl^-$$

is a *spontaneous* process, and so we can write

$$\tfrac{1}{2} H_2 + AgCl \rightleftharpoons H^+ + Ag + Cl^-; \quad E = +0.2222 \text{ v}$$

On the other hand, the emf for the second galvanic cell has an absolute magnitude of 0.763 v. However, the fact that the process

$$H_2 + Zn^{++} \rightleftharpoons 2 H^+ + Zn$$

is *nonspontaneous* can be indicated by the thermodynamic statement

$$H_2 + Zn^{++} \rightleftharpoons 2\,H^+ + Zn; \quad E = -0.763\ v$$

5. Notice that the standard potential for the silver chloride-silver metal electrode is $+0.2222$ v and that the standard potential for the zinc ion-zinc metal electrode is -0.763 v. When any half-reaction is written as a reduction (either by itself or combined in an overall reaction with the hydrogen gas-hydrogen ion half-reaction) and when all species involved are present in their standard states, the emf of this half-reaction (or the overall reaction, since the emf for the standard hydrogen electrode is zero) is identical in *sign* and *magnitude* to the standard potential for the half-reaction.

Standard-potential data are utilized for many types of thermodynamic calculations. In cases where reduction processes are involved, one may employ the data exactly as they appear in the table of standard potentials. Thus, for the reduction of dichromate to chromic ion, we obtain from the table

$$Cr_2O_7^= + 14\,H^+ + 6\,e \rightleftharpoons 2\,Cr^{+++} + 7\,H_2O; \quad E° = +1.33\ v$$

The positive sign for the emf indicates that, relative to the hydrogen ion-hydrogen gas half-reaction, the reduction is spontaneous. However, if we should desire to consider the oxidation of chromic ion to dichromate, both the direction of the half-reaction and the sign of the emf must be reversed; that is,

$$2\,Cr^{+++} + 7\,H_2O \rightleftharpoons Cr_2O_7^= + 14\,H^+ + 6\,e; \quad E° = -1.33\ v$$

Because emf is a thermodynamic quantity which depends on the direction of a reaction, we shall use subscripts to indicate the direction of the half-reaction to which each emf corresponds whenever we wish to write the emf value separately from the half-reaction. Thus, $E°_{Cr_2O_7^=,\,Cr^{+++}}$ or, more generally, $E_{Cr_2O_7^=,\,Cr^{+++}}$ written by itself in some expression (such as the Nernst equation) would denote the electromotive force for the half-reaction

$$Cr_2O_7^= + 14\,H^+ + 6\,e \rightleftharpoons 2\,Cr^{+++} + 7\,H_2O$$

$E_{Zn,\,Zn^{++}}$ would represent the emf for the half-reaction

$$Zn \rightleftharpoons Zn^{++} + 2\,e$$

and $E_{I_3^-,\,I^-}$ would stand for the emf of the half-reaction

$$I_3^- + 2\,e \rightleftharpoons 3\,I^-$$

FORMAL POTENTIALS

The use of standard potentials to make chemical and thermodynamic predictions is frequently unjustified and may even lead to serious error. This situation arises because the nature of solutions is so very complicated. One difficulty stems from the fact that aqueous solutions of analytical interest are usually so concentrated that activity coefficients cannot be reliably calculated. In turn, if activity coefficients are unknown, the activities of ions and molecules involved in half-reactions cannot be determined. Another problem is that the simple ionic and molecular species written in half-reactions do not necessarily represent the true state of affairs in aqueous solution. For example, the entry

$$Fe^{+++} + e \rightleftharpoons Fe^{++}; \quad E° = +0.771 \text{ v}$$

in the table of standard potentials applies to an aqueous solution in which the activities of the species $Fe(H_2O)_6^{+++}$ and $Fe(H_2O)_6^{++}$ are both unity. However, it is virtually impossible to prepare any aqueous solution containing just these species, so the validity of using this standard potential may be questioned. Most cations form complexes with anions present, and some highly charged cations also form polymeric species. In a concentrated hydrochloric acid medium, it is reasonable to expect the species of iron(III) to include $Fe(H_2O)_6^{+++}$, $Fe(H_2O)_5OH^{++}$, $Fe(H_2O)_3Cl_3$, $Fe(H_2O)_2Cl_4^-$, $Fe(H_2O)_4Cl_2^+$, $Fe_2(H_2O)_8(OH)_2^{++++}$, and others, and $Fe(H_2O)_6^{++}$, $Fe(H_2O)_5Cl^+$, and $Fe(H_2O)_4Cl_2$ are likely species of iron(II). Unfortunately, the identities of the various species and the equilibria and equilibrium constants which describe such a system are very difficult to ascertain. The general complexity of the iron(III)-iron(II) system tends to be the rule rather than the exception. Nevertheless, the use of standard potentials to predict chemical reactions is extremely successful.

The use of concentrations in formality and the corresponding use of formal potentials has been suggested as a means to overcome the uncertainties resulting from the variation of activity coefficients, from the formation of complexes, and from other chemical interactions. The **formality** of a solution, or the **formal** concentration of a solute, is expressed in terms of the number of gram formula weights of solute dissolved in 1 liter of solution. It is indicated by the symbol F. Specifying a formal concentration provides definite and useful information about how a solution is originally prepared, but it does not necessarily imply the form in which the solute actually exists after it dissolves. **Molarity** refers specifically to concentrations of actual molecules and ions present in solution at equilibrium and may or may not be synonymous with formality. A **formal potential** is defined as the potential (relative to the standard hydrogen electrode) of an electrode involving the half-reaction of interest in a specified electrolyte solution when the *formal concentrations* of the oxidant and reductant are both unity. In thermodynamic calculations, a formal potential is usually denoted by the symbol $E^{\circ\prime}$. As an example, the formal potential for the iron(III)-iron(II) half-reaction is $+0.70$ v in $1\,F$ hydrochloric acid. This differs significantly from the standard potential of $+0.771$ v for the iron(III)-iron(II) couple. In order to measure the formal potential, we might first prepare a solution by dissolving *1 formula weight* of solid $FeCl_3$ and *1 formula weight* of solid $FeCl_2$ in enough $1\,F$ hydrochloric acid to give *1 liter of solution*. The resulting solution would undoubtedly contain some or all of the various species listed in the preceding paragraph. Although we may not know what individual species of iron(III) and iron(II) are present or what their activities are, there is still 1 formula weight of iron(III)-containing species and 1 formula weight of iron(II)-containing species per liter of the $1\,F$ hydrochloric acid medium. Thus, if we immersed a platinum electrode into a portion of this solution and measured its potential versus the standard hydrogen electrode, the platinum electrode would exhibit a potential of $+0.70$ v relative to the hydrogen electrode.

Values for some formal potentials are included in Table 5-1. The specific electrolyte solutions to which these data pertain, e.g., $2\,F$ hydrochloric acid or $0.1\,F$ potassium chloride, are indicated in parentheses following the half-reactions. When available, a formal potential should be used for thermodynamic calculations if experimental conditions correspond closely to those used in the original measurement of the formal potential. In such a case, a much more reliable result will be obtained with a formal potential than with a standard potential. However, it is not a valid procedure to apply a formal potential for one system to an entirely different chemical situation.

THE NERNST EQUATION

The driving force for a chemical reaction, and thus the electromotive force, depends on the activities (concentrations) of reactants and products. We can derive an equation which relates electromotive force to the activities of the reactants and products by starting with the fundamental expression

$$\Delta G = \Delta G^{\circ} + RT \ln \frac{(C)^c (D)^d}{(A)^a (B)^b}$$

This equation gives the change in free energy ΔG for any general chemical process, such as

$$a A + b B \rightleftharpoons c C + d D$$

in terms of the *standard free-energy change* $\Delta G°$ for the same process and the activities of the reactants and products raised to appropriate powers.

It has already been indicated that the relation between electromotive force and free-energy change is

$$\Delta G = -nFE$$

and we may write the specific equation

$$\Delta G° = -nFE°$$

If we substitute the two latter expressions into the fundamental relation, the result is

$$-nFE = -nFE° + RT \ln \frac{(C)^c(D)^d}{(A)^a(B)^b}$$

If we divide each member of this expression by the term $-nF$, the familiar **Nernst equation** is obtained:

$$E = E° - \frac{RT}{nF} \ln \frac{(C)^c(D)^d}{(A)^a(B)^b}$$

For practical purposes, several simplifications of the Nernst equation are usually made. First, it is customary to employ concentrations rather than activities of reactant and product species. Second, base-ten or decimal logarithms are preferred to natural logarithms. Third, the temperature T is conventionally taken to be 298°K (25°C). If these changes are made, if the value used for R is 1.987 calories mole^{-1} degree^{-1}, and if F is taken to be 23,060 calories per faraday, the Nernst equation becomes

$$E = E° - \frac{0.05915}{n} \log \frac{[C]^c[D]^d}{[A]^a[B]^b}$$

For most calculations the numerical constant 0.05915, valid only for 25°C, is shortened to 0.059. This is the form in which the Nernst equation will be used throughout the remainder of this chapter.

The Nernst equation is strictly a thermodynamic relation in which E is the actual emf for a half-reaction or an overall cell reaction and $E°$ is the emf for the same half-reaction or overall reaction under standard-state conditions. Concentration terms should be expressed in conventional units. Thus, the concentrations of dissolved ionic and molecular species are given in molarities, and pressure in atmospheres is used for gases. The concentration of water molecules is taken to be unity, and concentrations of pure solids are likewise assumed to be unity. One final point should be mentioned. We stated earlier that emf is a thermodynamic quantity whose sign, + or −, is dependent on the direction of reaction. Therefore, the practice of adding subscripts to E and $E°$ in the Nernst equation to indicate the direction of the reaction of interest should be followed. The proper form for writing the Nernst equation will become more evident from the sample problems that follow.

EXAMPLE 4

Write the Nernst equation corresponding to the half-reaction

$$Cu^{++} + 2 e \rightleftharpoons Cu$$

The correct expression is

$$E_{Cu^{++},Cu} = E°_{Cu^{++},Cu} - \frac{0.059}{n} \log \frac{1}{[Cu^{++}]}$$

$$= +0.337 - \frac{0.059}{2} \log \frac{1}{[Cu^{++}]}$$

Several features of this equation should be noted. The arrangement of the subscripts (Cu^{++}, Cu) of E and $E°$ indicates the direction of reaction. The logarithmic term always contains products in the numerator and reactants in the denominator. The value for n of 2 is readily determined by inspection of the half-reaction. The significance of n is that it denotes the number of faradays or equivalents of electricity needed to reduce 1 mole of cupric ions to copper metal.

EXAMPLE 5

Write Nernst equations for each of the following half-reactions:

(1) $$2 H^+ + 2 e \rightleftharpoons H_2$$

$$E_{H^+,H_2} = E°_{H^+,H_2} - \frac{0.059}{n} \log \frac{p_{H_2}}{[H^+]^2} = 0.0000 - \frac{0.059}{2} \log \frac{p_{H_2}}{[H^+]^2}$$

(2) $$Cr_2O_7^= + 14 H^+ + 6 e \rightleftharpoons 2 Cr^{+++} + 7 H_2O$$

$$E_{Cr_2O_7^=,Cr^{+++}} = E^\circ_{Cr_2O_7^=,Cr^{+++}} - \frac{0.059}{n} \log \frac{[Cr^{+++}]^2}{[Cr_2O_7^=][H^+]^{14}}$$

$$= +1.33 - \frac{0.059}{6} \log \frac{[Cr^{+++}]^2}{[Cr_2O_7^=][H^+]^{14}}$$

(3) $$MnO_4^- + 8\,H^+ + 5\,e \rightleftharpoons Mn^{++} + 4\,H_2O$$

$$E_{MnO_4^-,Mn^{++}} = E^\circ_{MnO_4^-,Mn^{++}} - \frac{0.059}{n} \log \frac{[Mn^{++}]}{[MnO_4^-][H^+]^8}$$

$$= +1.51 - \frac{0.059}{5} \log \frac{[Mn^{++}]}{[MnO_4^-][H^+]^8}$$

Since electromotive force is independent of the quantity of chemical reaction, each of the preceding half-reactions could be multiplied or divided by an integer without altering the value of E obtained from the Nernst equation. For example, the dichromate-chromic ion half-reaction could be written as

$$\tfrac{1}{2}\,Cr_2O_7^= + 7\,H^+ + 3\,e \rightleftharpoons Cr^{+++} + 3\tfrac{1}{2}\,H_2O$$

and the corresponding Nernst equation would be

$$E_{Cr_2O_7^=,Cr^{+++}} = E^\circ_{Cr_2O_7^=,Cr^{+++}} - \frac{0.059}{n} \log \frac{[Cr^{+++}]}{[Cr_2O_7^=]^{1/2}[H^+]^7}$$

$$= +1.33 - \frac{0.059}{3} \log \frac{[Cr^{+++}]}{[Cr_2O_7^=]^{1/2}[H^+]^7}$$

which is mathematically identical to that written above.

Sometimes it is necessary or desirable to write a half-reaction as an oxidation rather than a reduction. The reversal of the direction of reaction necessitates an appropriate change in the Nernst equation. If we are interested in calculating E for the half-reaction

$$Mn^{++} + 4\,H_2O \rightleftharpoons MnO_4^- + 8\,H^+ + 5\,e$$

the proper form for the Nernst equation is

$$E_{Mn^{++},MnO_4^-} = E^\circ_{Mn^{++},MnO_4^-} - \frac{0.059}{n} \log \frac{[MnO_4^-][H^+]^8}{[Mn^{++}]}$$

$$= -1.51 - \frac{0.059}{5} \log \frac{[MnO_4^-][H^+]^8}{[Mn^{++}]}$$

Notice that the order of the subscripts for E and $E°$ has been appropriately reversed to show the direction of the half-reaction being considered. Also, the sign of $E°$ has been changed and the concentration terms in the logarithmic part of the equation have been inverted.

APPLICATIONS OF STANDARD POTENTIALS AND THE NERNST EQUATION

This section of the chapter is concerned with specific examples of various types of calculations which make use of standard-potential data and the Nernst equation.

CALCULATION OF THE ELECTROMOTIVE FORCE FOR AN OVERALL CELL REACTION

As pointed out previously, the potentiometric measurement of the emf of a galvanic cell is an ideal means for the determination of the driving force for a chemical process. This is so because the potentiometric method permits us to evaluate the driving force or free-energy change for the reaction under the condition of zero current flow. Thus, no net reaction occurs and the chemical system is undisturbed. However, if we attempt to measure the emf for the reaction while it is actually proceeding toward equilibrium, the value obtained will vary continuously with time because of changes in the concentrations (activities) of reactants and products. It would be extremely difficult to correlate an instantaneous value for the emf with the instantaneous concentrations of the reactant and product species. We shall now see how to calculate the emf for an overall cell reaction.

EXAMPLE 6

Calculate the emf for the overall reaction occurring in the galvanic cell

$$\text{Cu} \mid \text{Cu}^{++} \, (a = 1\,M) \parallel \text{Fe}^{++} \, (a = 1\,M), \text{Fe}^{+++} \, (a = 1\,M) \mid \text{Pt}$$

First, we should write the overall cell reaction according to the rule established earlier.

$$\text{Cu} + 2\,\text{Fe}^{+++} \rightleftharpoons \text{Cu}^{++} + 2\,\text{Fe}^{++}$$

This overall reaction can be viewed in terms of its component half-reactions,

$$Cu \rightleftharpoons Cu^{++} + 2\,e$$

and

$$2\,Fe^{+++} + 2\,e \rightleftharpoons 2\,Fe^{++}$$

Since the activities of all ions in the galvanic cell are unity and the activity of the copper metal electrode is also unity, the value for the emf of each half-reaction may be obtained directly from the table of standard potentials. Thus, we can write

$$E_{Cu,Cu^+} = E^\circ_{Cu,Cu^+} = -0.337\,v$$

and

$$E_{Fe^{+++},Fe^{++}} = E^\circ_{Fe^{+++},Fe^{++}} = +0.771\,v$$

Again, notice that, although we are considering two units of the iron(III)-iron(II) half-reaction, we do *not* multiply $E^\circ_{Fe^{+++},Fe^{++}}$ by a factor of two — emf is an intensity factor and does not depend on the quantity of reaction. In the present example, the emf for the overall cell reaction is just the sum of the emf values for the two separate half-reactions:

$$E_{overall} = E^\circ_{Cu,Cu^+} + E^\circ_{Fe^{+++},Fe^{++}} = -0.337 + 0.771 = +0.434\,v$$

In general, it is not permissible to add two intensity factors together as we have just done. For example, if one mixed a sample of a gas at pressure P_1 with a second gas sample at pressure P_2, the final pressure of the mixture would *not*, in general, be $(P_1 + P_2)$. To be correct, one should add together only so-called extensive variables such as ΔG or ΔG°.

We shall now repeat our calculation of the emf for the overall cell reaction starting with free-energy changes. It is *rigorously* true that the free-energy change for the overall reaction is equal to the sum of the free-energy changes for the two individual half-reactions:

$$\Delta G_{overall} = \Delta G_{Cu,Cu^+} + \Delta G_{Fe^{+++},Fe^{++}}$$

However, since

$$\Delta G = -nFE$$

we can write

$$-nFE_{\text{overall}} = -nFE_{\text{Cu,Cu}^{++}} - nFE_{\text{Fe}^{+++},\text{Fe}^{++}}$$

or

$$-nFE_{\text{overall}} = -nFE^{\circ}_{\text{Cu,Cu}^{++}} - nFE^{\circ}_{\text{Fe}^{+++},\text{Fe}^{++}}$$

Inspection of the two half-reactions, which when added give the overall cell reaction, shows that each involves *two electrons*, since the electrons must cancel to produce the net reaction. In addition, the overall cell reaction must itself involve *two electrons*. Accordingly, the value of n is the same for all three terms of the preceding equation. Dividing each term by the common factor $-nF$, we obtain

$$E_{\text{overall}} = E^{\circ}_{\text{Cu,Cu}^{++}} + E^{\circ}_{\text{Fe}^{+++},\text{Fe}^{++}}$$

which is the identical answer found by simply adding the emf values together at the start. The present situation is unique, however, because of the fact that n has the same value in both the overall cell reaction and the two half-reactions. The conclusion to be drawn from this discussion can be summarized in the form of a useful rule.

When two and only two half-reactions are combined to give an overall reaction with no net electrons appearing in it, the emf for the overall reaction is the algebraic sum of the emf values for the two appropriately written half-reactions. For all other calculations which do not fall into this category, it is absolutely required that the free-energy-change method be followed.

EXAMPLE 7

Calculate the emf for the overall reaction occurring in the galvanic cell

$$\text{Cu} \mid \text{Cu}^{++}(0.01\,M) \parallel \text{Fe}^{++}(0.1\,M),\ \text{Fe}^{+++}(0.02\,M) \mid \text{Pt}$$

The overall cell reaction and the two half-reactions are the same as for the preceding example:

$$\text{Cu} + 2\,\text{Fe}^{+++} \rightleftharpoons \text{Cu}^{++} + 2\,\text{Fe}^{++}$$
$$\text{Cu} \rightleftharpoons \text{Cu}^{++} + 2\,\text{e}$$
$$2\,\text{Fe}^{+++} + 2\,\text{e} \rightleftharpoons 2\,\text{Fe}^{++}$$

In agreement with the preceding rule, the emf for the overall cell reaction is the sum of the emf values for the half-reactions.

$$E_{overall} = E_{Cu,Cu^{++}} + E_{Fe^{+++},Fe^{++}}$$

For the present example, the concentrations of the various ions differ from unity, and so it is necessary to use the Nernst equation to calculate the emf for each half-reaction:

$$E_{Cu,Cu^{++}} = E^{\circ}_{Cu,Cu^{++}} - \frac{0.059}{n} \log [Cu^{++}]$$

$$= -0.337 - \frac{0.059}{2} \log (0.01)$$

$$= -0.337 - \frac{0.059}{2} (-2) = -0.278 \text{ v}$$

$$E_{Fe^{+++},Fe^{++}} = E^{\circ}_{Fe^{+++},Fe^{++}} - \frac{0.059}{n} \log \frac{[Fe^{++}]}{[Fe^{+++}]}$$

$$= +0.771 - \frac{0.059}{1} \log \frac{(0.1)}{(0.02)}$$

$$= +0.771 - 0.059 \log 5$$

$$= +0.771 - 0.059 (0.70) = +0.730 \text{ v}$$

$$E_{overall} = -0.278 + 0.730 = +0.452 \text{ v}$$

EXAMPLE 8

Calculate the emf for the overall reaction occurring in the galvanic cell

$$\text{Pb} \mid \text{PbSO}_4(s), \text{SO}_4^{=} (0.5\,M) \parallel \text{Ag}^+ (0.003\,M) \mid \text{Ag}$$

The overall cell reaction is

$$\text{Pb} + 2\,\text{Ag}^+ + \text{SO}_4^{=} \rightleftharpoons \text{PbSO}_4 + 2\,\text{Ag}$$

and the individual half-reactions are

$$\text{Pb} + \text{SO}_4^{=} \rightleftharpoons \text{PbSO}_4 + 2\,\text{e}$$

and

$$2\,\text{Ag}^+ + 2\,\text{e} \rightleftharpoons 2\,\text{Ag}$$

The electromotive force for the overall reaction is

$$E_{\text{overall}} = E_{\text{Pb},\text{PbSO}_4} + E_{\text{Ag}^+,\text{Ag}}$$

Again, it is necessary to use the Nernst equation in order to evaluate the emf values for the half-reactions:

$$E_{\text{Pb},\text{PbSO}_4} = E^{\circ}_{\text{Pb},\text{PbSO}_4} - \frac{0.059}{n} \log \frac{1}{[\text{SO}_4^=]}$$

$$= +0.356 - \frac{0.059}{2} \log \frac{1}{(0.5)}$$

$$= +0.356 - \frac{0.059}{2} \log 2 = +0.356 - \frac{0.059}{2}\,(0.30)$$

$$= +0.356 - 0.009 = +0.347\,\text{v}$$

$$E_{\text{Ag}^+,\text{Ag}} = E^{\circ}_{\text{Ag}^+,\text{Ag}} - \frac{0.059}{n} \log \frac{1}{[\text{Ag}^+]}$$

$$= +0.800 - \frac{0.059}{1} \log \frac{1}{(0.003)}$$

$$= +0.800 - 0.059 \log (3.33 \times 10^2)$$
$$= +0.800 - 0.059\,(2.52)$$
$$= +0.800 - 0.149 = +0.651\,\text{v}$$

$$E_{\text{overall}} = +0.347 + 0.651 = +0.998\,\text{v}$$

It is not strictly necessary that an overall chemical reaction be related to a galvanic cell in which that reaction will occur. For example, the statement of Example 8 could have been phrased as follows: Calculate the emf for the reaction

$$\text{Pb} + 2\,\text{Ag}^+ + \text{SO}_4^= \rightleftharpoons \text{PbSO}_4 + 2\,\text{Ag}$$

when the initial concentrations of silver ion and sulfate ion are 0.003 and 0.5 M, respectively. The method of solving the problem as well as the numerical result would be identical to that just presented, but the mention of any galvanic cell is completely forgotten. This discussion will be continued as we consider next the evaluation of equilibrium constants from standard-potential data.

CALCULATION OF EQUILIBRIUM CONSTANTS

One of the most widespread and useful applications of emf measurements is the evaluation of equilibrium constants for chemical reactions.

An important relation between the equilibrium constant and the emf for an overall reaction can be derived. The standard free-energy change for a reaction is related to the equilibrium constant by the equation

$$\Delta G° = -RT \ln K$$

In addition, the standard free-energy change and the emf for a reaction under standard-state conditions may be equated through the expression

$$\Delta G° = -nFE°$$

By combining these two equations, we obtain

$$RT \ln K = nFE°$$

or

$$\ln K = \frac{nFE°}{RT}$$

If we convert this relation for use with base-ten logarithms and substitute appropriate values for the various physical constants ($F = 23{,}060$ calories per faraday, $R = 1.987$ calories mole^{-1} degree^{-1}, and $T = 298°K$), the following useful result is obtained:

$$\log K = \frac{nE°}{0.059}$$

This equation is valid only for 25°C or 298°K. It should be noted that $E°$ is the emf for the reaction of interest under standard-state conditions, and that this value can be easily determined by proper combination of the standard-potential data from Table 5-1. Let us apply this equation to the solution of several problems.

EXAMPLE 9

Compute the equilibrium constant for the reaction

$$HAsO_2 + I_3^- + 2\,H_2O \rightleftharpoons H_3AsO_4 + 2\,H^+ + 3\,I^-$$

The equilibrium constant for this reaction may be expressed as

$$K = \frac{[H_3AsO_4][H^+]^2[I^-]^3}{[HAsO_2][I_3^-]}$$

The overall reaction is composed of the two half-reactions

$$HAsO_2 + 2\,H_2O \rightleftharpoons H_3AsO_4 + 2\,H^+ + 2\,e$$

and

$$I_3^- + 2\,e \rightleftharpoons 3\,I^-$$

both of which appear side by side in the table of standard potentials. In accord with previous sample calculations, we may write

$$E^\circ_{overall} = E^\circ_{HAsO_2,H_3AsO_4} + E^\circ_{I_3^-,I^-}$$

From data in Table 5-1, it follows that

$$E^\circ_{overall} = -0.559 + 0.536 = -0.023 \text{ v}$$

If this value is substituted into the expression for log K along with $n = 2$, we find that

$$\log K = \frac{nE^\circ}{0.059} = \frac{(2)(-0.023)}{0.059} = -0.780; \quad K = 0.166$$

EXAMPLE 10

Calculate the solubility-product constant for silver chloride from standard-potential data.

The equilibrium which expresses the solubility of silver chloride is

$$AgCl \rightleftharpoons Ag^+ + Cl^-$$

A search of Table 5-1 shows two half-reactions

$$Ag \rightleftharpoons Ag^+ + e$$

and

$$AgCl + e \rightleftharpoons Ag + Cl^-$$

which may be added together to yield the desired overall reaction. We can also write

$$E^\circ_{\text{overall}} = E^\circ_{\text{Ag,Ag}^+} + E^\circ_{\text{AgCl,Ag}} = -0.7995 + 0.2222 = -0.5773 \text{ v}$$

Substituting this latter value for E°_{overall} into our equation for log K, we obtain

$$\log K = \frac{nE^\circ}{0.059} = \frac{(1)(-0.5773)}{0.059} = -9.78$$

$$K = K_{\text{sp}} = 1.66 \times 10^{-10}$$

Using this approach, we can calculate the equilibrium constants for redox reactions, solubility products, formation or dissociation constants for complex ions, and ionization constants for acids and bases. The major requirement is that we be able to represent the desired reaction as the sum of appropriate half-reactions. If standard-potential data are available, the calculation may be performed as in the preceding two examples. However, if the pertinent standard potentials are unknown, it may be possible to set up a galvanic cell suitable for the experimental determination of the equilibrium constant. The following example will illustrate how this latter method can be accomplished.

EXAMPLE 11

Calculate the dissociation constant for the $\text{Ag}(\text{S}_2\text{O}_3)_2^=$ complex ion, which dissociates according to the equilibrium

$$\text{Ag}(\text{S}_2\text{O}_3)_2^= \rightleftharpoons \text{Ag}^+ + 2\,\text{S}_2\text{O}_3^=$$

if you are given the information that the emf of the following galvanic cell is 0.903 v:

$$-\text{Ag} \mid \text{Ag}(\text{S}_2\text{O}_3)_2^= \ (0.001\ M),\ \text{S}_2\text{O}_3^= \ (2\ M) \parallel \text{Ag}^+ \ (0.05\ M) \mid \text{Ag}+$$

The solution comprising the left-hand electrode could be prepared by dissolving 0.001 mole of silver nitrate and 2.002 moles of sodium thiosulfate in water to give 1 liter of solution. The nearly complete reaction between one Ag^+ ion and two $\text{S}_2\text{O}_3^=$ ions would produce essentially 0.001 M $\text{Ag}(\text{S}_2\text{O}_3)_2^=$ and leave 2.000 M $\text{S}_2\text{O}_3^=$. It should be pointed out that small concentrations of Ag^+ and $AgS_2O_3^-$ are in equilibrium with the $Ag(S_2O_3)_2^=$ complex in the left-hand compartment of the cell. The small concentration of silver ion is important because Ag^+ is involved in the equilibrium which we are studying. However, the presence of the $AgS_2O_3^-$ complex may be neglected because it is not involved directly in the equilibrium of interest. Note that it is unnecessary to specify the concentration of either Ag^+ or $AgS_2O_3^-$ in the left compartment because these are not independently variable but are governed by the stated concentrations of $Ag(S_2O_3)_2^=$ and $S_2O_3^=$.

We can write the half-reaction occurring in the left-hand compartment as

$$Ag + 2\,S_2O_3^= \rightleftharpoons Ag(S_2O_3)_2^= + e$$

and at the right-hand electrode we have

$$Ag^+ + e \rightleftharpoons Ag$$

The overall cell reaction is the sum of these two half-reactions:

$$Ag^+ + 2\,S_2O_3^= \rightleftharpoons Ag(S_2O_3)_2^=$$

The signs of the electrodes in the schematic or shorthand representation of the galvanic cell provide very useful information. These signs are automatically obtained as a consequence of the potentiometric measurement of emf. There is a tendency for electrons to accumulate at the left-hand electrode, which explains why it is the negative electrode. At the right-hand electrode, there is a tendency for a deficit of electrons, and so the right-hand electrode is positive. *These facts are true regardless of how the galvanic cell is oriented on the desk top; the silver-silver thiosulfate complex electrode is always negative and the silver-silver ion electrode is positive.* More important, these facts also indicate that the two half-reactions and the overall reaction written above are spontaneous processes. Therefore, the emf for the overall cell reaction is $+0.903$ v.

The emf for the overall cell reaction is the sum of the emf values for the two separate half-reactions

$$E_{\text{overall}} = E_{Ag,Ag(S_2O_3)_2^=} + E_{Ag^+,Ag}$$

The emf for the silver ion-silver metal half-reaction can be computed from the Nernst equation:

$$E_{Ag^+,Ag} = E^\circ_{Ag^+,Ag} - \frac{0.059}{n} \log \frac{1}{[Ag^+]}$$

$$= +0.800 - \frac{0.059}{1} \log \frac{1}{(0.05)}$$

$$= +0.800 - 0.059 \log 20 = +0.800 - 0.059 (1.30)$$

$$= +0.800 - 0.078 = +0.722 \text{ v}$$

Next, we can calculate the emf for the silver-silver thiosulfate electrode:

$$E_{Ag,Ag(S_2O_3)_2^=} = E_{overall} - E_{Ag^+,Ag} = +0.903 - 0.722 = +0.181 \text{ v}$$

Although $E^\circ_{Ag,Ag(S_2O_3)_2^=}$ is unknown, it can be calculated from the Nernst equation as follows:

$$E_{Ag,Ag(S_2O_3)_2^=} = E^\circ_{Ag,Ag(S_2O_3)_2^=} - \frac{0.059}{n} \log \frac{[Ag(S_2O_3)_2^=]}{[S_2O_3^=]^2}$$

$$E^\circ_{Ag,Ag(S_2O_3)_2^=} = E_{Ag,Ag(S_2O_3)_2^=} + \frac{0.059}{n} \log \frac{[Ag(S_2O_3)_2^=]}{[S_2O_3^=]^2}$$

$$= +0.181 + \frac{0.059}{1} \log \frac{(0.001)}{(2)^2}$$

$$= +0.181 + 0.059 \log (2.5 \times 10^{-4})$$

$$= +0.181 + 0.059 (-3.60) = +0.181 - 0.212$$

$$= -0.031 \text{ v}$$

Even though we have not quite arrived at the dissociation constant for the $Ag(S_2O_3)_2^=$ complex, this problem has already demonstrated how standard potentials are determined from galvanic cells. The standard potential E° for the $Ag(S_2O_3)_2^=$-Ag couple (half-reaction written as a *reduction*) is $+0.031$ v relative to the standard hydrogen electrode.

The calculation of the dissociation constant for the $Ag(S_2O_3)_2^=$ complex can now proceed as shown in Example 10 for the solubility product of silver chloride. The dissociation reaction

$$Ag(S_2O_3)_2^= \rightleftharpoons Ag^+ + 2 S_2O_3^=$$

is a combination of the half-reactions

$$Ag(S_2O_3)_2^{\equiv} + e \rightleftharpoons Ag + 2\,S_2O_3^{\equiv}$$

and

$$Ag \rightleftharpoons Ag^+ + e$$

The emf for the dissociation equilibrium under standard-state conditions can be written as

$$E^\circ_{\text{overall}} = E^\circ_{Ag(S_2O_3)_2^{\equiv},Ag} + E^\circ_{Ag,Ag^+} = +0.031 - 0.800 = -0.769\,\text{v}$$

When this value is substituted into the equation for $\log K$, the result is

$$\log K = \frac{nE^\circ}{0.059} = \frac{(1)(-0.769)}{0.059} = -13.0$$

$$K = K_{\text{diss}} = 1.0 \times 10^{-13}$$

CALCULATION OF THE STANDARD POTENTIAL FOR AN UNKNOWN HALF-REACTION

Another application of standard-potential data is the evaluation of standard potentials for half-reactions which do not appear in Table 5-1. The type of calculation involved differs from any considered previously.

EXAMPLE 12

Calculate the standard potential which pertains to the half-reaction

$$Cu^+ + e \rightleftharpoons Cu$$

The emf for this reduction half-reaction under standard-state conditions is identical in sign and magnitude to the standard potential for the copper(I)-copper metal electrode. However, the standard potential is not to be found in Table 5-1, and so it must be calculated from other information. Two entries which do appear in the table are

$$Cu^+ \rightleftharpoons Cu^{++} + e$$

and

$$Cu^{++} + 2e \rightleftharpoons Cu$$

which, if added together in the manner just written, will yield the desired half-reaction.

The present problem cannot be solved by simple addition of the emf values for the latter two half-reactions because the numbers of electrons involved in the three half-reactions are not identical. The rule stated in our discussion of Example 6 indicates that the method of addition of free-energy changes must be followed here. The fundamental equation

$$\Delta G^{\circ}_{Cu^+,Cu} = \Delta G^{\circ}_{Cu^+,Cu^{++}} + \Delta G^{\circ}_{Cu^{++},Cu}$$

may be expressed in terms of standard free-energy changes because we wish to consider all substances, Cu, Cu^+, and Cu^{++}, in their standard states at unit activity. Each free-energy term can be related to the electromotive force for the appropriate half-reaction. Thus,

$$-nFE^{\circ}_{Cu^+,Cu} = -nFE^{\circ}_{Cu^+,Cu^{++}} - nFE^{\circ}_{Cu^{++},Cu}$$

If we substitute values for n from each half-reaction written above and values for $E^{\circ}_{Cu^+,Cu^{++}}$ and $E^{\circ}_{Cu^{++},Cu}$ from Table 5-1, the equation becomes

$$-1 \, FE^{\circ}_{Cu^+,Cu} = -1 \, F(-0.153) - 2 \, F(+0.337)$$

By dividing each term of this expression by $-F$, we can simplify the relation to

$$E^{\circ}_{Cu^+,Cu} = -0.153 + 0.674 = +0.521 \text{ v}$$

Thus, the standard potential for the copper(I)-copper metal electrode is $+0.521$ v versus the standard hydrogen electrode.

EXAMPLE 13

Calculate the standard potential for the half-reaction

$$SeO_4^= + 8H^+ + 6e \rightleftharpoons Se + 4H_2O$$

The two half-reactions in Table 5-1 from which the desired standard potential can be computed are as follows:

$$SeO_4^= + 4\,H^+ + 2\,e \rightleftharpoons H_2SeO_3 + H_2O; \quad E° = +1.15\,v$$
$$H_2SeO_3 + 4\,H^+ + 4\,e \rightleftharpoons Se + 3\,H_2O; \qquad E° = +0.740\,v$$

The free-energy-change relation is

$$\Delta G°_{SeO_4^=,Se} = \Delta G°_{SeO_4^=,H_2SeO_3} + \Delta G°_{H_2SeO_3,Se}$$

As the next step, we may write

$$-nFE°_{SeO_4^=,Se} = -nFE°_{SeO_4^=,H_2SeO_3} - nFE°_{H_2SeO_3,Se}$$

If we substitute values for n and for emf from the above half-reactions, it follows that

$$-6\,FE°_{SeO_4^=,Se} = -2\,F\,(+1.15) - 4\,F\,(+0.740)$$

or

$$6\,E°_{SeO_4^=,Se} = 2\,(+1.15) + 4\,(+0.740)$$

Solution of the preceding expression yields

$$E°_{SeO_4^=,Se} = \tfrac{1}{3}\,(+1.15) + \tfrac{2}{3}\,(+0.740)$$
$$= +0.383 + 0.493 = +0.876\,v$$

This result is the standard potential for the selenate-selenium metal electrode relative to the standard hydrogen electrode.

DIRECT POTENTIOMETRY

As indicated by the Nernst equation, the electromotive force of a galvanic cell depends upon the activities (concentrations) of the reducing and oxidizing agents in equilibrium with the electrodes. In certain well-defined situations, the magnitude of the electromotive force of a galvanic cell can be related by means of the Nernst equation to the concentration or activity of a single desired species, providing the technique known as **direct potentiometry.** Herein lies one of the most frequently encountered practical applications of electrochemical phenomena.

Probably the most important practical use of direct potentiometry is the determination of pH. The activity or concentration of hydrogen ions in solution plays a critical role in biochemical processes, in the rates of many organic and inorganic reactions, and in a wide variety of separations and measurements in analytical chemistry. A galvanic cell for the potentiometric measurement of pH comprises two electrodes. One is a stable reference electrode, and the other is an indicator electrode which responds to hydrogen ion.

As a reference electrode for pH measurement, it is necessary to select one whose potential remains constant regardless of the pH of the solution being measured. The most commonly used reference electrode is the **saturated calomel electrode** (SCE), which is composed of metallic mercury and solid mercurous chloride (calomel) in contact with, and in equilibrium with, a saturated aqueous solution of potassium chloride. The electrochemical equilibrium which characterizes the behavior of a calomel electrode is represented by the half-reaction

$$Hg_2Cl_2(s) \rightleftharpoons 2\,Hg(s) + 2\,Cl^-$$

and the corresponding Nernst equation can be written as

$$E_{Hg_2Cl_2,Hg} = E^{\circ}_{Hg_2Cl_2,Hg} - \frac{0.059}{2} \log\,[Cl^-]^2$$

An inspection of this relation reveals that the potential of a saturated calomel electrode depends only on the chloride ion concentration (activity). Since mercurous chloride is very insoluble, the concentration of chloride ion is governed almost entirely by the amount of potassium chloride used in the preparation of the electrode. As listed in Table 5-1, the potential of this reference electrode is $+0.2415$ v versus the normal hydrogen electrode at 25°C.

Saturated calomel electrodes are commercially available, one of the common varieties being depicted in Figure 5-5. The smaller, inner tube contains an amalgamated platinum wire which leads eventually to the external circuit. In addition, the inner tube is packed with a thick paste of

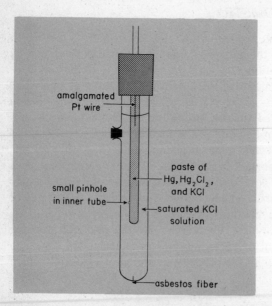

amalgamated
Pt wire

small pinhole
in inner tube

paste of
Hg, Hg₂Cl₂,
and KCl

saturated KCl
solution

asbestos fiber

FIGURE 5-5 Common form of commercially available saturated calomel reference electrode.

metallic mercury, mercurous chloride, and potassium chloride. The outer tube is filled with a saturated potassium chloride solution; a few crystals of solid potassium chloride can be added to ensure saturation at all times. Electrolytic contact between the inner and outer compartments of this electrode is obtained by means of a small pinhole in the side of the inner tube. Finally, electrolytic contact between the electrode itself and the sample solution is provided through a porous asbestos fiber sealed into the tip of the outer tube.

Numerous electrodes sensitive to pH have been devised, including the hydrogen electrode itself as shown in Figure 5-4. However, the glass membrane electrode is most widely employed. One form of this electrode is illustrated in Figure 5-6. A thin-walled bulb, fabricated from a special glass which is highly sensitive to the hydrogen ion activity of a solution, is sealed to the bottom of an ordinary glass tube. Inside the glass bulb is a dilute aqueous hydrochloric acid solution, usually $0.1\,M$ in concentration. A silver wire coated with a layer of silver chloride is immersed into the hydrochloric acid medium. The silver wire is extended upward through the resin-filled tube to provide electrical contact to the external circuit.

A glass membrane electrode in combination with the saturated calomel reference electrode provides the galvanic cell usually employed for practical pH measurements in the analytical chemical laboratory. The shorthand representation for such a cell is

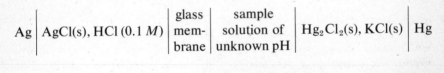

$$\text{Ag}\;\Big|\;\text{AgCl(s), HCl}\,(0.1\,M)\;\Big|\;\begin{array}{c}\text{glass}\\\text{mem-}\\\text{brane}\end{array}\;\Big|\;\begin{array}{c}\text{sample}\\\text{solution of}\\\text{unknown pH}\end{array}\;\Big|\;\text{Hg}_2\text{Cl}_2\text{(s), KCl(s)}\;\Big|\;\text{Hg}$$

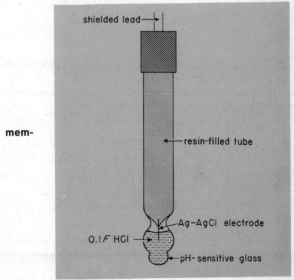

FIGURE 5-6 Glass membrane electrode.

shielded lead

resin-filled tube

Ag–AgCl electrode

0.1 F HCl

pH-sensitive glass

Each vertical line in the present galvanic cell representation denotes a phase boundary across which an electromotive force or potential develops. Therefore, the overall electromotive force for this galvanic cell is composed of five parts: (1) the potential of the silver-silver chloride electrode, (2) the potential between the hydrochloric acid solution inside the glass electrode and the inner wall of the glass membrane, (3) the potential between the outer wall of the glass membrane and the solution of unknown pH, (4) a liquid-junction potential between the solution of unknown pH and the saturated calomel electrode, and (5) the potential of the saturated calomel electrode.

Many careful experimental studies have led to the conclusion that the overall electromotive force, E_{cell}, for such a cell is related to the pH of the unknown sample by the expression

$$E_{cell} = K + 0.059 \text{ pH}$$

where the constant K includes the first, second, fourth, and fifth sources of potential just listed. However, the value of K can never be precisely known because the liquid-junction potential is uncertain. Therefore, all practical pH determinations necessarily involve a calibration procedure in which the pH of an unknown solution is compared to the pH of a standard buffer. If we transfer a portion of some standard buffer into the galvanic cell and measure the electromotive force of the cell, it follows that

$$(E_{cell})_s = K + 0.059 \text{ (pH)}_s$$

where the subscript s pertains to the standard buffer. Similarly, if an unknown solution is present in the cell, we obtain

$$(E_{cell})_x = K + 0.059 \text{ (pH)}_x$$

where the subscript x refers to the unknown solution. When the latter two relationships are combined, the result is

$$(\text{pH})_x = (\text{pH})_s + \frac{(E_{cell})_x - (E_{cell})_s}{0.059}$$

which has been adopted at the National Bureau of Standards as the *operational definition* of pH. Implicit in this operational or practical definition is the assumption that K has the same value when either the standard buffer or the unknown sample is present in the galvanic cell. In other words, the value of K must remain constant if this definition of pH is to be truly valid. In practice, one attempts to minimize the uncertainty by selecting a standard buffer with a pH as close as possible to that of the unknown sample. A list of accepted pH values for various standard buffers is presented in Table 5-2. For example, if the unknown solution has a pH close to 4, it is preferable that the standard buffer be potassium acid phthalate, the latter having a pH of 4.01 at 25°C.

For optimum conditions, when the pH values of the standard buffer and unknown sample are essentially identical, the uncertainty in the measured pH of an unknown solution is about ±0.02 pH unit. It is noteworthy that pH meters are available commercially from which one can read pH values with a precision of ±0.003 unit or better, a feature which is frequently useful for studying *changes* in the pH of a system under carefully controlled conditions. However, such precision must not be misconstrued, for the accuracy of the measurements is still no better than one or two hundredths of a pH unit.

A *direct-reading* pH meter is essentially a vacuum tube voltmeter in which the electromotive force of the galvanic cell is impressed across a very high resistance and the resulting current is amplified and passed through an ammeter whose dial face is calibrated directly in pH units. The *potentiometric* or *null-detector* instrument is the second type of pH meter. It incorporates a relatively straightforward potentiometer circuit, except that the usual galvanometer is replaced with a vacuum tube amplifier. The direct-reading pH meter is especially convenient for use in potentiometric acid-base titrations, where the variation of pH as a function of added titrant is more important than any individual value of pH. Direct-reading instruments are usually accurate to ±0.1 pH unit. On the other hand, null-detector pH meters yield pH values with accuracies of 0.01 to 0.02 pH unit, and consequently they are preferable for precise measurements. Both types of instruments must be standardized according to the operational definition of pH discussed earlier.

It should be noted that in direct potentiometry a state of equilibrium

TABLE 5-2 pH VALUES OF STANDARD BUFFERS*

Temperature, °C	Potassium Tetroxalate, 0.05 M	Potassium Hydrogen Tartrate, Saturated at 25°C	Potassium Acid Phthalate, 0.05 M	KH_2PO_4, 0.025 M; Na_2HPO_4, 0.025 M	Borax, 0.01 M
0	1.666	—	4.003	6.984	9.464
10	1.670	—	3.998	6.923	9.332
20	1.675	—	4.002	6.881	9.225
25	1.679	3.557	4.008	6.865	9.180
30	1.683	3.552	4.015	6.853	9.139
40	1.694	3.547	4.035	6.838	9.068
50	1.707	3.549	4.060	6.833	9.011

*Values taken with permission from R. G. Bates: *Determination of pH,* John Wiley & Sons, Inc., New York, 1964, p. 76. The uncertainties in these values are about ±0.005 unit at 25°C, but somewhat larger at other temperatures.

exists within each half-cell, in the sense that the oxidized and reduced forms of a chemical species are in equilibrium with one another. However, the two half-cells which comprise the complete galvanic cell are generally not in equilibrium with each other. We will now conclude this chapter with a consideration of oxidation-reduction systems which are in a state of equilibrium.

CALCULATION OF CONCENTRATIONS IN SYSTEMS AT EQUILIBRIUM

Determination of the equilibrium concentration of one or more species of an oxidation-reduction system is essentially no different than the calculations encountered in the three preceding chapters concerning precipitation, acid-base, and complex-formation reactions. In fact, the only distinctively new feature introduced in the present chapter is the method described on pages 226 to 231 for determining the numerical value of an equilibrium constant from standard-potential data. Therefore, the following examples, four of which involve the calculation of the concentration of one or more species in a system at equilibrium, will serve as a review of several concepts which have been discussed throughout this book.

EXAMPLE 14

Arsenious acid can be oxidized with triiodide ion to form arsenic acid and iodide according to the following reaction:

$$HAsO_2 + I_3^- + 2\,H_2O \rightleftharpoons H_3AsO_4 + 2\,H^+ + 3\,I^-$$

If, in one particular experiment, the final concentrations of $HAsO_2$ and H_3AsO_4 were identical, the equilibrium iodide concentration was $0.100\,M$, and the pH was maintained constant at 1.00, what was the equilibrium concentration of triiodide ion? Usually, it would be necessary to compute the equilibrium constant for the preceding reaction from appropriate standard potentials listed in Table 5-1. However, as shown in Example 9, the equilibrium constant is 0.166, so we may write

$$\frac{[H_3AsO_4][H^+]^2[I^-]^3}{[HAsO_2][I_3^-]} = 0.166$$

Inasmuch as $[HAsO_2] = [H_3AsO_4]$, and the hydrogen ion and iodide ion concentrations are both $0.100\,M$, this expression becomes

$$\frac{(0.100)^2(0.100)^3}{[I_3^-]} = 0.166$$

which, when solved, yields

$$[I_3^-] = 6.02 \times 10^{-5} \, M$$

EXAMPLE 15

Calculate the equilibrium concentrations of cadmium(II) and lead(II) ions resulting when a 0.200 M lead nitrate solution is treated with an excess of pure cadmium metal.

Cadmium metal reduces lead(II) to the elemental state and is oxidized to cadmium(II) in the process:

$$Cd + Pb^{++} \rightleftharpoons Cd^{++} + Pb$$

It should be evident that the net reaction is composed of the following two half-reactions:

$$Cd \rightleftharpoons Cd^{++} + 2 \, e$$
$$Pb^{++} + 2 \, e \rightleftharpoons Pb$$

By combining standard-potential data listed in Table 5-1, we can obtain the standard potential for the overall reaction

$$E^\circ_{overall} = E^\circ_{Cd,Cd^{++}} + E^\circ_{Pb^{++},Pb}$$
$$E^\circ_{overall} = 0.403 - 0.126 = +0.277 \, v$$

as well as the corresponding equilibrium constant:

$$\log K = \frac{nE^\circ}{0.059} = \frac{(2)(+0.277)}{0.059} = 9.39$$
$$K = 2.45 \times 10^9$$

Therefore, when a state of chemical equilibrium prevails, the expression

$$\frac{[Cd^{++}]}{[Pb^{++}]} = 2.45 \times 10^9$$

must be satisfied. Returning to the original statement of the problem, we see that the equilibrium concentration of cadmium ion can be symbolized by $[Cd^{++}]$, whereas the concentration of lead ion is given by the relation

$$[Pb^{++}] = 0.200 - [Cd^{++}]$$

If the latter relationship is substituted into the equilibrium expression

$$\frac{[Cd^{++}]}{0.200 - [Cd^{++}]} = 2.45 \times 10^9$$

the result is

$$[Cd^{++}] = 4.90 \times 10^8 - 2.45 \times 10^9 [Cd^{++}]$$

or

$$2.45 \times 10^9 [Cd^{++}] + [Cd^{++}] = 4.90 \times 10^8$$

Since the *second* term on the left-hand side of the equation is negligible compared to the *first* term, we may write

$$2.45 \times 10^9 [Cd^{++}] = 4.90 \times 10^8$$

$$[Cd^{++}] = \frac{4.90 \times 10^8}{2.45 \times 10^9} = 0.200 \, M$$

In view of the facts that we have just shown the *equilibrium* cadmium ion concentration to be $0.200 \, M$ and that the *original* lead ion concentration was $0.200 \, M$, it might appear that the *final* concentration of lead ion is zero. This cannot be true, because no reaction can ever be exactly 100 per cent complete, although the position of chemical equilibrium may lie exceedingly far toward the right. To compute the final lead ion concentration, it is necessary to substitute the cadmium ion concentration $(0.200 \, M)$ into the equilibrium expression as follows:

$$\frac{[Cd^{++}]}{[Pb^{++}]} = 2.45 \times 10^9$$

$$\frac{(0.200)}{[Pb^{++}]} = 2.45 \times 10^9$$

$$[Pb^{++}] = \frac{(0.200)}{2.45 \times 10^9} = 8.16 \times 10^{-11} \, M$$

Although our calculations are perfectly valid, we could have saved considerable time and effort by recognizing the equilibrium constant for the overall reaction to be so large $(K = 2.45 \times 10^9)$ that the reduction of $0.200 \, M$ lead ion by cadmium metal is virtually complete and, therefore, that the final concentration of cadmium ion must be equal to the original lead ion concentration. When this fact is realized, it is a simple matter to obtain the equilibrium concentration of lead ion as shown in the last three preceding equations.

EXAMPLE 16

Calculate the final concentration of Fe^{++} ion in a solution prepared by mixing 50.0 ml each of 0.0200 M Fe^{++} and Ce^{++++} solutions, both being 1 F in sulfuric acid.

These two species react to establish the equilibrium

$$Fe^{++} + Ce^{++++} \rightleftharpoons Fe^{+++} + Ce^{+++}$$

which is composed of the half-reactions

$$Fe^{++} \rightleftharpoons Fe^{+++} + e$$

and

$$Ce^{++++} + e \rightleftharpoons Ce^{+++}$$

Because the reaction of interest occurs in a 1 F sulfuric acid solution, it is appropriate to use the *formal* potentials to calculate the equilibrium constant in this medium. First, we can write

$$E^{\circ\prime}_{\text{overall}} = E^{\circ\prime}_{Fe^{++},Fe^{+++}} + E^{\circ\prime}_{Ce^{++++},Ce^{+++}}$$

$$E^{\circ\prime}_{\text{overall}} = -0.68 + 1.44 = +0.76 \text{ v}$$

and, next, we can evaluate the equilibrium constant:

$$\log K = \frac{nE^{\circ\prime}}{0.059} = \frac{(1)(+0.76)}{0.059} = 12.9$$

$$K = 7.9 \times 10^{12}$$

From the information given in the statement of the problem, we can conclude that the *total* iron concentration is 0.0100 M; similarly, the *total* concentration of cerium is 0.0100 M. Moreover, the large value for the equilibrium constant means that the reaction proceeds far toward the right and that essentially all of the iron and cerium exist as iron(III) and cerium(III), respectively. Thus,

$$[Fe^{+++}] = 0.0100 \, M \quad \text{and} \quad [Ce^{+++}] = 0.0100 \, M$$

In addition, since identical quantities of Fe^{++} and Ce^{++++} were mixed, and since these species react in a one-to-one ratio, equal concentrations of each ion must remain; so

$$[Fe^{++}] = [Ce^{++++}]$$

Substituting these various relationships into the equilibrium expression

$$\frac{[Fe^{+++}][Ce^{+++}]}{[Fe^{++}][Ce^{++++}]} = 7.9 \times 10^{12}$$

we obtain

$$\frac{(0.0100)(0.0100)}{[Fe^{++}]^2} = 7.9 \times 10^{12}$$

$$[Fe^{++}]^2 = 1.27 \times 10^{-17}$$

$$[Fe^{++}] = 3.56 \times 10^{-9} M$$

EXAMPLE 17

For the same chemical system discussed in the preceding example, calculate the equilibrium concentrations of all four species in a solution prepared by mixing 12.5 ml of 0.0200 M cerium(IV) sulfate with 20.0 ml of 0.0200 M iron(II) sulfate.

We have mixed $(12.5)(0.0200)$ or 0.250 millimole of Ce^{++++} with $(20.0)(0.0200)$ or 0.400 millimole of Fe^{++}, and the total volume of the solution is 32.5 ml. Since the position of equilibrium for the forward reaction has previously been shown to lie far toward the right, it is reasonable to assert that virtually all of the cerium(IV) will be reduced to cerium(III) by the excess of iron(II) and that an equal amount of iron(III) will be produced. Accordingly, 0.250 millimole each of Ce^{+++} and Fe^{+++} exists at equilibrium, and 0.150 millimole of Fe^{++} remains unreacted. Dividing the number of millimoles of each species by the solution volume in milliliters, we obtain the molar concentrations of the three ions:

$$[Ce^{+++}] = \frac{0.250 \text{ millimole}}{32.5 \text{ ml}} = 0.00769 M$$

$$[Fe^{+++}] = \frac{0.250 \text{ millimole}}{32.5 \text{ ml}} = 0.00769 M$$

$$[Fe^{++}] = \frac{0.150 \text{ millimole}}{32.5 \text{ ml}} = 0.00462 M$$

In order to calculate the very small, residual concentration of Ce^{++++}, it is necessary to employ the equilibrium-constant expression:

$$\frac{[Fe^{+++}][Ce^{+++}]}{[Fe^{++}][Ce^{++++}]} = 7.9 \times 10^{12}$$

$$\frac{(0.00769)(0.00769)}{(0.00462)[Ce^{++++}]} = 7.9 \times 10^{12}$$

$$[Ce^{++++}] = 1.62 \times 10^{-15} M$$

EXAMPLE 18

If the electromotive force of the galvanic cell

$$-Pt, H_2(0.5 \text{ atm}) \mid \text{solution of unknown pH} \mid Hg_2Cl_2(s),$$
$$KCl(s) \mid Hg+$$

is 0.366 v, calculate the pH of the unknown solution, neglecting the liquid-junction potential.

Using the conventions described earlier in this chapter, we may write the reaction for this galvanic cell as

$$H_2 + Hg_2Cl_2(s) + 2 K^+ \rightleftharpoons 2 H^+ + 2 Hg + 2 KCl(s)$$

and the two half-reactions as

$$H_2 \rightleftharpoons 2 H^+ + 2 e$$

and

$$Hg_2Cl_2(s) + 2 K^+ + 2 e \rightleftharpoons 2 Hg + 2 KCl(s)$$

In addition, the emf for the overall cell reaction is given by the sum of the emf values for these two half-reactions; that is,

$$E_{\text{overall}} = E_{H_2,H^+} + E_{Hg_2Cl_2,Hg}$$

where E_{overall} is stated to be $+0.366$ v and $E_{Hg_2Cl_2,Hg}$, corresponding to the potential of the saturated calomel electrode, is listed in Table 5-1 as $+0.242$ v versus the normal hydrogen electrode. Substitution of these quantities into the preceding relation gives

$$+0.366 = E_{H_2,H^+} + 0.242$$

or

$$E_{H_2,H^+} = +0.124 \text{ v}$$

If we now write the Nernst equation for the hydrogen gas–hydrogen ion couple

$$E_{H_2,H^+} = +0.124 = E^\circ_{H_2,H^+} - \frac{0.059}{2} \log \frac{[H^+]^2}{p_{H_2}}$$

and note that $E^\circ_{H_2,H^+} = 0$ v by definition and that $p_{H_2} = 0.5$ atm for the particular galvanic cell being considered, the hydrogen ion concentration and, therefore, the pH of the unknown sample may be obtained as follows:

$$+0.124 = 0 - \frac{0.059}{2} \log \frac{[H^+]^2}{(0.5)}$$

$$+0.248 = -0.059 \log \frac{[H^+]^2}{(0.5)}$$

$$-\frac{0.248}{0.059} = -4.20 = \log \frac{[H^+]^2}{(0.5)}$$

$$10^{-4.20} = 6.3 \times 10^{-5} = \frac{[H^+]^2}{(0.5)}$$

$$[H^+]^2 = (0.5)(6.3 \times 10^{-5}) = 3.15 \times 10^{-5}$$

$$[H^+] = 5.61 \times 10^{-3} M$$

$$pH = 2.25$$

EXAMPLE 19

If the electromotive force of the galvanic cell

$$-Cu \,|\, Cu^{++} (0.0100 \, M) \,||\, Ag^+ \,|\, Ag+$$

is 0.353 v, what must be the concentration of silver ion in the right-hand half-cell?

We may represent the overall reaction

$$Cu + 2 \, Ag^+ \rightleftharpoons Cu^{++} + 2 \, Ag$$

which occurs in this electrochemical cell as the sum of the following two half-reactions:

$$Cu \rightleftharpoons Cu^{++} + 2 \, e$$

$$2 \, Ag^+ + 2 \, e \rightleftharpoons 2 \, Ag$$

Following the procedure developed earlier in this chapter, we can write the relation

$$E_{overall} = E_{Cu,Cu^{++}} + E_{Ag^+,Ag}$$

In order to obtain the desired silver ion concentration, it is necessary to find $E_{Ag^+,Ag}$, which requires that $E_{overall}$ and $E_{Cu,Cu^{++}}$ be known. Since the overall emf of the cell is stated to be $+0.353$ v, we must determine $E_{Cu,Cu^{++}}$. To do this, let us write the Nernst equation

$$E_{Cu,Cu^{++}} = E^{\circ}_{Cu,Cu^{++}} - \frac{0.059}{2} \log [Cu^{++}]$$

where $E^{\circ}_{Cu,Cu^{++}}$ is listed as -0.337 v versus the normal hydrogen electrode in Table 5-1 and where the concentration of cupric ion is $0.0100\,M$. When the latter two quantities are inserted into the Nernst equation, we have

$$E_{Cu,Cu^{++}} = -0.337 - \frac{0.059}{2} \log (0.0100)$$

$$E_{Cu,Cu^{++}} = -0.337 + 0.059 = -0.278 \text{ v}$$

Next, the value of $E_{Ag^+,Ag}$ can be computed as follows:

$$E_{Ag^+,Ag} = E_{overall} - E_{Cu,Cu^{++}}$$

$$E_{Ag^+,Ag} = +0.353 - (-0.278) = +0.631 \text{ v}$$

Finally, we can employ the Nernst equation for the silver ion-silver metal couple to evaluate the concentration of silver ion:

$$E_{Ag^+,Ag} = E^{\circ}_{Ag^+,Ag} - 0.059 \log \frac{1}{[Ag^+]}$$

$$+0.631 = +0.800 - 0.059 \log \frac{1}{[Ag^+]}$$

$$-0.169 = -0.059 \log \frac{1}{[Ag^+]}$$

$$\frac{0.169}{0.059} = \log \frac{1}{[Ag^+]} = 2.86$$

$$\frac{1}{[Ag^+]} = 7.25 \times 10^2$$

$$[Ag^+] = 1.38 \times 10^{-3} M$$

QUESTIONS AND PROBLEMS

1. Define or characterize each of the following terms: oxidation, reduction, oxidant, reductant, anode, cathode, galvanic cell, and electrolytic cell.

2. Describe clearly how the electromotive force or emf of a galvanic cell is measured experimentally.

3. Write the shorthand cell representation for each of the following galvanic cells:

(a) A metallic silver electrode in a $0.015\,F$ silver nitrate solution connected, through a potassium nitrate salt bridge to eliminate the liquid-junction potential, to a $0.028\,F$ nickel chloride solution into which a nickel metal rod is immersed.

(b) A platinum wire in a mixture of $0.10\,M$ cerium(IV) and $0.05\,M$ cerium(III) in a $1\,F$ sulfuric acid solution which is in contact through a permeable membrane with a $10\,F$ sodium hydroxide solution containing $0.05\,M$ permanganate ion (MnO_4^-) and $0.001\,M$ manganate ion $(MnO_4^=)$ in which a gold wire electrode is immersed.

(c) A palladium wire in a $0.025\,F$ hydrochloric acid solution which is saturated with hydrogen gas at a pressure of $0.5\,atm$ and which is connected, through a potassium chloride salt bridge to minimize the liquid-junction potential, to another half-cell consisting of a zinc metal rod immersed in a $0.04\,F$ zinc nitrate solution.

4. Write the shorthand cell representation of a galvanic cell which could be employed to determine the solubility-product constant of silver chloride. In other words, construct a suitable cell in which the cell reaction is

$$AgCl(s) \rightleftharpoons Ag^+ + Cl^-$$

5. Write the shorthand cell representation of a galvanic cell which can be used to measure the ion-product constant for water. In other words, construct a cell for which the overall reaction is

$$H_2O \rightleftharpoons H^+ + OH^-$$

6. Write the Nernst equation which corresponds to each of the following half-reactions:

(a) $Cd + 4 CN^- \rightleftharpoons Cd(CN)_4^= + 2 e$

(b) $Cu^{++} + I^- + e \rightleftharpoons CuI(s)$

(c) $TiO^{++} + 2 H^+ + e \rightleftharpoons Ti^{+++} + H_2O$

(d) $Mn^{++} + 2 H_2O \rightleftharpoons MnO_2 + 4 H^+ + 2 e$

(e) $2 Hg^{++} + 2 e \rightleftharpoons Hg_2^{++}$

(f) $Hg_2SO_4(s) + 2 e \rightleftharpoons 2 Hg + SO_4^=$

7. Calculate the actual emf for the overall reaction occurring in each of the following galvanic cells:

(a) $Ni \mid Ni^{++} (0.200\,M) \parallel Ag^+ (0.00500\,M) \mid Ag$

(b) $Pt \mid I^- (0.500\,M),$
$$I_3^- (0.0300\,M) \parallel Cd^{++} (0.100\,M) \mid Cd$$

(c) $Pb \mid Pb^{++} (0.0250\,M) \parallel Cu^{++} (0.300\,M) \mid Cu$

(d) $Ag \mid AgCl(s),\ Cl^- (0.100\,M) \parallel Hg_2SO_4(s),$
$$SO_4^= (2.00\,M) \mid Hg$$

(e) $Pt \mid VO_2^+ (0.0200\,M),\ VO^{++} (0.100\,M),$
$$H^+(0.500\,M) \parallel Tl^+(0.0400\,M) \mid Tl$$

8. Define or characterize each of the following terms: liquid-junction potential, platinum black, standard (or normal) hydrogen electrode, half-reaction, standard potential, and formal potential.

9. For each of the following galvanic cells: (a) Write the two half-reactions and the overall cell reaction, (b) calculate the actual emf for each cell from the Nernst equation, (c) calculate the equilibrium constant for each cell reaction, and (d) identify the anode and cathode and label the electrodes appropriately with either a + or − sign.

$Cu \mid CuSO_4(0.02\,F) \parallel Fe^{++}(0.2\,M),\ Fe^{+++}(0.01\,M),\ HCl(1\,F) \mid Pt$

$Pt \mid Pu^{++++}(0.1\,M),\ Pu^{+++}(0.2\,M) \parallel AgCl(s),\ HCl(0.03\,F) \mid Ag$

$Pt \mid KBr(0.2\,F),\ Br_3^-(0.03\,M) \parallel Ce^{++++}(0.01\,M),$
$$Ce^{+++}(0.002\,M),\ H_2SO_4(1\,F) \mid Pt$$

$Pt,\ Cl_2(0.1\ atm) \mid HCl(2.0\,F) \parallel HCl(0.1\,F) \mid H_2(0.5\ atm),\ Pt$

$Zn \mid ZnCl_2(0.02\,F) \parallel Na_2SO_4(0.1\,F),\ PbSO_4(s) \mid Pb$

$Pt \mid UO_2^{++}(0.005\,M),\ U^{++++}(0.1\,M),$
$$HClO_4(0.2\,F) \parallel HBr(0.3\,F),\ AgBr(s) \mid Ag$$

10. Compute the equilibrium constant for the reaction

$$AuCl_4^- + 2 Au + 2 Cl^- \rightleftharpoons 3 AuCl_2^-$$

from the standard potentials for the following half-reactions:

$$AuCl_2^- + e \rightleftharpoons Au + 2 Cl^-; \qquad E° = +1.154\ v$$
$$AuCl_4^- + 2 e \rightleftharpoons AuCl_2^- + 2 Cl^-; \qquad E° = +0.926\ v$$

11. Evaluate the equilibrium constant for each of the following reactions:

(a) $Ag + Fe^{+++} \rightleftharpoons Ag^+ + Fe^{++}$

(b) $2 Cr^{++} + Co^{++} \rightleftharpoons 2 Cr^{+++} + Co$

(c) $Br_2(aq) + 3 I^- \rightleftharpoons 2 Br^- + I_3^-$

(d) $2 V^{+++} + UO_2^{++} \rightleftharpoons 2 VO^{++} + U^{++++}$

(e) $2 Co^{+++} + Co \rightleftharpoons 3 Co^{++}$

12. Evaluate the equilibrium constant for the formation of the triiodide ion,

$$I_2(aq) + I^- \rightleftharpoons I_3^-$$

from the knowledge that

$$I_2(aq) + 2 e \rightleftharpoons 2 I^-; \quad E° = +0.6197 \text{ v}$$

and

$$I_3^- + 2 e \rightleftharpoons 3 I^-; \quad E° = +0.5355 \text{ v}$$

13. Calculate the solubility-product constant for copper(I) iodide,

$$CuI(s) \rightleftharpoons Cu^+ + I^-$$

given the following information:

$$Cu^{++} + e \rightleftharpoons Cu^+; \quad E° = +0.153 \text{ v}$$

and

$$Cu^{++} + I^- + e \rightleftharpoons CuI(s); \quad E° = +0.86 \text{ v}$$

14. Given that

$$Ag + 2 CN^- \rightleftharpoons Ag(CN)_2^- + e; \quad E° = +0.31 \text{ v}$$

and

$$Ag \rightleftharpoons Ag^+ + e; \quad E° = -0.80 \text{ v}$$

calculate the equilibrium (dissociation) constant for the following reaction:

$$Ag(CN)_2^- \rightleftharpoons Ag^+ + 2 CN^-$$

15. Calculate the standard potential ($E°$) for the half-reaction

$$Au^+ + e \rightleftharpoons Au$$

from the following data:

$$Au^{+++} + 2e \rightleftharpoons Au^+; \quad E° = +1.41 \text{ v}$$
$$Au^{+++} + 3e \rightleftharpoons Au; \quad E° = +1.50 \text{ v}$$

16. Given the following data

$$MnO_4^- + 8H^+ + 5e \rightleftharpoons Mn^{++} + 4H_2O; \quad E° = +1.51 \text{ v}$$

$$Mn^{+++} + e \rightleftharpoons Mn^{++}; \quad E° = +1.51 \text{ v}$$

calculate the standard potential ($E°$) for

$$MnO_4^- + 8H^+ + 4e \rightleftharpoons Mn^{+++} + 4H_2O$$

17. Consider the following galvanic cell:

$Pt \mid PuO_2^{++}(0.01 \ M), \ Pu^{++++}(0.001 \ M),$
$$H^+(0.1 \ M) \parallel Cu^{++}(0.001 \ M) \mid Cu$$

  (a) Write the two pertinent half-reactions and the overall cell reaction.
  (b) Calculate the $E°$ and the equilibrium constant for the overall cell reaction.
  (c) Calculate the actual emf of the galvanic cell.
  (d) Which electrode is the negative electrode?
  (e) A bar of pure copper metal weighing 127 gm was placed into 1 liter of a 0.0500 F $PuO_2(ClO_4)_2$ solution. The pH of this solution was maintained constant at exactly 3.00. What was the concentration of PuO_2^{++} at equilibrium?

18. Given the following data,

$$PtCl_4^= + 2e \rightleftharpoons Pt + 4Cl^-; \quad E° = +0.73 \text{ v}$$
$$PtCl_6^= + 4e \rightleftharpoons Pt + 6Cl^-; \quad E° = +0.72 \text{ v}$$

calculate the $E°$ and the equilibrium constant (to two significant figures) for the reaction

$$2 PtCl_4^= \rightleftharpoons Pt + PtCl_6^= + 2Cl^-$$

19. Consider the following galvanic cell:

$Pt \mid Cr^{+++}(0.30 \ M), \ Cr^{++}(0.010 \ M) \parallel AgCl(s), \ Cl^-(0.025 \ M) \mid Ag$

What will be the qualitative effect of each of the following upon the emf of the galvanic cell:

(a) The addition of 10 grams of solid silver chloride to the right half-cell?

(b) The dissolution of 10 grams of sodium chloride in the right half-cell?

(c) The addition of 100 ml of water to the left half-cell?

(d) The addition of some soluble chromium(III) salt to the left half-cell?

(e) The dissolution of some silver nitrate in the right half-cell?

20. Consider the following galvanic cell:

$$Pt \mid Fe^{+++}(0.01\ M),\ Fe^{++}(0.02\ M),$$
$$H^+(1\ M) \parallel H^+(1\ M) \mid H_2(1\ atm),\ Pt$$

What will be the qualitative effect of each of the following upon the emf of this galvanic cell:

(a) The addition of 50 ml of 1 M acid to the left half-cell?

(b) The addition of some soluble iron(II) salt to the left half-cell?

(c) The addition of a small amount of solid potassium permanganate to the left half-cell?

(d) The decrease of the pressure of hydrogen gas in the right half-cell?

21. Calculate the equilibrium constant for each of the following reactions:

(a) $Ce^{++++} + Fe(CN)_6^{\equiv} \rightleftharpoons Ce^{+++} +$
$Fe(CN)_6^{\equiv}$ (1 F $HClO_4$ medium)

(b) $Pb + SnCl_6^{=} \rightleftharpoons Pb^{++} + SnCl_4^{=} + 2\ Cl^-$ (1 F HCl medium)

(c) $5\ Fe^{++} + MnO_4^- + 8\ H^+ \rightleftharpoons 5\ Fe^{+++} + Mn^{++} + 4\ H_2O$

(d) $Fe^{++} + Cu^{++} \rightleftharpoons Fe^{+++} + Cu^+$

22. From data given in Appendix 4, evaluate the standard potentials for each of the following half-reactions:

(a) $3\ IO_3^- + 18\ H^+ + 16\ e \rightleftharpoons I_3^- + 9\ H_2O$

(b) $IO_3^- + 6\ H^+ + 2\ Cl^- + 4\ e \rightleftharpoons ICl_2^- + 3\ H_2O$

(c) $BrO_3^- + 6\ H^+ + 6\ e \rightleftharpoons Br^- + 3\ H_2O$

23. Determine the equilibrium constant for the reaction

$$BrO_3^- + 5\ Br^- + 6\ H^+ \rightleftharpoons 3\ Br_2 + 3\ H_2O$$

and compute the concentration of free bromine in a solution of pH 7.00 containing 0.1000 F potassium bromate and 0.70 F potassium bromide.

24. From standard-potential data given in Appendix 4, cal-

culate the solubility of bromine in water at 25°C and calculate the equilibrium constant for the reaction

$$Br_2(aq) + Br^- \rightleftharpoons Br_3^-$$

25. Calculate the electromotive force of the following galvanic cell, assuming the absence of liquid-junction potentials:

$$Hg \mid Hg_2Cl_2(s), KCl(1.0\ F) \parallel Ag^+(0.00250\ M) \mid Ag$$

26. The following galvanic cell was constructed for the measurement of the dissociation constant of a weak monoprotic acid, HA:

$$-Pt, H_2(0.8\ atm) \mid HA(0.5\ F), NaCl(1.0\ F), AgCl(s) \mid Ag+$$

If the observed electromotive force of this cell was 0.568 v, what is the dissociation constant for the weak acid?

27. Repeat the calculation of Example 14 on page 238, except assume that the pH is 7.00. With the aid of Le Châtelier's principle, explain the difference in the triiodide ion concentration at the two different pH values.

28. Calculate the equilibrium concentrations of cobalt(II) and thallium(I) ions resulting when a 0.250 M cobalt(II) sulfate, $CoSO_4$, solution is treated with an excess of pure thallium metal.

29. Titanium(III) may be oxidized by iron(III) in an acidic solution, as shown by the reaction

$$Ti^{+++} + Fe^{+++} + H_2O \rightleftharpoons TiO^{++} + Fe^{++} + 2\ H^+$$

Calculate the final concentration of Ti^{+++} ion in a solution prepared by mixing 25.0 ml each of 0.0200 M Ti^{+++} and Fe^{+++} solutions, both being 1 F in sulfuric acid.

30. As described earlier in this chapter, cerium(IV) and iron(II) react to form cerium(III) and iron(III).

$$Ce^{++++} + Fe^{++} \rightleftharpoons Ce^{+++} + Fe^{+++}$$

(a) Calculate the equilibrium concentrations of all four species in a solution prepared by mixing 5.0 ml of 0.0500 M cerium(IV) sulfate with 25.0 ml of 0.0150 M iron(II) sulfate. Assume that the solutions contain 1 F sulfuric acid.

(b) Calculate the equilibrium concentrations of all four species in a solution prepared by mixing 25.0 ml of 0.0200 M cerium(IV) sulfate with 17.0 ml of

0.0200 M iron(II) sulfate. Assume that the solutions contain 1 F sulfuric acid.

31. Calculate the standard potential ($E°$) for the half-reaction

$$WO_3(s) + 2 H^+ + 2 e \rightleftharpoons WO_2(s) + H_2O$$

from the following data:

$$2 WO_2(s) + H_2O \rightleftharpoons W_2O_5(s) + 2 H^+ + 2 e; \quad E° = +0.043 \text{ v}$$
$$2 WO_3(s) + 2 H^+ + 2 e \rightleftharpoons W_2O_5(s) + H_2O; \quad E° = -0.030 \text{ v}$$

32. The hypothetical galvanic cell

$$-A \mid A^{++} \parallel B^{++} \mid B+$$

has an emf of $+0.360$ v when the concentrations of A^{++} and B^{++} are equal. What will be the observed emf of the cell if the concentration of A^{++} is 0.100 M and the concentration of B^{++} is $1.00 \times 10^{-4} M$?

33. Given the following standard-potential data,

$$Cd^{++} + 2 e \rightleftharpoons Cd; \quad E° = -0.403 \text{ v}$$
$$Fe^{++} + 2 e \rightleftharpoons Fe; \quad E° = -0.440 \text{ v}$$

calculate the equilibrium concentration of cadmium ion when a 0.0500 M cadmium ion solution is shaken with an excess of pure iron filings.

34. Consider the following galvanic cell:

$$Cd \mid Cd^{++}(0.100 \, M) \parallel Hg^{++}(0.000300 \, M) \mid Hg$$

(a) Write the two half-reactions which occur in this cell when the electrodes are connected with a conducting wire.
(b) Write the overall cell reaction.
(c) Calculate the $E°$ for the overall cell reaction.
(d) Calculate the actual emf of the galvanic cell.

35. Consider the following two galvanic cells and assume that the copper electrode of the first cell is permanently connected to the iron electrode of the second cell, as shown below:

$$\begin{array}{l} \text{Cu} \mid Cu^{++}(0.100 \, M) \parallel Pb^{++}(0.200 \, M) \mid Pb \\ \text{Fe} \mid Fe^{++}(0.300 \, M) \parallel Ag^+(0.500 \, M) \mid Ag \end{array}$$

(a) Calculate what emf would be observed or measured if a potentiometer were connected across the Pb and Ag electrodes.

(b) Which electrode is the negative electrode?

(c) Suppose that you connect the Ag and Pb electrodes with a conducting wire. Write the half-reaction which would occur at each of the four electrodes, being sure to *write each half-reaction in the direction in which it proceeds spontaneously*.

36. Cadmium metal reacts with vanadium(III) according to the reaction

$$Cd + 2 V^{+++} \rightleftharpoons Cd^{++} + 2 V^{++}$$

If a 0.0750 M vanadium(III) solution is shaken with an excess of cadmium metal, what will be the concentrations of V^{+++}, V^{++}, and Cd^{++} at equilibrium?

37. Tin(II) is often employed to reduce iron(III) to iron(II) in a hydrochloric acid medium.

$$SnCl_4^= + 2 Fe^{+++} + 2 Cl^- \rightleftharpoons SnCl_6^= + 2 Fe^{++}$$

If 1.00 ml of 0.0500 M tin(II) is added to 22.00 ml of 0.00450 M iron(III), what will be the equilibrium concentrations of $SnCl_4^=$, $SnCl_6^=$, Fe^{++}, and Fe^{+++}? Assuming that the solution is 1 F in hydrochloric acid, use the appropriate formal-potential data in Table 5-1.

38. With reference to Example 19 on page 244, what must be the silver ion concentration in the right half-cell in order for the electromotive force of the galvanic cell to be exactly zero?

39. If the electromotive force of the galvanic cell

$$+Pb \mid Pb^{++}(0.0860 \, M) \parallel Tl^+ \mid Tl-$$

is 0.280 v, what must be the concentration of thallium ion in the right half-cell?

40. The electromotive force of the galvanic cell

$$-Ag \mid AgCl(s), Cl^-(0.100 \, M) \parallel Fe^{+++}(0.0200 \, M), Fe^{++} \mid Pt+$$

is 0.319 v, what must be the concentration of Fe^{++} in the right half-cell? Assume that the solution in the right half-cell is 1 F in sulfuric acid.

41. If the electromotive force of the galvanic cell

$$-Pt, H_2(0.250 \text{ atm}) \mid \text{solution of unknown pH} \parallel AgCl(s),$$
$$Cl^-(1.00 \, M) \mid Ag+$$

is 0.621 v, what is the pH of the unknown sample?

Appendix 1

SOLUBILITY PRODUCT CONSTANTS*

(All values are valid at or near room temperature.)

Substance	Formula	K_{sp}
Aluminum hydroxide	$Al(OH)_3$	2×10^{-32}
Barium arsenate	$Ba_3(AsO_4)_2$	7.7×10^{-51}
Barium carbonate	$BaCO_3$	8.1×10^{-9}
Barium chromate	$BaCrO_4$	2.4×10^{-10}
Barium fluoride	BaF_2	1.7×10^{-6}
Barium iodate	$Ba(IO_3)_2 \cdot 2H_2O$	1.5×10^{-9}
Barium oxalate	$BaC_2O_4 \cdot H_2O$	2.3×10^{-8}
Barium sulfate	$BaSO_4$	1.08×10^{-10}
Beryllium hydroxide	$Be(OH)_2$	7×10^{-22}
Bismuth iodide	BiI_3	8.1×10^{-19}
Bismuth phosphate	$BiPO_4$	1.3×10^{-23}
Bismuth sulfide	Bi_2S_3	1×10^{-97}
Cadmium arsenate	$Cd_3(AsO_4)_2$	2.2×10^{-33}
Cadmium hydroxide	$Cd(OH)_2$	5.9×10^{-15}
Cadmium oxalate	$CdC_2O_4 \cdot 3H_2O$	1.5×10^{-8}
Cadmium sulfide	CdS	7.8×10^{-27}
Calcium arsenate	$Ca_3(AsO_4)_2$	6.8×10^{-19}
Calcium carbonate	$CaCO_3$	8.7×10^{-9}
Calcium fluoride	CaF_2	4.0×10^{-11}
Calcium hydroxide	$Ca(OH)_2$	5.5×10^{-6}
Calcium iodate	$Ca(IO_3)_2 \cdot 6H_2O$	6.4×10^{-7}
Calcium oxalate	$CaC_2O_4 \cdot H_2O$	2.6×10^{-9}
Calcium phosphate	$Ca_3(PO_4)_2$	2.0×10^{-29}
Calcium sulfate	$CaSO_4$	1.9×10^{-4}
Cerium(III) hydroxide	$Ce(OH)_3$	2×10^{-20}
Cerium(III) iodate	$Ce(IO_3)_3$	3.2×10^{-10}
Cerium(III) oxalate	$Ce_2(C_2O_4)_3 \cdot 9H_2O$	3×10^{-29}
Chromium(II) hydroxide	$Cr(OH)_2$	1.0×10^{-17}
Chromium(III) hydroxide	$Cr(OH)_3$	6×10^{-31}
Cobalt(II) hydroxide	$Co(OH)_2$	2×10^{-16}
Cobalt(III) hydroxide	$Co(OH)_3$	1×10^{-43}
Copper(II) arsenate	$Cu_3(AsO_4)_2$	7.6×10^{-36}
Copper(I) bromide	$CuBr$	5.2×10^{-9}
Copper(I) chloride	$CuCl$	1.2×10^{-6}
Copper(I) iodide	CuI	5.1×10^{-12}

* See footnotes at end of table.

Substance	Formula	K_{sp}
Copper(II) iodate	$Cu(IO_3)_2$	7.4×10^{-8}
Copper(I) sulfide	Cu_2S	2×10^{-47}
Copper(II) sulfide	CuS	9×10^{-36}
Copper(I) thiocyanate	$CuSCN$	4.8×10^{-15}
Iron(III) arsenate	$FeAsO_4$	5.7×10^{-21}
Iron(II) carbonate	$FeCO_3$	3.5×10^{-11}
Iron(II) hydroxide	$Fe(OH)_2$	8×10^{-16}
Iron(III) hydroxide	$Fe(OH)_3$	4×10^{-38}
Lead arsenate	$Pb_3(AsO_4)_2$	4.1×10^{-36}
Lead bromide	$PbBr_2$	3.9×10^{-5}
Lead carbonate	$PbCO_3$	3.3×10^{-14}
Lead chloride	$PbCl_2$	1.6×10^{-5}
Lead chromate	$PbCrO_4$	1.8×10^{-14}
Lead fluoride	PbF_2	3.7×10^{-8}
Lead iodate	$Pb(IO_3)_2$	2.6×10^{-13}
Lead iodide	PbI_2	7.1×10^{-9}
Lead oxalate	PbC_2O_4	4.8×10^{-10}
Lead sulfate	$PbSO_4$	1.6×10^{-8}
Lead sulfide	PbS	8×10^{-28}
Magnesium ammonium phosphate	$MgNH_4PO_4$	2.5×10^{-13}
Magnesium arsenate	$Mg_3(AsO_4)_2$	2.1×10^{-20}
Magnesium carbonate	$MgCO_3 \cdot 3H_2O$	1×10^{-5}
Magnesium fluoride	MgF_2	6.5×10^{-9}
Magnesium hydroxide	$Mg(OH)_2$	1.2×10^{-11}
Magnesium oxalate	$MgC_2O_4 \cdot 2H_2O$	1×10^{-8}
Manganese(II) hydroxide	$Mn(OH)_2$	1.9×10^{-13}
[a]Mercury(I) bromide	Hg_2Br_2	5.8×10^{-23}
[a]Mercury(I) chloride	Hg_2Cl_2	1.3×10^{-18}
[a]Mercury(I) iodide	Hg_2I_2	4.5×10^{-29}
[a]Mercury(I) sulfate	Hg_2SO_4	7.4×10^{-7}
Mercury(II) sulfide	HgS	4×10^{-53}
[a]Mercury(I) thiocyanate	$Hg_2(SCN)_2$	3.0×10^{-20}
Nickel arsenate	$Ni_3(AsO_4)_2$	3.1×10^{-26}
Nickel carbonate	$NiCO_3$	6.6×10^{-9}
Nickel hydroxide	$Ni(OH)_2$	6.5×10^{-18}
Nickel sulfide	NiS	3×10^{-19}
Silver arsenate	Ag_3AsO_4	1×10^{-22}
Silver bromate	$AgBrO_3$	5.77×10^{-5}
Silver bromide	$AgBr$	5.25×10^{-13}
Silver carbonate	Ag_2CO_3	8.1×10^{-12}
Silver chloride	$AgCl$	1.78×10^{-10}
Silver chromate	Ag_2CrO_4	2.45×10^{-12}
Silver cyanide	$Ag[Ag(CN)_2]$	5.0×10^{-12}
Silver iodate	$AgIO_3$	3.02×10^{-8}
Silver iodide	AgI	8.31×10^{-17}
Silver oxalate	$Ag_2C_2O_4$	3.5×10^{-11}
[b]Silver oxide	Ag_2O	2.6×10^{-8}
Silver phosphate	Ag_3PO_4	1.3×10^{-20}
Silver sulfate	Ag_2SO_4	1.6×10^{-5}
Silver sulfide	Ag_2S	2×10^{-49}
Silver thiocyanate	$AgSCN$	1.00×10^{-12}

Substance	Formula	K_{sp}
Strontium carbonate	$SrCO_3$	1.1×10^{-10}
Strontium chromate	$SrCrO_4$	3.6×10^{-5}
Strontium fluoride	SrF_2	2.8×10^{-9}
Strontium iodate	$Sr(IO_3)_2$	3.3×10^{-7}
Strontium oxalate	$SrC_2O_4 \cdot H_2O$	1.6×10^{-7}
Strontium sulfate	$SrSO_4$	3.8×10^{-7}
Thallium(I) bromate	$TlBrO_3$	8.5×10^{-5}
Thallium(I) bromide	$TlBr$	3.4×10^{-6}
Thallium(I) chloride	$TlCl$	1.7×10^{-4}
Thallium(I) chromate	Tl_2CrO_4	9.8×10^{-13}
Thallium(I) iodate	$TlIO_3$	3.1×10^{-6}
Thallium(I) iodide	TlI	6.5×10^{-8}
Thallium(I) sulfide	Tl_2S	5×10^{-21}
Tin(II) sulfide	SnS	1×10^{-25}
Titanium(III) hydroxide	$Ti(OH)_3$	1×10^{-40}
Zinc arsenate	$Zn_3(AsO_4)_2$	1.3×10^{-28}
Zinc carbonate	$ZnCO_3$	1.4×10^{-11}
Zinc ferrocyanide	$Zn_2Fe(CN)_6$	4.1×10^{-16}
Zinc hydroxide	$Zn(OH)_2$	1.2×10^{-17}
Zinc oxalate	$ZnC_2O_4 \cdot 2H_2O$	2.8×10^{-8}
Zinc phosphate	$Zn_3(PO_4)_2$	9.1×10^{-33}
Zinc sulfide	ZnS	1×10^{-21}

Although water appears in the formulas of a number of substances, it is not included in the solubility-product expression.

[a] All mercury(I) compounds contain the dimeric species Hg_2^{++}. Therefore, the solubility reaction and solubility-product expression are represented in general by:

$$(Hg_2)_mX_n \rightleftharpoons m\,Hg_2^{++} + n\,X^{-2m/n}; \quad K_{sp} = [Hg_2^{++}]^m[X^{-2m/n}]^n$$

[b] $\frac{1}{2}Ag_2O + \frac{1}{2}H_2O \rightleftharpoons Ag^+ + OH^-; \quad K_{sp} = [Ag^+][OH^-]$

Appendix 2

IONIZATION CONSTANTS FOR ACIDS AND BASES

(All values are valid at or near room temperature.)

Acids

Acid	Ionization Equilibrium	
Acetic	$CH_3COOH \rightleftharpoons CH_3COO^- + H^+;$	$K = 1.75 \times 10^{-5}$
Alanine	$\underset{\underset{+NH_3}{\mid}}{CH_3CHCOOH} \rightleftharpoons \underset{\underset{+NH_3}{\mid}}{CH_3CHCOO^-} + H^+;$	$K_1 = 4.5 \times 10^{-3}$
	$\underset{\underset{+NH_3}{\mid}}{CH_3CHCOO^-} \rightleftharpoons \underset{\underset{NH_2}{\mid}}{CH_3CHCOO^-} + H^+;$	$K_2 = 1.3 \times 10^{-10}$
Arsenic	$H_3AsO_4 \rightleftharpoons H_2AsO_4^- + H^+;$	$K_1 = 6.0 \times 10^{-3}$
	$H_2AsO_4^- \rightleftharpoons HAsO_4^{--} + H^+;$	$K_2 = 1.0 \times 10^{-7}$
	$HAsO_4^{--} \rightleftharpoons AsO_4^{---} + H^+;$	$K_3 = 3.0 \times 10^{-12}$
Arsenious	$HAsO_2 \rightleftharpoons AsO_2^- + H^+;$	$K_1 = 6 \times 10^{-10}$
Benzoic	$C_6H_5COOH \rightleftharpoons C_6H_5COO^- + H^+;$	$K = 6.3 \times 10^{-5}$
Carbonic	$H_2CO_3 \rightleftharpoons HCO_3^- + H^+;$	$K_1 = 4.47 \times 10^{-7}$
	$HCO_3^- \rightleftharpoons CO_3^{--} + H^+;$	$K_2 = 4.68 \times 10^{-11}$
Chloroacetic	$ClCH_2COOH \rightleftharpoons ClCH_2COO^- + H^+;$	$K = 1.54 \times 10^{-3}$
Chromic	$H_2CrO_4 \rightleftharpoons HCrO_4^- + H^+;$	$K_1 = 0.18$
	$HCrO_4^- \rightleftharpoons CrO_4^{--} + H^+;$	$K_2 = 3.3 \times 10^{-6}$
Formic	$HCOOH \rightleftharpoons HCOO^- + H^+;$	$K = 1.76 \times 10^{-4}$
Glycine	$+NH_3CH_2COOH \rightleftharpoons +NH_3CH_2COO^- + H^+;$	$K_1 = 4.5 \times 10^{-3}$
	$+NH_3CH_2COO^- \rightleftharpoons NH_2CH_2COO^- + H^+;$	$K_2 = 1.7 \times 10^{-10}$
Hydrocyanic	$HCN \rightleftharpoons CN^- + H^+;$	$K = 7.2 \times 10^{-10}$
Hydrofluoric	$HF \rightleftharpoons F^- + H^+;$	$K = 6.7 \times 10^{-4}$
Hydrogen sulfide	$H_2S \rightleftharpoons HS^- + H^+;$	$K_1 = 9.1 \times 10^{-8}$
	$HS^- \rightleftharpoons S^{--} + H^+;$	$K_2 = 1.2 \times 10^{-15}$
Hypochlorous	$HClO \rightleftharpoons ClO^- + H^+;$	$K = 1.1 \times 10^{-8}$
Iodic	$HIO_3 \rightleftharpoons IO_3^- + H^+;$	$K = 0.2$

Acids (continued)

Acid	Ionization Equilibrium	
Nitrous	$HNO_2 \rightleftharpoons NO_2^- + H^+$;	$K = 5.1 \times 10^{-4}$
Oxalic	$H_2C_2O_4 \rightleftharpoons HC_2O_4^- + H^+$;	$K_1 = 6.5 \times 10^{-2}$
	$HC_2O_4^- \rightleftharpoons C_2O_4^{--} + H^+$;	$K_2 = 6.1 \times 10^{-5}$

Phenol

$$\rightleftharpoons \quad + H^+; \qquad K = 1.1 \times 10^{-10}$$

Phosphoric	$H_3PO_4 \rightleftharpoons H_2PO_4^- + H^+$;	$K_1 = 7.5 \times 10^{-3}$
	$H_2PO_4^- \rightleftharpoons HPO_4^{--} + H^+$;	$K_2 = 6.2 \times 10^{-8}$
	$HPO_4^{--} \rightleftharpoons PO_4^{---} + H^+$;	$K_3 = 4.8 \times 10^{-13}$
Phosphorous	$H_3PO_3 \rightleftharpoons H_2PO_3^- + H^+$;	$K_1 = 5 \times 10^{-2}$
	$H_2PO_3^- \rightleftharpoons HPO_3^{--} + H^+$;	$K_2 = 2.6 \times 10^{-7}$
Propionic	$CH_3CH_2COOH \rightleftharpoons CH_3CH_2COO^- + H^+$; $K = 1.3 \times 10^{-5}$	

Salicylic

$$\rightleftharpoons \quad + H^+; \quad K = 1.38 \times 10^{-4}$$

Sulfamic	$NH_2SO_3H \rightleftharpoons NH_2SO_3^- + H^+$;	$K = 0.10$
Sulfuric	$H_2SO_4 \rightleftharpoons HSO_4^- + H^+$;	$K_1 \gg 1$
	$HSO_4^- \rightleftharpoons SO_4^{--} + H^+$;	$K_2 = 1.2 \times 10^{-2}$
Sulfurous	$H_2SO_3 \rightleftharpoons HSO_3^- + H^+$;	$K_1 = 1.7 \times 10^{-2}$
	$HSO_3^- \rightleftharpoons SO_3^{--} + H^+$;	$K_2 = 6.5 \times 10^{-8}$

Bases

Base	Ionization Equilibrium	
Ammonia	$NH_3 + H_2O \rightleftharpoons NH_4^+ + OH^-$;	$K = 1.80 \times 10^{-5}$

Aniline

$$+ H_2O \rightleftharpoons \quad + OH^-; \qquad K = 4.0 \times 10^{-10}$$

Ethanolamine	$HOCH_2CH_2NH_2 + H_2O \rightleftharpoons HOCH_2CH_2NH_3^+ + OH^-$;	
	$K = 3.2 \times 10^{-5}$	
Ethylamine	$CH_3CH_2NH_2 + H_2O \rightleftharpoons CH_3CH_2NH_3^+ + OH^-$;	
	$K = 4.3 \times 10^{-4}$	
Ethylenediamine	$NH_2CH_2CH_2NH_2 + H_2O \rightleftharpoons NH_2CH_2CH_2NH_3^+ + OH^-$;	
	$K_1 = 8.5 \times 10^{-5}$	
	$NH_2CH_2CH_2NH_3^+ + H_2O \rightleftharpoons {}^+NH_3CH_2CH_2NH_3^+ + OH^-$;	
	$K_2 = 7.1 \times 10^{-8}$	
Hydrazine	$H_2NNH_2 + H_2O \rightleftharpoons H_2NNH_3^+ + OH^-$; $K = 1.3 \times 10^{-6}$	
Hydroxylamine	$HONH_2 + H_2O \rightleftharpoons HONH_3^+ + OH^-$; $K = 9.1 \times 10^{-9}$	
Methylamine	$CH_3NH_2 + H_2O \rightleftharpoons CH_3NH_3^+ + OH^-$; $K = 4.8 \times 10^{-4}$	

Bases (continued)

Base	Ionization Equilibrium

Pyridine

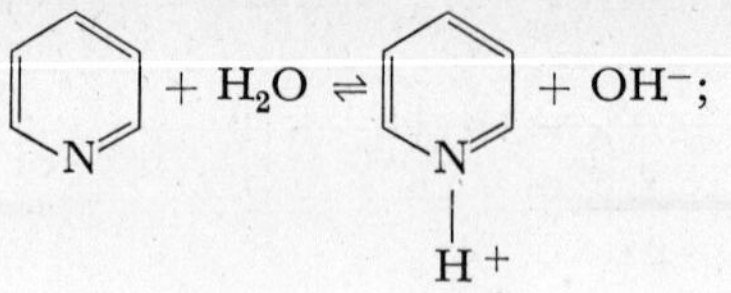

$$\text{(pyridine)} + H_2O \rightleftharpoons \text{(pyridinium, N–H}^+\text{)} + OH^-; \qquad K = 1.7 \times 10^{-9}$$

Tris(hydroxymethyl)-
aminomethane

$$(HOCH_2)_3CNH_2 + H_2O \rightleftharpoons (HOCH_2)_3CNH_3^+ + OH^-;$$
$$K = 1.2 \times 10^{-6}$$

It is common practice to designate the above reactions of acids and bases as ionization equilibria. However, it is much more correct to consider them as *proton-transfer* equilibria, because all such reactions involve the transfer of a proton from a Brönsted-Lowry acid to a Brönsted-Lowry base.

All acid ionizations listed above pertain to water as solvent, the latter acting as the Brönsted-Lowry base (proton acceptor). Thus, the complete proton-transfer reaction for acetic acid should be written as

$$CH_3COOH + H_2O \rightleftharpoons CH_3COO^- + H_3O^+; \quad K = 1.75 \times 10^{-5}$$

to show clearly the true nature of this equilibrium. Other equilibria for acids can be similarly written.

On the other hand, correct proton-transfer reactions are listed above for the various bases, although it should be noted that water acts as a Brönsted-Lowry acid by donating one of its protons to the base.

Appendix 3

STEPWISE AND OVERALL FORMATION CONSTANTS FOR METAL ION COMPLEXES*

(All values are valid at or near room temperature.)

Ammonia, NH_3

$Ag^+ + NH_3 = AgNH_3^+$	$K_1 = 2.5 \times 10^3$
$AgNH_3^+ + NH_3 = Ag(NH_3)_2^+$	$K_2 = 1.0 \times 10^4$
$Cd^{++} + NH_3 = CdNH_3^{++}$	$K_1 = 400$
$CdNH_3^{++} + NH_3 = Cd(NH_3)_2^{++}$	$K_2 = 130$
$Cd(NH_3)_2^{++} + NH_3 = Cd(NH_3)_3^{++}$	$K_3 = 25$
$Cd(NH_3)_3^{++} + NH_3 = Cd(NH_3)_4^{++}$	$K_4 = 8$
$Cd(NH_3)_4^{++} + NH_3 = Cd(NH_3)_5^{++}$	$K_5 = 0.5$
$Cd(NH_3)_5^{++} + NH_3 = Cd(NH_3)_6^{++}$	$K_6 = 0.02$
$Co^{++} + NH_3 = CoNH_3^{++}$	$K_1 = 130$
$CoNH_3^{++} + NH_3 = Co(NH_3)_2^{++}$	$K_2 = 40$
$Co(NH_3)_2^{++} + NH_3 = Co(NH_3)_3^{++}$	$K_3 = 10$
$Co(NH_3)_3^{++} + NH_3 = Co(NH_3)_4^{++}$	$K_4 = 5$
$Co(NH_3)_4^{++} + NH_3 = Co(NH_3)_5^{++}$	$K_5 = 1$
$Co(NH_3)_5^{++} + NH_3 = Co(NH_3)_6^{++}$	$K_6 = 0.2$
$Co^{+++} + NH_3 = CoNH_3^{+++}$	$K_1 = 2.0 \times 10^7$
$CoNH_3^{+++} + NH_3 = Co(NH_3)_2^{+++}$	$K_2 = 5.0 \times 10^6$
$Co(NH_3)_2^{+++} + NH_3 = Co(NH_3)_3^{+++}$	$K_3 = 1.3 \times 10^6$
$Co(NH_3)_3^{+++} + NH_3 = Co(NH_3)_4^{+++}$	$K_4 = 4.0 \times 10^5$
$Co(NH_3)_4^{+++} + NH_3 = Co(NH_3)_5^{+++}$	$K_5 = 1.3 \times 10^5$
$Co(NH_3)_5^{+++} + NH_3 = Co(NH_3)_6^{+++}$	$K_6 = 2.5 \times 10^4$
$Cu^+ + NH_3 = CuNH_3^+$	$K_1 = 8.0 \times 10^5$
$CuNH_3^+ + NH_3 = Cu(NH_3)_2^+$	$K_2 = 8.0 \times 10^4$
$Cu^{++} + NH_3 = CuNH_3^{++}$	$K_1 = 1.3 \times 10^4$
$CuNH_3^{++} + NH_3 = Cu(NH_3)_2^{++}$	$K_2 = 3.2 \times 10^3$
$Cu(NH_3)_2^{++} + NH_3 = Cu(NH_3)_3^{++}$	$K_3 = 800$
$Cu(NH_3)_3^{++} + NH_3 = Cu(NH_3)_4^{++}$	$K_4 = 130$
$Cu(NH_3)_4^{++} + NH_3 = Cu(NH_3)_5^{++}$	$K_5 = 0.32$
$Hg^{++} + NH_3 = HgNH_3^{++}$	$K_1 = 6.3 \times 10^8$
$HgNH_3^{++} + NH_3 = Hg(NH_3)_2^{++}$	$K_2 = 5.0 \times 10^8$
$Hg(NH_3)_2^{++} + NH_3 = Hg(NH_3)_3^{++}$	$K_3 = 10$
$Hg(NH_3)_3^{++} + NH_3 = Hg(NH_3)_4^{++}$	$K_4 = 8$
$Ni^{++} + NH_3 = NiNH_3^{++}$	$K_1 = 630$
$NiNH_3^{++} + NH_3 = Ni(NH_3)_2^{++}$	$K_2 = 160$
$Ni(NH_3)_2^{++} + NH_3 = Ni(NH_3)_3^{++}$	$K_3 = 50$
$Ni(NH_3)_3^{++} + NH_3 = Ni(NH_3)_4^{++}$	$K_4 = 16$
$Ni(NH_3)_4^{++} + NH_3 = Ni(NH_3)_5^{++}$	$K_5 = 5$

* See footnote at end of table.

Ammonia, NH_3 (continued)

$Ni(NH_3)_5^{++} + NH_3 = Ni(NH_3)_6^{++}$ $K_6 = 1$

$Zn^{++} + NH_3 = ZnNH_3^{++}$ $K_1 = 190$

$ZnNH_3^{++} + NH_3 = Zn(NH_3)_2^{++}$ $K_2 = 210$

$Zn(NH_3)_2^{++} + NH_3 = Zn(NH_3)_3^{++}$ $K_3 = 250$

$Zn(NH_3)_3^{++} + NH_3 = Zn(NH_3)_4^{++}$ $K_4 = 110$

Bromide, Br^-

$Bi^{+++} + Br^- = BiBr^{++}$ $K_1 = 2.0 \times 10^4$

$BiBr^{++} + Br^- = BiBr_2^+$ $K_2 = 18$

$BiBr_2^+ + Br^- = BiBr_3$ $K_3 = 2.2$

$BiBr_3 + Br^- = BiBr_4^-$ $K_4 = 85$

$Cd^{++} + Br^- = CdBr^+$ $K_1 = 56$

$CdBr^+ + Br^- = CdBr_2$ $K_2 = 3.9$

$CdBr_2 + Br^- = CdBr_3^-$ $K_3 = 9.5$

$CdBr_3^- + Br^- = CdBr_4^{--}$ $K_4 = 2.4$

$Hg^{++} + Br^- = HgBr^+$ $K_1 = 1.1 \times 10^9$

$HgBr^+ + Br^- = HgBr_2$ $K_2 = 1.9 \times 10^8$

$HgBr_2 + Br^- = HgBr_3^-$ $K_3 = 260$

$HgBr_3^- + Br^- = HgBr_4^{--}$ $K_4 = 18$

$Pb^{++} + Br^- = PbBr^+$ $K_1 = 14$

$PbBr^+ + Br^- = PbBr_2$ $K_2 = 5.9$

$PbBr_2 + 2\,Br^- = PbBr_4^{--}$ $K_3K_4 = 13$

$Zn^{++} + Br^- = ZnBr^+$ $K_1 = 0.25$

Chloride, Cl^-

$Bi^{+++} + Cl^- = BiCl^{++}$ $K_1 = 270$

$BiCl^{++} + Cl^- = BiCl_2^+$ $K_2 = 100$

$BiCl_2^+ + Cl^- = BiCl_3$ $K_3 = 25$

$BiCl_3 + Cl^- = BiCl_4^-$ $K_4 = 2.5$

$BiCl_4^- + Cl^- = BiCl_5^{--}$ $K_5 = 3.2$

$Cd^{++} + Cl^- = CdCl^+$ $K_1 = 22$

$CdCl^+ + Cl^- = CdCl_2$ $K_2 = 2.7$

$CdCl_2 + Cl^- = CdCl_3^-$ $K_3 = 2.5$

$Cu^+ + 2\,Cl^- = CuCl_2^-$ $\beta_2 = 5.0 \times 10^4$

$Fe^{+++} + Cl^- = FeCl^{++}$ $K_1 = 30$

$FeCl^{++} + Cl^- = FeCl_2^+$ $K_2 = 4.5$

$FeCl_2^+ + Cl^- = FeCl_3$ $K_3 = 0.10$

$Hg^{++} + Cl^- = HgCl^+$ $K_1 = 1.9 \times 10^5$

$HgCl^+ + Cl^- = HgCl_2$ $K_2 = 3.2 \times 10^7$

$HgCl_2 + Cl^- = HgCl_3^-$ $K_3 = 14$

$HgCl_3^- + Cl^- = HgCl_4^{--}$ $K_4 = 10$

$Pb^{++} + Cl^- = PbCl^+$ $K_1 = 44$

$PbCl^+ + 2\,Cl^- = PbCl_3^-$ $K_2K_3 = 1.7$

Cyanide, CN^-

$Ag^+ + 2\,CN^- = Ag(CN)_2^-$ $\beta_2 = 1.26 \times 10^{21}$

$Cd^{++} + CN^- = CdCN^+$ $K_1 = 3.5 \times 10^5$

$CdCN^+ + CN^- = Cd(CN)_2$ $K_2 = 1.2 \times 10^5$

$Cd(CN)_2 + CN^- = Cd(CN)_3^-$ $K_3 = 5.0 \times 10^4$

$Cd(CN)_3^- + CN^- = Cd(CN)_4^{--}$ $K_4 = 3.6 \times 10^3$

$Co^{++} + 6\,CN^- = Co(CN)_6^{----}$ $\beta_6 = 1.0 \times 10^{19}$

$Cu^+ + 2\,CN^- = Cu(CN)_2^-$ $\beta_2 = 1.0 \times 10^{24}$

$Cu(CN)_2^- + CN^- = Cu(CN)_3^{--}$ $K_3 = 3.9 \times 10^4$

$Hg^{++} + CN^- = HgCN^+$ $K_1 = 1.0 \times 10^{18}$

Cyanide, CN^- (continued)

$$HgCN^+ + CN^- = Hg(CN)_2 \qquad\qquad K_2 = 5.0 \times 10^{16}$$
$$Hg(CN)_2 + CN^- = Hg(CN)_3^- \qquad\qquad K_3 = 6.3 \times 10^3$$
$$Hg(CN)_3^- + CN^- = Hg(CN)_4^{--} \qquad\qquad K_4 = 1.0 \times 10^3$$
$$Ni^{++} + 4\ CN^- = Ni(CN)_4^{--} \qquad\qquad \beta_4 = 1.0 \times 10^{22}$$
$$Zn^{++} + 3\ CN^- = Zn(CN)_3^- \qquad\qquad \beta_3 = 3.2 \times 10^{17}$$
$$Zn(CN)_3^- + CN^- = Zn(CN)_4^{--} \qquad\qquad K_4 = 500$$

Ethylenediamine, $H_2NCH_2CH_2NH_2$ (en)

$$Ag^+ + en = Ag(en)^+ \qquad\qquad K_1 = 5.0 \times 10^4$$
$$Ag(en)^+ + en = Ag(en)_2^+ \qquad\qquad K_2 = 1.4 \times 10^3$$
$$Cd^{++} + en = Cd(en)^{++} \qquad\qquad K_1 = 3.0 \times 10^5$$
$$Cd(en)^{++} + en = Cd(en)_2^{++} \qquad\qquad K_2 = 3.6 \times 10^4$$
$$Cd(en)_2^{++} + en = Cd(en)_3^{++} \qquad\qquad K_3 = 120$$
$$Co^{++} + en = Co(en)^{++} \qquad\qquad K_1 = 7.8 \times 10^5$$
$$Co(en)^{++} + en = Co(en)_2^{++} \qquad\qquad K_2 = 6.9 \times 10^4$$
$$Co(en)_2^{++} + en = Co(en)_3^{++} \qquad\qquad K_3 = 1.3 \times 10^3$$
$$Co^{+++} + 3\ en = Co(en)_3^{+++} \qquad\qquad \beta_3 = 4.9 \times 10^{48}$$
$$Cu^+ + 2\ en = Cu(en)_2^+ \qquad\qquad \beta_2 = 6.3 \times 10^{10}$$
$$Cu^{++} + en = Cu(en)^{++} \qquad\qquad K_1 = 3.5 \times 10^{10}$$
$$Cu(en)^{++} + en = Cu(en)_2^{++} \qquad\qquad K_2 = 1.1 \times 10^9$$
$$Hg^{++} + 2\ en = Hg(en)_2^{++} \qquad\qquad \beta_2 = 2.5 \times 10^{23}$$
$$Ni^{++} + en = Ni(en)^{++} \qquad\qquad K_1 = 4.6 \times 10^7$$
$$Ni(en)^{++} + en = Ni(en)_2^{++} \qquad\qquad K_2 = 2.5 \times 10^6$$
$$Ni(en)_2^{++} + en = Ni(en)_3^{++} \qquad\qquad K_3 = 3.4 \times 10^4$$
$$Zn^{++} + en = Zn(en)^{++} \qquad\qquad K_1 = 5.1 \times 10^5$$
$$Zn(en)^{++} + en = Zn(en)_2^{++} \qquad\qquad K_2 = 4.6 \times 10^4$$
$$Zn(en)_2^{++} + en = Zn(en)_3^{++} \qquad\qquad K_3 = 51$$

Ethylenediaminetetraacetate, $(^-OOCCH_2)_2NCH_2CH_2N(CH_2COO^-)_2$ or (Y^{-4})

$$Al^{+++} + Y^{-4} = AlY^- \qquad\qquad K_1 = 1.35 \times 10^{16}$$
$$Ba^{++} + Y^{-4} = BaY^{--} \qquad\qquad K_1 = 5.75 \times 10^7$$
$$Cd^{++} + Y^{-4} = CdY^{--} \qquad\qquad K_1 = 2.88 \times 10^{16}$$
$$Ca^{++} + Y^{-4} = CaY^{--} \qquad\qquad K_1 = 5.01 \times 10^{10}$$
$$Co^{++} + Y^{-4} = CoY^{--} \qquad\qquad K_1 = 2.04 \times 10^{16}$$
$$Cu^{++} + Y^{-4} = CuY^{--} \qquad\qquad K_1 = 6.30 \times 10^{18}$$
$$Ga^{+++} + Y^{-4} = GaY^- \qquad\qquad K_1 = 1.86 \times 10^{20}$$
$$In^{+++} + Y^{-4} = InY^- \qquad\qquad K_1 = 8.91 \times 10^{24}$$
$$Fe^{++} + Y^{-4} = FeY^{--} \qquad\qquad K_1 = 2.14 \times 10^{14}$$
$$Fe^{+++} + Y^{-4} = FeY^- \qquad\qquad K_1 = 1.3 \times 10^{25}$$
$$Pb^{++} + Y^{-4} = PbY^{--} \qquad\qquad K_1 = 1.10 \times 10^{18}$$
$$Mg^{++} + Y^{-4} = MgY^{--} \qquad\qquad K_1 = 4.90 \times 10^8$$
$$Mn^{++} + Y^{-4} = MnY^{--} \qquad\qquad K_1 = 1.10 \times 10^{14}$$
$$Hg^{++} + Y^{-4} = HgY^{--} \qquad\qquad K_1 = 6.30 \times 10^{21}$$

Ethylenediaminetetraacetate,
($^-$OOCCH$_2$)$_2$NCH$_2$CH$_2$N(CH$_2$COO$^-$)$_2$ or (Y^{-4}) (continued)

Ni^{++} + Y^{-4} = NiY^{--}	$K_1 = 4.16 \times 10^{18}$
Sc^{+++} + Y^{-4} = ScY$^-$	$K_1 = 1.3 \times 10^{23}$
Ag$^+$ + Y^{-4} = AgY^{---}	$K_1 = 2.09 \times 10^7$
Sr^{++} + Y^{-4} = SrY^{--}	$K_1 = 4.26 \times 10^8$
Th^{++++} + Y^{-4} = ThY	$K_1 = 1.6 \times 10^{23}$
Ti^{+++} + Y^{-4} = TiY$^-$	$K_1 = 2.0 \times 10^{21}$
TiO^{++} + Y^{-4} = TiOY^{--}	$K_1 = 2.0 \times 10^{17}$
V^{++} + Y^{-4} = VY^{--}	$K_1 = 5.01 \times 10^{12}$
V^{+++} + Y^{-4} = VY$^-$	$K_1 = 8.0 \times 10^{25}$
VO^{++} + Y^{-4} = VOY^{--}	$K_1 = 5.89 \times 10^{18}$
Y^{+++} + Y^{-4} = YY$^-$	$K_1 = 1.23 \times 10^{18}$
Zn^{++} + Y^{-4} = ZnY^{--}	$K_1 = 3.16 \times 10^{16}$

Iodide, I$^-$

Bi^{+++} + 6 I$^-$ = BiI$_6$$^{---}$	$\beta_6 = 2.5 \times 10^{19}$
Cd^{++} + I$^-$ = CdI$^+$	$K_1 = 190$
CdI$^+$ + I$^-$ = CdI$_2$	$K_2 = 44$
CdI$_2$ + I$^-$ = CdI$_3$$^-$	$K_3 = 12$
CdI$_3$$^-$ + I$^-$ = CdI$_4$$^{--}$	$K_4 = 13$
Cu$^+$ + 2 I$^-$ = CuI$_2$$^-$	$\beta_2 = 5.8 \times 10^8$
Hg^{++} + I$^-$ = HgI$^+$	$K_1 = 7.4 \times 10^{12}$
HgI$^+$ + I$^-$ = HgI$_2$	$K_2 = 8.9 \times 10^{10}$
HgI$_2$ + I$^-$ = HgI$_3$$^-$	$K_3 = 6.0 \times 10^3$
HgI$_3$$^-$ + I$^-$ = HgI$_4$$^{--}$	$K_4 = 170$
Pb^{++} + I$^-$ = PbI$^+$	$K_1 = 20$
PbI$^+$ + I$^-$ = PbI$_2$	$K_2 = 30$
PbI$_2$ + I$^-$ = PbI$_3$$^-$	$K_3 = 4$
PbI$_3$$^-$ + I$^-$ = PbI$_4$$^{--}$	$K_4 = 3$

Thiocyanate, SCN$^-$

Ag$^+$ + 2 SCN$^-$ = Ag(SCN)$_2$$^-$	$\beta_2 = 3.7 \times 10^7$
Ag(SCN)$_2$$^-$ + SCN$^-$ = Ag(SCN)$_3$$^{--}$	$K_3 = 320$
Ag(SCN)$_3$$^{--}$ + SCN$^-$ = Ag(SCN)$_4$$^{---}$	$K_4 = 10$
Cu$^+$ + 2 SCN$^-$ = Cu(SCN)$_2$$^-$	$\beta_2 = 1.3 \times 10^{12}$
Cu(SCN)$_2$$^-$ + SCN$^-$ = Cu(SCN)$_3$$^{--}$	$K_3 = 1.5 \times 10^5$
Fe^{+++} + SCN$^-$ = FeSCN^{++}	$K_1 = 138$
FeSCN^{++} + SCN$^-$ = Fe(SCN)$_2$$^+$	$K_2 = 20$
Hg^{++} + 2 SCN$^-$ = Hg(SCN)$_2$	$\beta_2 = 3.1 \times 10^{17}$
Hg(SCN)$_2$ + 2 SCN$^-$ = Hg(SCN)$_4$$^{--}$	$K_3K_4 = 5.8 \times 10^3$

Thiosulfate, S$_2$O$_3$$^{--}$

Ag$^+$ + S$_2$O$_3$$^{--}$ = AgS$_2$O$_3$$^-$	$K_1 = 6.6 \times 10^8$
AgS$_2$O$_3$$^-$ + S$_2$O$_3$$^{--}$ = Ag(S$_2$O$_3$)$_2$$^{---}$	$K_2 = 4.4 \times 10^4$
Cd^{++} + S$_2$O$_3$$^{--}$ = CdS$_2$O$_3$	$K_1 = 8.3 \times 10^3$
CdS$_2$O$_3$ + S$_2$O$_3$$^{--}$ = Cd(S$_2$O$_3$)$_2$$^{--}$	$K_2 = 330$
Cu$^+$ + S$_2$O$_3$$^{--}$ = CuS$_2$O$_3$$^-$	$K_1 = 1.9 \times 10^{10}$
CuS$_2$O$_3$$^-$ + S$_2$O$_3$$^{--}$ = Cu(S$_2$O$_3$)$_2$$^{---}$	$K_2 = 90$
Hg^{++} + 2 S$_2$O$_3$$^{--}$ = Hg(S$_2$O$_3$)$_2$$^{--}$	$\beta_2 = 2.8 \times 10^{29}$
Hg(S$_2$O$_3$)$_2$$^{--}$ + S$_2$O$_3$$^{--}$ = Hg(S$_2$O$_3$)$_3$$^{----}$	$K_3 = 290$
Pb^{++} + 2 S$_2$O$_3$$^{--}$ = Pb(S$_2$O$_3$)$_2$$^{--}$	$\beta_2 = 1.3 \times 10^5$

*Discussions of the formulation and significance of stepwise (K_n) and overall (B_n) formation constants are presented in Chapter 4.

Appendix 4

STANDARD AND FORMAL POTENTIALS FOR HALF-REACTIONS*

(All values pertain to 25°C and are quoted in volts with respect to the normal hydrogen electrode, taken to have a standard potential of zero.)

Half-Reaction	$E°$
Aluminum	
$Al^{+++} + 3\ e = Al$	-1.66
$Al(OH)_4^- + 3\ e = Al + 4\ OH^-$	-2.35
Antimony	
$Sb_2O_5 + 6\ H^+ + 4\ e = 2\ SbO^+ + 3\ H_2O$	$+0.581$
$Sb + 3\ H^+ + 3\ e = SbH_3$	-0.51
Arsenic	
$H_3AsO_4 + 2\ H^+ + 2\ e = HAsO_2 + 2\ H_2O$	$+0.559$
$HAsO_2 + 3\ H^+ + 3\ e = As + 2\ H_2O$	$+0.248$
$As + 3\ H^+ + 3\ e = AsH_3$	-0.60
Barium	
$Ba^{++} + 2\ e = Ba$	-2.90
Beryllium	
$Be^{++} + 2\ e = Be$	-1.85
Bismuth	
$BiCl_4^- + 3\ e = Bi + 4\ Cl^-$	$+0.16$
$BiO^+ + 2\ H^+ + 3\ e = Bi + H_2O$	$+0.32$
Boron	
$H_2BO_3^- + 5\ H_2O + 8\ e = BH_4^- + 8\ OH^-$	-1.24
$H_2BO_3^- + H_2O + 3\ e = B + 4\ OH^-$	-1.79
Bromine	
$2\ BrO_3^- + 12\ H^+ + 10\ e = Br_2 + 6\ H_2O$	$+1.52$
$Br_2(aq) + 2\ e = 2\ Br^-$	$+1.087$[a]
$Br_2(l) + 2\ e \rightleftharpoons 2\ Br^-$	$+1.065$[a]
$Br_3^- + 2\ e = 3\ Br^-$	$+1.05$
Cadmium	
$Cd^{++} + 2\ e = Cd$	-0.403
$Cd(CN)_4^{--} + 2\ e = Cd + 4\ CN^-$	-1.09
$Cd(NH_3)_4^{++} + 2\ e = Cd + 4\ NH_3$	-0.61

* See footnotes at end of table.

265

Half-Reaction	$E°$
Calcium	
$Ca^{++} + 2\,e = Ca$	-2.87
Carbon	
$2\,CO_2 + 2\,H^+ + 2\,e = H_2C_2O_4$	-0.49
Cerium	
$Ce^{++++} + e = Ce^{+++}$ $(1\,F\,HClO_4)$	$+1.70$
$Ce^{++++} + e = Ce^{+++}$ $(1\,F\,HNO_3)$	$+1.61$
$Ce^{++++} + e = Ce^{+++}$ $(1\,F\,H_2SO_4)$	$+1.44$
Cesium	
$Cs^+ + e = Cs$	-2.92
Chlorine	
$Cl_2 + 2\,e = 2\,Cl^-$	$+1.3595$
$2\,ClO_3^- + 12\,H^+ + 10\,e = Cl_2 + 6\,H_2O$	$+1.47$
$ClO_3^- + 2\,H^+ + e = ClO_2 + H_2O$	$+1.15$
$HClO + H^+ + 2\,e = Cl^- + H_2O$	$+1.49$
$2\,HClO + 2\,H^+ + 2\,e = Cl_2 + 2\,H_2O$	$+1.63$
Chromium	
$Cr_2O_7^{--} + 14\,H^+ + 6\,e = 2\,Cr^{+++} + 7\,H_2O$	$+1.33$
$Cr^{+++} + e = Cr^{++}$	-0.41
$Cr^{++} + 2\,e = Cr$	-0.91
$CrO_4^{--} + 4\,H_2O + 3\,e = Cr(OH)_3 + 5\,OH^-$	-0.13
Cobalt	
$Co^{+++} + e = Co^{++}$	$+1.842$
$Co(NH_3)_6^{+++} + e = Co(NH_3)_6^{++}$	$+0.1$
$Co(OH)_3 + e = Co(OH)_2 + OH^-$	$+0.17$
$Co^{++} + 2\,e = Co$	-0.277
$Co(CN)_6^{---} + e = Co(CN)_6^{----}$	-0.84
Copper	
$Cu^{++} + 2\,e = Cu$	$+0.337$
$Cu^{++} + e = Cu^+$	$+0.153$
$Cu^{++} + I^- + e = CuI$	$+0.86$
$Cu^{++} + 2\,CN^- + e = Cu(CN)_2^-$	$+1.12$
$Cu(CN)_2^- + e = Cu + 2\,CN^-$	-0.43
$Cu(NH_3)_4^{++} + e = Cu(NH_3)_2^+ + 2\,NH_3$	-0.01
$Cu^{++} + 2\,Cl^- + e = CuCl_2^-$	$+0.463$
$CuCl_2^- + e = Cu + 2\,Cl^-$	$+0.177$
Fluorine	
$F_2 + 2\,e = 2\,F^-$	$+2.87$
Gold	
$Au^{+++} + 2\,e = Au^+$	$+1.41$
$Au^{+++} + 3\,e = Au$	$+1.50$
$Au(CN)_2^- + e = Au + 2\,CN^-$	-0.60
$AuCl_2^- + e = Au + 2\,Cl^-$	$+1.15$
$AuCl_4^- + 2\,e = AuCl_2^- + 2\,Cl^-$	$+0.926$
$AuBr_2^- + e = Au + 2\,Br^-$	$+0.959$
$AuBr_4^- + 2\,e = AuBr_2^- + 2\,Br^-$	$+0.802$

Half-Reaction	$E°$
Hydrogen	
$2 H^+ + 2 e = H_2$	0.0000
$2 H_2O + 2 e = H_2 + 2 OH^-$	-0.828
Iodine	
$I_2(aq) + 2 e = 2 I^-$	$+0.6197^b$
$I_3^- + 2 e = 3 I^-$	$+0.5355$
$I_2(s) + 2 e = 2 I^-$	$+0.5345^b$
$2 IO_3^- + 12 H^+ + 10 e = I_2 + 6 H_2O$	$+1.20$
$2 ICl_2^- + 2 e = I_2 + 4 Cl^-$	$+1.06$
Iron	
$Fe^{+++} + e = Fe^{++}$	$+0.771$
$Fe^{+++} + e = Fe^{++}$ $\quad$ $(1 F HCl)$	$+0.70$
$Fe^{+++} + e = Fe^{++}$ $\quad$ $(1 F H_2SO_4)$	$+0.68$
$Fe^{+++} + e = Fe^{++}$ $\quad$ $(0.5 F H_3PO_4 - 1 F H_2SO_4)$	$+0.61$
$Fe(CN)_6^{---} + e = Fe(CN)_6^{----}$	$+0.36$
$Fe(CN)_6^{---} + e = Fe(CN)_6^{----}$ $\quad$ $(1 F HCl or HClO_4)$	$+0.71$
$Fe^{++} + 2 e = Fe$	-0.440
Lead	
$Pb^{++} + 2 e = Pb$	-0.126
$PbSO_4 + 2 e = Pb + SO_4^{--}$	-0.3563
$PbO_2 + SO_4^{--} + 4 H^+ + 2 e = PbSO_4 + 2 H_2O$	$+1.685$
$PbO_2 + 4 H^+ + 2 e = Pb^{++} + 2 H_2O$	$+1.455$
Lithium	
$Li^+ + e = Li$	-3.045
Magnesium	
$Mg^{++} + 2 e = Mg$	-2.37
$Mg(OH)_2 + 2 e = Mg + 2 OH^-$	-2.69
Manganese	
$Mn^{++} + 2 e = Mn$	-1.18
$MnO_4^- + 4 H^+ + 3 e = MnO_2 + 2 H_2O$	$+1.695$
$MnO_4^- + 8 H^+ + 5 e = Mn^{++} + 4 H_2O$	$+1.51$
$MnO_2 + 4 H^+ + 2 e = Mn^{++} + 2 H_2O$	$+1.23$
$MnO_4^- + e = MnO_4^{--}$	$+0.564$
$Mn^{+++} + e = Mn^{++}$ $\quad$ $(8 F H_2SO_4)$	$+1.51$
Mercury	
$2 Hg^{++} + 2 e = Hg_2^{++}$	$+0.920$
$Hg^{++} + 2 e = Hg$	$+0.854$
$Hg_2^{++} + 2 e = 2 Hg$	$+0.789$
$Hg_2SO_4 + 2 e = 2 Hg + SO_4^{--}$	$+0.6151$
$HgCl_4^{--} + 2 e = Hg + 4 Cl^-$	$+0.48$
$Hg_2Cl_2 + 2 e = 2 Hg + 2 Cl^-$ $\quad$ $(0.1 F KCl)$	$+0.334$
$Hg_2Cl_2 + 2 e = 2 Hg + 2 Cl^-$ $\quad$ $(1 F KCl)$	$+0.280$
$Hg_2Cl_2 + 2 K^+ + 2 e = 2 Hg + 2 KCl(s)$	$+0.2415$
(saturated calomel electrode)	
Molybdenum	
$Mo^{+6} + e = Mo^{+5}$ $\quad$ $(2 F HCl)$	$+0.53$
$Mo^{++++} + e = Mo^{+++}$ $\quad$ $(4 F H_2SO_4)$	$+0.1$

Half-Reaction	$E°$
Neptunium	
$Np^{++++} + e = Np^{+++}$	$+0.147$
$NpO_2^+ + 4 H^+ + e = Np^{++++} + 2 H_2O$	$+0.75$
$NpO_2^{++} + e = NpO_2^+$	$+1.15$
Nickel	
$Ni^{++} + 2 e = Ni$	-0.24
$NiO_2 + 4 H^+ + 2 e = Ni^{++} + 2 H_2O$	$+1.68$
Nitrogen	
$NO_2 + H^+ + e = HNO_2$	$+1.07$
$NO_2 + 2 H^+ + 2 e = NO + H_2O$	$+1.03$
$HNO_2 + H^+ + e = NO + H_2O$	$+1.00$
$NO_3^- + 4 H^+ + 3 e = NO + 2 H_2O$	$+0.96$
$NO_3^- + 3 H^+ + 2 e = HNO_2 + H_2O$	$+0.94$
$NO_3^- + 2 H^+ + e = NO_2 + H_2O$	$+0.80$
$N_2 + 5 H^+ + 4 e = N_2H_5^+$	-0.23
Osmium	
$OsO_4 + 8 H^+ + 8 e = Os + 4 H_2O$	$+0.85$
$OsCl_6^{--} + e = OsCl_6^{---}$	$+0.85$
$OsCl_6^{---} + e = Os^{++} + 6 Cl^-$	$+0.4$
$Os^{++} + 2 e = Os$	$+0.85$
Oxygen	
$O_3 + 2 H^+ + 2 e = O_2 + H_2O$	$+2.07$
$H_2O_2 + 2 H^+ + 2 e = 2 H_2O$	$+1.77$
$O_2 + 4 H^+ + 4 e = 2 H_2O$	$+1.229$
$H_2O_2 + 2 e = 2 OH^-$	$+0.88$
$O_2 + 2 H^+ + 2 e = H_2O_2$	$+0.682$
Palladium	
$Pd^{++} + 2 e = Pd$	$+0.987$
$PdCl_6^{--} + 2 e = PdCl_4^{--} + 2 Cl^-$	$+1.288$
$PdCl_4^{--} + 2 e = Pd + 4 Cl^-$	$+0.623$
Phosphorus	
$H_3PO_4 + 2 H^+ + 2 e = H_3PO_3 + H_2O$	-0.276
$H_3PO_3 + 2 H^+ + 2 e = H_3PO_2 + H_2O$	-0.50
Platinum	
$PtCl_6^{--} + 2 e = PtCl_4^{--} + 2 Cl^-$	$+0.68$
$PtBr_6^{--} + 2 e = PtBr_4^{--} + 2 Br^-$	$+0.59$
$Pt(OH)_2 + 2 H^+ + 2 e = Pt + 2 H_2O$	$+0.98$
Plutonium	
$PuO_2^+ + 4 H^+ + e = Pu^{++++} + 2 H_2O$	$+1.15$
$PuO_2^{++} + 4 H^+ + 2 e = Pu^{++++} + 2 H_2O$	$+1.067$
$Pu^{++++} + e = Pu^{+++}$	$+0.97$
$PuO_2^{++} + e = PuO_2^+$	$+0.93$
Potassium	
$K^+ + e = K$	-2.925
Radium	
$Ra^{++} + 2 e = Ra$	-2.92

Half-Reaction	$E°$

Rubidium

$Rb^+ + e = Rb$ -2.925

Selenium

$SeO_4^{--} + 4 H^+ + 2 e = H_2SeO_3 + H_2O$ $+1.15$
$H_2SeO_3 + 4 H^+ + 4 e = Se + 3 H_2O$ $+0.740$
$Se + 2 H^+ + 2 e = H_2Se$ -0.40

Silver

$Ag^+ + e = Ag$ $+0.7995$
$Ag^{++} + e = Ag^+$ $(4 F HNO_3)$ $+1.927$
$AgCl + e = Ag + Cl^-$ $+0.2222$
$AgBr + e = Ag + Br^-$ $+0.073$
$AgI + e = Ag + I^-$ -0.151
$Ag_2O + H_2O + 2 e = 2 Ag + 2 OH^-$ $+0.342$
$Ag_2S + 2 e = 2 Ag + S^{--}$ -0.71

Sodium

$Na^+ + e = Na$ -2.714

Strontium

$Sr^{++} + 2 e = Sr$ -2.89

Sulfur

$S + 2 H^+ + 2 e = H_2S$ $+0.141$
$S_4O_6^{--} + 2 e = 2 S_2O_3^{--}$ $+0.08$
$SO_4^{--} + 4 H^+ + 2 e = H_2SO_3 + H_2O$ $+0.17$
$S_2O_8^{--} + 2 e = 2 SO_4^{--}$ $+2.01$
$SO_4^{--} + H_2O + 2 e = SO_3^{--} + 2 OH^-$ -0.93
$2 H_2SO_3 + 2 H^+ + 4 e = S_2O_3^{--} + 3 H_2O$ $+0.40$
$2 SO_3^{--} + 3 H_2O + 4 e = S_2O_3^{--} + 6 OH^-$ -0.58
$SO_3^{--} + 3 H_2O + 4 e = S + 6 OH^-$ -0.66

Thallium

$Tl^{+++} + 2 e = Tl^+$ $+1.25$
$Tl^+ + e = Tl$ -0.3363

Tin

$Sn^{++} + 2 e = Sn$ -0.136
$Sn^{++++} + 2 e = Sn^{++}$ $+0.154$
$SnCl_6^{--} + 2 e = SnCl_4^{--} + 2 Cl^-$ $(1 F HCl)$ $+0.14$
$Sn(OH)_6^{--} + 2 e = HSnO_2^- + H_2O + 3 OH^-$ -0.93
$HSnO_2^- + H_2O + 2 e = Sn + 3 OH^-$ -0.91

Titanium

$Ti^{++} + 2 e = Ti$ -1.63
$Ti^{+++} + e = Ti^{++}$ -0.37
$TiO^{++} + 2 H^+ + e = Ti^{+++} + H_2O$ $+0.10$
$Ti^{++++} + e = Ti^{+++}$ $(5 F H_3PO_4)$ -0.15

Tungsten

$W^{+6} + e = W^{+5}$ $(12 F HCl)$ $+0.26$
$W^{+5} + e = W^{+4}$ $(12 F HCl)$ -0.3
$W(CN)_8^{---} + e = W(CN)_8^{----}$ $+0.48$
$2 WO_3(s) + 2 H^+ + 2 e = W_2O_5(s) + H_2O$ -0.03
$W_2O_5(s) + 2 H^+ + 2 e = 2 WO_2(s) + H_2O$ -0.043

Half-Reaction	$E°$
Uranium	
$U^{++++} + e = U^{+++}$	-0.61
$UO_2^{++} + e = UO_2^+$	$+0.05$
$UO_2^{++} + 4\,H^+ + 2\,e = U^{++++} + 2\,H_2O$	$+0.334$
$UO_2^+ + 4\,H^+ + e = U^{++++} + 2\,H_2O$	$+0.62$
Vanadium	
$VO_2^+ + 2\,H^+ + e = VO^{++} + H_2O$	$+1.000$
$VO^{++} + 2\,H^+ + e = V^{+++} + H_2O$	$+0.361$
$V^{+++} + e = V^{++}$	-0.255
$V^{++} + 2\,e = V$	-1.18
Zinc	
$Zn^{++} + 2\,e = Zn$	-0.763
$Zn(NH_3)_4^{++} + 2\,e = Zn + 4\,NH_3$	-1.04
$Zn(CN)_4^{--} + 2\,e = Zn + 4\,CN^-$	-1.26
$Zn(OH)_4^{--} + 2\,e = Zn + 4\,OH^-$	-1.22

The *standard potential* for a redox couple is defined on page 210 as the emf or potential (sign and magnitude) of an electrode consisting of that redox couple under standard-state conditions measured in a galvanic cell against the normal hydrogen electrode at 25°C.

Formal potentials, properly designated by the symbol $E^{°\prime}$ and defined on page 216, are italicized in the above table. The solution condition to which each formal potential pertains is written in parentheses following the half-reaction.

[a] The half-reaction and standard potential

$$Br_2(aq) + 2\,e = 2\,Br^-; \quad E° = +1.087 \text{ v}$$

pertain to the system in which the activity of dissolved molecular bromine, Br_2, as well as the activity of the bromide ion, is unity in water. Actually, this is an impossible situation because the solubility of Br_2 in water is only about 0.21 M at 25°C.

On the other hand, the half-reaction and standard potential

$$Br_2(l) + 2\,e = 2\,Br^-; \quad E° = +1.065 \text{ v}$$

apply to an electrode system in which excess *liquid* bromine is in equilibrium with an aqueous solution containing bromide ion at unit activity. It follows that an aqueous solution in equilibrium with liquid bromine will be saturated with respect to molecular bromine at a concentration (activity) of 0.21 M.

Thus, these two standard potentials are different because the former refers to the (hypothetical) situation in which the concentration (activity) of $Br_2(aq)$ is taken to be unity, whereas the latter refers to the physically real situation for which the concentration (activity) of $Br_2(aq)$ is only 0.21 M.

[b] The reason for the difference between the two entries

$$I_2(aq) + 2\,e = 2\,I^-; \quad E° = +0.6197 \text{ v}$$

and

$$I_2(s) + 2\,e = 2\,I^-; \quad E° = +0.5345 \text{ v}$$

is essentially the same as that stated in the preceding footnote. The first half-reaction requires (hypothetically) an aqueous molecular iodine concentration or activity of unity, whereas the second half-reaction specifies that excess *solid* iodine be in equilibrium with an aqueous, iodide solution of unit activity. Since the solubility of molecular iodine in water at 25°C is approximately 0.00133 M, it is impossible to ever have an aqueous solution containing 1 M molecular iodine. Thus, the standard potential for the second half-reaction will be considerably less oxidizing or less positive than the value for the first half-reaction.

Appendix 5

ANSWERS TO NUMERICAL PROBLEMS

Chapter 1

1. 0.0172; 0.0828; 0.0258
2. 0.00444
7. 0.00755; 0.000772
8. 0.0123; 35.0; 189
9. 4.25; 1.21×10^4
10. 1.01×10^{-6}; 2.86×10^{-8}; 1.26×10^{-6}
11. 0.0247
12. 1.72×10^{-4}
13. 7.65
14. 3.16×10^{-7}
15. 0.0240
16. 50.6; 50.6
18. 0.0741; 2.76×10^{-4}
19. 33.1
20. 0.033
21. 0.725; 0.525
23. 4.66×10^{-4}; 0.388
25. 0.153; 0.306; 1.78×10^{-4}
26. +78.12; +31.1; −16.73; −24.14; −17.05; +59.9; +38.9
27. 8.7×10^{-6}; 6.8×10^5; 1.0×10^{-39}; 4.8×10^{18}; 8.3×10^{-17}

Chapter 2

10. 1.78×10^{-4}; 2.52×10^{-13}; 1.42×10^{-16}; 1.24×10^{-11}
11. 8.8×10^{-14}; 7.5×10^{-3}; 2.6×10^{-3}; 1.3×10^{-5}; 6.2×10^{-4}
12. 2.5×10^{-8}; 5.6×10^{-2}; 2.0×10^{-7}; 3.93; 5.20×10^{-3}
14. 1.08×10^{-16}
15. 7.29×10^{-4}
16. 3.2×10^{-10}; 2.6×10^{-6}
17. 4.4×10^{-12}
18. 7.1×10^{-10}; 7.1×10^{-12}
19. 2.6×10^{-5}; 2.6×10^{-9}
20. 3.9×10^{-6}; 1.3×10^{-9}; 4.0×10^{-7}; 3.2×10^{-6}; 2.5×10^{-7}; 5.0×10^{-8}
21. 4.8×10^{-4}
22. 8.2×10^{-6}; 8.7×10^{-6}
23. 3.2

Chapter 2   *(continued)*

24. 9.1×10^{-7}
25.   0.20
26. 1.8×10^{-4}; 4.3×10^{-3}; 4.4×10^{-3}; 8.8×10^{-5}
27. 1.0×10^{-8}
28. 1.82×10^{-4}; 6.05×10^{-7}; 1.82×10^{-4}
29.   0.26
30. 3.5×10^{-5}
31. 2.2×10^{-27}
33. 3.2×10^{-4}
34. 4.2×10^{-4}
35. 2×10^{-8}
36. 7.8×10^{-26}
37. 1.65×10^{-4}; 7.9×10^{-6}; 1.8×10^{-4}; 2.3
38. 1.3×10^{-6}
39. 1.4×10^{-9}
41. 5.05×10^{-6}; 50
42. 5.3×10^{-3}; 6.5×10^{-3}; 1.7×10^{-4}
43. 1.35×10^{-13}; 1.4×10^{-8}; 7.2×10^{-14}
44.   9.3
45. 1.4×10^{-13}

Chapter 3

4. 6.16×10^{-7}; 4.26×10^{-5}; 1.82×10^{-12}; 1.29×10^{-9}; 6.61×10^{-4}
5. 6.61×10^{-11}; 1.82×10^{-5}; 4.47×10^{-12}; 2.04×10^{-2}; 5.89×10^{-8}
6.   1.82; 4.70; 9.20; −0.16; 5.41
7.   1.00; 0.40; 11.73; 12.40; −0.14; 7.00; 3.38; 2.72; 4.92; 9.20; 5.13; 8.88
8.   1.30
9.   4.76
10.   1.0 to 27.8
11.   1.0 to 7.2
12. 1.62×10^{-7}; 6.79
17.   1.24; 6.2×10^{-8}
18. 4.5×10^{-12}; 2.2×10^{-3}; 0.265
19.   0.283; 7.9×10^{-7}; 3.70
20. 1.86×10^{-3}; 1.86×10^{-3}; 0.265
21.   0.340; 1.3×10^{-6}; 10.30
22.   9.33
23.   1.20; 6.5×10^{-8}
24. 1.58×10^{-2}; 1.58×10^{-2}; 0.484

Chapter 3 *(continued)*

25. 0.100; 1.31×10^{-8}; 10.17
26. 0.0078; 0.0078; 0.092
27. 0.67; 3.15×10^{-6}; 8.50
28. 0.0260; 6.9×10^{-4}; 1.45×10^{-11}; 6.9×10^{-4}
30. 9.87
31. 5.05
32. 9.63
33. 7.6×10^{-4}
34. 1.64 to 5.7×10^4
35. 2.47
36. 1.19
37. 4.67
38. 11.50
39. 9.73
40. 5.75
41. 7.03
42. 11.72
43. 3.66
44. 4.97
45. 12.38
46. 9.22
47. 5.17

Chapter 4

6. 0.41; 0.27; 0.15; 0.13; 0.04; 4.1×10^{-4}; 2.7×10^{-4}; 1.5×10^{-4}; 1.3×10^{-4}; 4.0×10^{-5}
7. 4.88×10^{-3}; 3.90×10^{-2}; 7.80×10^{-2}; 2.54×10^{-2}
8. 0.625
9. 5.22×10^{-7}; 2.10×10^{-5}
10. 7.5×10^{-10}; 7.5×10^{-7}; 3.0×10^{-3}
11. 1.3×10^{-11}; 6.1×10^{-9}; 7.3×10^{-7}; 2.7×10^{-5}; 3.3×10^{-4}; 1.2×10^{-3}; 9.2×10^{-4}
12. 2.07×10^{-20}; 0.0421; 0.0462
13. 2.0×10^{-10}; 3.2×10^{-7}; 0.0251
18. 1.45×10^{-3}
19. 10.26
20. 4.49×10^{-20}; 1.42×10^{-12}; 9.74×10^{-6}; 0.0213; 3.69×10^{-3}
21. 9.56; 1.74×10^{-20}; 6.32×10^{-13}; 4.96×10^{-6}; 1.25×10^{-2}; 2.50×10^{-3}
22. 3.92×10^{-8}

Chapter 4 *(continued)*
23. 7.55×10^{-19}
25. 4.89×10^{-8}

Chapter 5

7. $+0.925; -0.950; +0.495; +0.325; -1.342$
9. $+0.336; 2.0 \times 10^{12}$; Cu anode; $-0.64; 2 \times 10^{-13}$; Pt cathode; $+0.414; 1.59 \times 10^{13}$; left Pt anode; $-1.361; 8.0 \times 10^{-47}$; left Pt cathode; $+0.487; 6.3 \times 10^{13}$; Zn anode; $-0.109; 1.4 \times 10^{-9}$; Pt cathode
10. 1.9×10^{-8}
11. $0.328; 3.23 \times 10^4; 4.95 \times 10^{18}; 0.122; 6.75 \times 10^{71}$
12. 708
13. 1.0×10^{-12}
14. 1.48×10^{-19}
15. $+1.68$
16. $+1.51$
17. $-0.73; 1.8 \times 10^{-25}; -0.73$; copper electrode is negative; 4.6×10^{-16}
18. $+0.010; 4.8$
21. $6.3 \times 10^{16}; 1.4 \times 10^9; 8.0 \times 10^{61}; 3.6 \times 10^{-11}$
22. $+1.174; +1.24; +1.45$
23. $4.90 \times 10^{36}; 0.00435$
24. $0.180; 18.0$
25. 0.367
26. 3.08×10^{-12}
27. 6.02×10^{-17}
28. $2.5 \times 10^{-3}; 0.500$
29. 1.20×10^{-7}
30. $8.33 \times 10^{-3}; 8.33 \times 10^{-3}; 4.2 \times 10^{-3}; 2.1 \times 10^{-15}; 8.1 \times 10^{-3}; 8.1 \times 10^{-3}; 3.8 \times 10^{-3}; 2.18 \times 10^{-15}$
31. -0.0365
32. $+0.271$
33. 2.6×10^{-3}
34. $+1.257; +1.183$
35. 1.691; lead electrode is negative
36. $4.54 \times 10^{-5}; 0.0750; 0.0375$
37. $2.0 \times 10^{-5}; 2.15 \times 10^{-3}; 4.30 \times 10^{-3}; 1.41 \times 10^{-11}$
38. 1.41×10^{-9}
39. 0.0191
40. 0.490
41. 7.06

Appendix 6

TABLE OF ATOMIC WEIGHTS

(Based on Carbon-12)

	Symbol	Atomic No.	Atomic Weight		Symbol	Atomic No.	Atomic Weight
Actinium	Ac	89	227	Mercury	Hg	80	200.59
Aluminum	Al	13	26.9815	Molybdenum	Mo	42	95.94
Americium	Am	95	[243]*	Neodymium	Nd	60	144.24
Antimony	Sb	51	121.75	Neon	Ne	10	20.183
Argon	Ar	18	39.948	Neptunium	Np	93	[237]
Arsenic	As	33	74.9216	Nickel	Ni	28	58.71
Astatine	At	85	[210]	Niobium	Nb	41	92.906
Barium	Ba	56	137.34	Nitrogen	N	7	14.0067
Berkelium	Bk	97	[249]	Nobelium	No	102	[253]
Beryllium	Be	4	9.0122	Osmium	Os	76	190.2
Bismuth	Bi	83	208.980	Oxygen	O	8	15.9994
Boron	B	5	10.811	Palladium	Pd	46	106.4
Bromine	Br	35	79.909	Phosphorus	P	15	30.9738
Cadmium	Cd	48	112.40	Platinum	Pt	78	195.09
Calcium	Ca	20	40.08	Plutonium	Pu	94	[242]
Californium	Cf	98	[251]	Polonium	Po	84	210
Carbon	C	6	12.01115	Potassium	K	19	39.102
Cerium	Ce	58	140.12	Praseodymium	Pr	59	140.907
Cesium	Cs	55	132.905	Promethium	Pm	61	[145]
Chlorine	Cl	17	35.453	Protactinium	Pa	91	231
Chromium	Cr	24	51.996	Radium	Ra	88	226.05
Cobalt	Co	27	58.9332	Radon	Rn	86	222
Copper	Cu	29	63.54	Rhenium	Re	75	186.2
Curium	Cm	96	[247]	Rhodium	Rh	45	102.905
Dysprosium	Dy	66	162.50	Rubidium	Rb	37	85.47
Einsteinium	Es	99	[254]	Ruthenium	Ru	44	101.07
Erbium	Er	68	167.26	Samarium	Sm	62	150.35
Europium	Eu	63	151.96	Scandium	Sc	21	44.956
Fermium	Fm	100	[253]	Selenium	Se	34	78.96
Fluorine	F	9	18.9984	Silicon	Si	14	28.086
Francium	Fr	87	[223]	Silver	Ag	47	107.870
Gadolinium	Gd	64	157.25	Sodium	Na	11	22.9898
Gallium	Ga	31	69.72	Strontium	Sr	38	87.62
Germanium	Ge	32	72.59	Sulfur	S	16	32.064
Gold	Au	79	196.967	Tantalum	Ta	73	180.948
Hafnium	Hf	72	178.49	Technetium	Tc	43	[99]
Helium	He	2	4.0026	Tellurium	Te	52	127.60
Holmium	Ho	67	164.930	Terbium	Tb	65	158.924
Hydrogen	H	1	1.00797	Thallium	Tl	81	204.37
Indium	In	49	114.82	Thorium	Th	90	232.038
Iodine	I	53	126.9044	Thulium	Tm	69	168.934
Iridium	Ir	77	192.2	Tin	Sn	50	118.69
Iron	Fe	26	55.847	Titanium	Ti	22	47.90
Krypton	Kr	36	83.80	Tungsten	W	74	183.85
Lanthanum	La	57	138.91	Uranium	U	92	238.03
Lawrencium	Lw	103	[257]	Vanadium	V	23	50.942
Lead	Pb	82	207.19	Xenon	Xe	54	131.30
Lithium	Li	3	6.939	Ytterbium	Yb	70	173.04
Lutetium	Lu	71	174.97	Yttrium	Y	39	88.905
Magnesium	Mg	12	24.312	Zinc	Zn	30	65.37
Manganese	Mn	25	54.9380	Zirconium	Zr	40	91.22
Mendelevium	Md	101	[256]				

*A value given in brackets denotes the mass number of the longest-lived or best-known isotope.

Appendix 7

TABLE OF LOGARITHMS

	0	1	2	3	4	5	6	7	8	9
1.0	.0000	.0043	.0086	.0128	.0170	.0212	.0253	.0294	.0334	.0374
1.1	.0414	.0453	.0492	.0531	.0569	.0607	.0645	.0682	.0719	.0755
1.2	.0792	.0828	.0864	.0899	.0934	.0969	.1004	.1038	.1072	.1106
1.3	.1139	.1173	.1206	.1239	.1271	.1303	.1335	.1367	.1399	.1430
1.4	.1461	.1492	.1523	.1553	.1584	.1614	.1644	.1673	.1703	.1732
1.5	.1761	.1790	.1818	.1847	.1875	.1903	.1931	.1959	.1987	.2014
1.6	.2041	.2068	.2095	.2122	.2148	.2175	.2201	.2227	.2253	.2279
1.7	.2304	.2330	.2355	.2380	.2405	.2430	.2455	.2480	.2504	.2529
1.8	.2553	.2577	.2601	.2625	.2648	.2672	.2695	.2718	.2742	.2765
1.9	.2788	.2810	.2833	.2856	.2878	.2900	.2923	.2945	.2967	.2989
2.0	.3010	.3032	.3054	.3075	.3096	.3118	.3139	.3160	.3181	.3201
2.1	.3222	.3243	.3263	.3284	.3304	.3324	.3345	.3365	.3385	.3404
2.2	.3424	.3444	.3464	.3483	.3502	.3522	.3541	.3560	.3579	.3598
2.3	.3617	.3636	.3655	.3674	.3692	.3711	.3729	.3747	.3766	.3784
2.4	.3802	.3820	.3838	.3856	.3874	.3892	.3909	.3927	.3945	.3962
2.5	.3979	.3997	.4014	.4031	.4048	.4065	.4082	.4099	.4116	.4133
2.6	.4150	.4166	.4183	.4200	.4216	.4232	.4249	.4265	.4281	.4298
2.7	.4314	.4330	.4346	.4362	.4378	.4393	.4409	.4425	.4440	.4456
2.8	.4472	.4487	.4502	.4518	.4533	.4548	.4564	.4579	.4594	.4609
2.9	.4624	.4639	.4654	.4669	.4683	.4698	.4713	.4728	.4742	.4757
3.0	.4771	.4786	.4800	.4814	.4829	.4843	.4857	.4871	.4886	.4900
3.1	.4914	.4928	.4942	.4955	.4969	.4983	.4997	.5011	.5024	.5038
3.2	.5051	.5065	.5079	.5092	.5105	.5119	.5132	.5145	.5159	.5172
3.3	.5185	.5198	.5211	.5224	.5237	.5250	.5263	.5276	.5289	.5302
3.4	.5315	.5328	.5340	.5353	.5366	.5378	.5391	.5403	.5416	.5428
3.5	.5441	.5453	.5465	.5478	.5490	.5502	.5514	.5527	.5539	.5551
3.6	.5563	.5575	.5587	.5599	.5611	.5623	.5635	.5647	.5658	.5670
3.7	.5682	.5694	.5705	.5717	.5729	.5740	.5752	.5763	.5775	.5786
3.8	.5798	.5809	.5821	.5832	.5843	.5855	.5866	.5877	.5888	.5899
3.9	.5911	.5922	.5933	.5944	.5955	.5966	.5977	.5988	.5999	.6010
4.0	.6021	.6031	.6042	.6053	.6064	.6075	.6085	.6096	.6107	.6117
4.1	.6128	.6138	.6149	.6160	.6170	.6180	.6191	.6201	.6212	.6222
4.2	.6232	.6243	.6253	.6263	.6274	.6284	.6294	.6304	.6314	.6325
4.3	.6335	.6345	.6355	.6365	.6375	.6385	.6395	.6405	.6415	.6425
4.4	.6435	.6444	.6454	.6464	.6474	.6484	.6493	.6503	.6513	.6522
4.5	.6532	.6542	.6551	.6561	.6571	.6580	.6590	.6599	.6609	.6618
4.6	.6628	.6637	.6646	.6656	.6665	.6675	.6684	.6693	.6702	.6712
4.7	.6721	.6730	.6739	.6749	.6758	.6767	.6776	.6785	.6794	.6803
4.8	.6812	.6821	.6830	.6839	.6848	.6857	.6866	.6875	.6884	.6893
4.9	.6902	.6911	.6920	.6938	.6937	.6946	.6955	.6964	.6972	.6981
5.0	.6990	.6998	.7007	.7016	.7024	.7033	.7042	.7050	.7059	.7067
5.1	.7076	.7084	.7093	.7101	.7110	.7118	.7126	.7135	.7143	.7152
5.2	.7160	.7168	.7177	.7185	.7193	.7202	.7210	.7218	.7226	.7235
5.3	.7243	.7251	.7259	.7267	.7275	.7284	.7292	.7300	.7308	.7316
5.4	.7324	.7332	.7340	.7348	.7356	.7364	.7372	.7380	.7388	.7396
5.5	.7404	.7412	.7419	.7427	.7435	.7443	.7451	.7459	.7466	.7474
5.6	.7482	.7490	.7497	.7505	.7513	.7520	.7528	.7536	.7543	.7551
5.7	.7559	.7566	.7574	.7582	.7589	.7597	.7604	.7612	.7619	.7627
5.8	.7634	.7642	.7649	.7657	.7664	.7672	.7679	.7686	.7694	.7701
5.9	.7709	.7716	.7723	.7731	.7738	.7745	.7752	.7760	.7767	.7774

	0	1	2	3	4	5	6	7	8	9
6.0	.7782	.7789	.7796	.7803	.7810	.7818	.7825	.7832	.7839	.7846
6.1	.7853	.7860	.7868	.7875	.7882	.7889	.7896	.7903	.7910	.7917
6.2	.7924	.7931	.7938	.7945	.7952	.7959	.7966	.7973	.7980	.7987
6.3	.7993	.8000	.8007	.8014	.8021	.8028	.8035	.8041	.8048	.8055
6.4	.8062	.8069	.8075	.8082	.8089	.8096	.8102	.8109	.8116	.8122
6.5	.8129	.8136	.8142	.8149	.8156	.8162	.8169	.8176	.8182	.8189
6.6	.8195	.8202	.8209	.8215	.8222	.8228	.8235	.8241	.8248	.8254
6.7	.8261	.8267	.8274	.8280	.8287	.8293	.8299	.8306	.8312	.8319
6.8	.8325	.8331	.8338	.8344	.8351	.8357	.8363	.8370	.8376	.8382
6.9	.8388	.8395	.8401	.8407	.8414	.8420	.8426	.8432	.8439	.8445
7.0	.8451	.8457	.8463	.8470	.8476	.8482	.8488	.8494	.8500	.8506
7.1	.8513	.8519	.8525	.8531	.8537	.8543	.8549	.8555	.8561	.8567
7.2	.8573	.8579	.8585	.8591	.8597	.8603	.8609	.8615	.8621	.8627
7.3	.8633	.8639	.8645	.8651	.8657	.8663	.8669	.8675	.8681	.8686
7.4	.8692	.8698	.8704	.8710	.8716	.8722	.8727	.8733	.8739	.8745
7.5	.8751	.8756	.8762	.8768	.8774	.8779	.8785	.8791	.8797	.8802
7.6	.8808	.8814	.8820	.8825	.8831	.8837	.8842	.8848	.8854	.8859
7.7	.8865	.8871	.8876	.8882	.8887	.8893	.8899	.8904	.8910	.8915
7.8	.8921	.8927	.8932	.8938	.8943	.8949	.8954	.8960	.8965	.8971
7.9	.8976	.8982	.8987	.8993	.8998	.9004	.9009	.9015	.9020	.9026
8.0	.9031	.9036	.9042	.9047	.9053	.9058	.9063	.9069	.9074	.9079
8.1	.9085	.9090	.9096	.9101	.9106	.9112	.9117	.9122	.9128	.9133
8.2	.9138	.9143	.9149	.9154	.9159	.9165	.9170	.9175	.9180	.9186
8.3	.9191	.9196	.9201	.9206	.9212	.9217	.9222	.9227	.9232	.9238
8.4	.9243	.9248	.9253	.9258	.9263	.9269	.9274	.9279	.9284	.9289
8.5	.9294	.9299	.9304	.9309	.9315	.9320	.9325	.9330	.9335	.9340
8.6	.9345	.9350	.9355	.9360	.9365	.9370	.9375	.9380	.9385	.9390
8.7	.9395	.9400	.9405	.9410	.9415	.9420	.9425	.9430	.9435	.9440
8.8	.9445	.9450	.9455	.9460	.9465	.9469	.9474	.9479	.9484	.9489
8.9	.9494	.9499	.9504	.9509	.9513	.9518	.9523	.9528	.9533	.9538
9.0	.9542	.9547	.9552	.9557	.9562	.9566	.9571	.9576	.9581	.9586
9.1	.9590	.9595	.9600	.9605	.9609	.9614	.9619	.9624	.9628	.9633
9.2	.9638	.9643	.9647	.9652	.9657	.9661	.9666	.9671	.9675	.9680
9.3	.9685	.9689	.9694	.9699	.9703	.9708	.9713	.9717	.9722	.9727
9.4	.9731	.9736	.9741	.9745	.9750	.9754	.9759	.9763	.9768	.9773
9.5	.9777	.9782	.9786	.9791	.9795	.9800	.9805	.9809	.9814	.9818
9.6	.9823	.9827	.9832	.9836	.9841	.9845	.9850	.9854	.9859	.9863
9.7	.9868	.9872	.9877	.9881	.9886	.9890	.9894	.9899	.9903	.9908
9.8	.9912	.9917	.9921	.9926	.9930	.9934	.9939	.9943	.9948	.9952
9.9	.9956	.9961	.9965	.9969	.9974	.9978	.9983	.9987	.9991	.9996

Index